THE HONEY BEE

A Guide For Beekeepers

By Vernon R. Vickery
Ph.D., F.E.S.C.,F.R.E.S.

Published by
Particle Press

Particle Press
P.o. Box 132
Westmount, Quebec
Canada H3Z 2T1

Edited by **Edwin Vickery**
Type and layout on the Amiga by **Eyo Sama and Jacqui Summers**
Cover Design by **Sword in Stone Productions**
Cover Art by **Geoff Isherwood**
Production Coordinator: **Roger Broughton**
Printing by **L'Éclaireur, Beauce, Quebec**
Printed and bound in Canada

*"No living creature, not even man,
has achieved in the center of his sphere,
what the bee has achieved"*

Maeterlinck, 1901

Dedication

I take great pleasure in dedicating this book to two friends of very long standing, who helped me immeasurably in the days when I worked with them in Nova Scotia, from 1947 to 1961:

Endel A. Karmo, former Provincial Apiarist

and

Malcolm E. Neary, former Provincial Entomologist

In addition I must add a dedication to *Apis mellifera*, the fascinating little creatures that to me have been a constant source of inspiration.

FOREWORD

During the years that I was actively engaged in teaching about bees and their doings, my students asked me every year to please write my class notes as a book. Little did they know that I did not use class notes - nothing more than a course outline and some headings or data on a few file cards. When I retired I had very little to assist others who would take over the teaching chores, other than a library of more than 2000 colour slides that I had used as illustrations during classes. Some of these I obtained from others but most were my own.

From time to time, former students still call me for beekeeping advice and invariably ask "When will you write that book ?" Retired people are supposed to have more time in which to do such things but you can't prove it by me. At any rate, and at long last, here is the book.

After I completed the first draft, laboriously punched into my computer at home (I have always been a two-finger typist) I sent copies to two of the most knowledgeable and reputable people of long experience in apiculture in Canada: Endel A. Karmo, who for many years was Provincial Apiarist in Nova Scotia and who still keeps honey bees for honey and pollination; and Jack Arnott, Science Editor of Canadian Beekeeping. The final draft has benefitted much from their suggestions.

Unless otherwise stated in the captions, the illustrations are from my camera. A fee has been paid to Andromeda Productions, Elmira, New York, for use of three pictures, namely Figures 1.5; 1.16; and 3.4. I prepared the line drawings in pencil (some were adapted from other sources). Judith Nowlan and Geoff Isherwood completed some of them in ink for publication and others were computer generated by my son Edwin. Geoff Isherwood also drew the bee for the cover.

Two people who were particularly helpful in recent years need to be acknowledged here. Neil Duffy worked with me at Macdonald College in the apiary and in the classroom. His efforts are greatly appreciated. Susan Willis assisted me in the apiary during several summers. I could always leave everything to her and she never failed to exceed my expectations.

My wife Muriel has helped all along the way. She kept bees too until she became more and more sensitive to the stings of the little creatures. My son Edwin, who often had assisted me in demonstrations with bees in the past, has been very helpful in taking my efforts from manuscript to the completed book.

I have enjoyed writing this book and I hope it will provide enjoyment and information to many for many years to come.

Vernon R. Vickery, 102 Souvenir Drive, Pincourt, Quebec, J7V 3N8
June 30, 1990.

TABLE OF CONTENTS (Quick Reference)

TABLE OF CONTENTS (Detailed)

APPENDIX A

COLOUR PLATES 1, 2, 3, 4

INTRODUCING THE HONEY BEE

Honey bees are unique in the world of insects. There are about 100,000 species of insects in the Order Hymenoptera, the Order to which the honey bee belongs, but none of the others come close to rivalling the honey bee which, surely, is man's favourite insect. Sir Vincent Wigglesworth, the famed insect physiologist, made this comment: "the honey-bee is as far above the general run of other insects as man is above all his fellow mammals" (Wigglesworth, 1987).

Robacker (1988) agrees with Wigglesworth and states: "of the more than one million estimated species of insects, few have evolved the high capacity for learning possessed by the honey bee". He goes on to discuss capacity of learning by bees. They can learn by association like we do. They also can forget, again like we do. Unlike our language which is learned, the dance language of the bees is genetically fixed. Learning language is instinctive in humans, and the acquiring of bee language by bees also is instinctive. "The fundamental difference is the amount of leeway allowed by the genetic program of the animal : There is a tremendous amount for humans and essentially none for honey bees" (Robacker, 1988).

The average life span of a bee is too short to make possible much associative behaviour between bees and beekeeper - although I have met beekeepers who swore that their bees knew them !

All animals are given two names. These names are always Latin or are latinized. This is because Latin is a "dead" language and does not change. The Latin name of a species is the same in every country regardless of the native language or type of alphabet of that country. The first, the generic name, is shared by a group of related species; the second, the specific name, refers only to the species to which it is applied. Thus, man is *Homo sapiens* and the honey bee is *Apis mellifera*. Some times subspecies are recognized. These are variations which are geographically separated from each other but which can still interbreed if they are brought together. A subspecies is given a third name, which follows the species name. The Italian honey bee is called *Apis mellifera ligustica* Spinola and the Caucasian honey bee is called *Apis mellifera caucasica* Gorbatschew. Generic names are always capitalized; specific and subspecific names are never capitalized. As these names are Latinized they are always printed in italics. The name following the species or subspecies name is that of the person who first described the species or subspecies.

The Importance of the Honey Bee

How many people realize that the use of sugarcane and sugar beets started only a few hundred years ago, since the discovery of the Americas by European explorers? Before that time, honey was the main source of carbohydrates used by mankind.

The world production of honey is approximately 600,000 metric tons annually. This

Fig 1.1: Cave picture in Spain, *ca.* 9000 years old, female honey gatherer.

comes from about 50,000,000 colonies of honey bees kept by about 6,500,000 bee-keepers (Crane, 1975). If we allow an average price of Canadian $2.00 per kilogram (a low figure for most highly developed countries) the annual value of honey is more than 12 hundred million dollars. Canadian production per colony is about the highest in the world, with an average of more than 55 kilograms. The total production in Canada varies from 25 to 38 million kg. If this is valued at Canadian $2.00 per kg. the figure is 50 to 76 million dollars. Honey ranks very respectably in comparison with other agricultural crops.

Honey bees produce beeswax. The rule of thumb yield of beeswax is 1 kg. for each 100 kg. of surplus honey removed from the hives. The Canadian annual yield of beeswax is 250,000 kg. or more. At a low price of $5.00 per kg., the wax is worth Can. $1,250,000.00. Wax from bees is used extensively in production of fine quality candles, particularly for churches and religious organizations, as well as for grafting wax, pharmaceuticals and art work, to name but a few.

Honey bees also provide an essential service in pollinating plants. In many cases cross-pollination is essential so that seed can be produced. In the case of many fruit crops, if no seeds are produced there will be no fruit !! Most of our tree fruits such as apples, citrus fruits, pears, plums and many others, would cease to be available to us as food if there were no pollinating insects. The same is true of strawberries, raspberries and other small fruits, pumpkins, squash and other cucurbit crops, most tree-borne nut crops, and all of the legume crops, including alfalfa and clovers, which provide so much of the essential food supply for our domesticated livestock. How do we place a monetary value on pollination services? The best estimate that we have considers that the pollination service provided by honey bees in a year is valued at 10 to 20 times the value of the honey produced that year. If we go back to the conservative value assigned to Canadian honey production of 50 to 76 million Canadian dollars we find the annual pollination service is worth between 500 million and 1.5 billion dollars per year. For many seasons the value certainly exceeds a billion dollars. Levin (1983) gave a figure for value of crops produced by pollination in the United States of 19.5 billion dollars annually.

If we total the value of honey, of wax, of other minor hive products such as propolis, pollen and royal jelly, and pollination service, we arrive at more than one and one-half billion dollars contributed each year to Canadian agriculture and to the well being of citizens of Canada.

There are other factors too to be considered. Certainly many beekeepers operate their colonies on a commercial basis to make profit, but there are a great many others, the "hobby" beekeepers who are fascinated by the little creatures and keep bees for their own relaxation and enjoyment. I am at a loss to be able to assign a dollar value to "peace of mind", but many times over the past 30 and more years when I have been in a bad mood - anything ranging from sorrow to frustration or melancholia to rage - in fact any time when my spirits needed a boost, the bees invariably supplied it. I am not alone in this; many beekeepers who keep bees for "fun" have expressed a similar opinion. The bees have done more for me than a "hive" of psychiatrists ever could.

Beekeeping in History

The history of beekeeping or at least "bee-robbing" is undoubtedly much older than the recorded history of man. The association of man and honey bee may be older than the association of man with any other animal. Primitive man learned to locate the nests of bees in hollow trees or crevices in rocks. Once he had tasted honey he soon learned how to steal it from a nest. No doubt this was sometimes a rather painful experience. The early association is portrayed by a painting on rock in a rock shelter in a mountainous area of Spain. The painting (Fig. 1.1) which shows a human figure, unmistakably female, gathering honey, is thought to have been made 9,000 years ago. The female figure may be using smoke to stupefy the bees. Although it is difficult to be certain about this, it is certain that man discovered early that smoke would help when harvesting honeycombs.

Beekeeping was well developed when ancient Egypt was in its ascent. Honey bees were kept there in clay pots, no doubt because someone found a swarm which had entered an empty clay water pot and claimed it as their home. Migratory beekeeping was known to the Egyptians. They kept stacks of clay cylinders (Fig. 1.2), each with its colony of bees on boats or rafts that they propelled along the river Nile, following successions of plants in bloom. Such clay pots, usually with detachable bottoms for honey gathering, can be found in Egypt today.

The ancient Egyptians revered the little insect to the extent that they considered it a "Royal" insect and used a stylized honeybee as a symbol for the "ruler of upper Egypt" in the "cartouche", the hieroglyphic representation of the names of the Pharaohs or Kings (Fig. 1.3).

As man discovered techniques for working various natural products, he employed them in making "nests" for honey bees. Basket-work hives led to the production of the "straw skep", a

Fig 1.2:
"Mud" hives,
Cairo, Egypt.

Fig 1.3: Cartouche of a Pharaoh, *ca.* 4000 years old. Note stylized bee. Egyptian museum, Cairo, Egypt.

hive which persisted until late in the 19th century and is still used today in countries where they are allowed (Fig. 1.4). Skeps, box hives, or any hives with fixed frames or combs, are illegal in Canada. Sections of hollow logs, or even boxes have been used as bee hives and are still used to some extent in central Africa.

Using these primitive hives, man learned very little about what went on inside them. For thousands of years man killed off colonies and used the products they had stored, at the same time providing more empty containers that bees could inhabit when they swarmed. With this type of beekeeping, with "hives" of limited size, swarming was inevitable and usually was frequent.

From the dawn of time to the 16th century beekeeping hardly changed at all. The following is the beekeepers calendar as described by Crane (1975), "in early summer he caught and hived the swarms which issued; in late summer he killed the bees in most of his hives, cut out the combs and strained the honey from the wax; in the fall, if necessary, he provided food for the remaining hives, which he overwintered. Burning sulfur was commonly used for killing the bees."

One large bee was known to exist in each colony but it was not realized that she was the queen - the mother. She was commmonly called the "king". The sexes of the bees and their role in the colony was not understood and it was not known whether the bees secreted wax or found it somewhere. The role of bees in pollination was unknown and their essential part in production of seeds and fruits escaped notice until relatively modern times. Beekeepers did not even associate the visits of bees to flowers with the honey that they produced.

Mickel Jacob, a German, in 1568 published a description of the honey bees raising a queen from eggs or very young larvae. This was the initial breakthrough which stimulated critical observation of the bees in several European countries. In 1586, a Spanish beekeeper, Luis Mendez de Torres, discovered the role of the "queen" as the egg producer, the mother of the colony. Spain and England were at war at the time and it is not known whether this discovery reached England or whether Charles Butler discovered the queen role independently. In 1609, he published a book," Feminine Monarchie" in which he showed that drone bees were males. Some time later, 1637, there appeared the "Discourse of Historie of Bees" by Richard Remmant. He had observed that worker bees were females.

Years passed before the story of the mating of queen and drone became known. In 1771, Anton Janscha of Slovenia, published a description of the event. Janscha was honoured 200 years later by Jugoslavia, which issued a stamp (Scott 1983, No. 1147) bearing his likeness. Thus the recognition of the castes of honey bees, and their role in colony structure and survival, gradually became known.

The role of the bees in pollination became known in 1750, when an Englishman, Arthur Dobbs, discovered that the pollen which the bees gathered was responsible for fertilizing the flower in order to produce seed. He also observed the trait of "fidelity to plant species" when he noticed that bees gathered pollen from only one kind of flower on a trip from the hive to the field and back to the hive. The role of bees in pollination was confirmed and clearly established by the work of a German, C.K. Sprenge, in 1793. The blind beekeeper, François Hüber, a Swiss, put it all together and in 1792 published a paper which became the foundation of the science of apiculture as we know it today.

As early as the year 1500 beekeepers began to devise methods for taking the honey without killing the bees. One such method was "driving" the bees. The "hive" containing the colony, presumably a straw skep, was turned upside down and an empty one was placed above it with the open ends in contact. By drumming on the sides of the lower hive the bees were forced to move upward to the empty one. Several colonies were driven into the empty hive. The beekeeper would then feed these bees and keep them for winter, leaving the other hives free of bees so that he could harvest the honey crop very easily.

Many types of wooden box hives were devised. Hüber developed a "leaf-hive" in which the combs opened like the pages of a book, a hive which was useful for observation but impractical for honey production. The period of 200 years between 1650 and 1850 produced a series of hives with top bars and frames. None of them was very successful as, in every case, the bees attached their combs to the side walls of the hive as well as to the top bars, so that the combs were not removable except by cutting them out.

One innovation developed in Greece which might have assisted the would-be inventors of new hives, had the idea received wide dissemination. Woven basket hives had been used in Greece for many centuries. For some unknown reason some beekeepers began to use the baskets upside down, then covering the open "top" with with bars about four cm wide. Flat bars would not have helped as the bees would likely have attached their combs across rather than along them. However, the bars used were not flat but were somewhat rounded beneath pro-

Fig 1.4: Straw skep. This one has not been used by the bees.

INTRODUCING THE HONEY BEE 5

viding a ridge along which the bees attached their combs, one to each bar. Coupled with this was the fact that the hive was widest at the top so that the bees built their combs attached to the bars but not to the sides of the hive. This inovation occurred very early; the date or even the century is not known. It is quite probable that Aristotle used this type of hive. His descriptions of the life of the bee in his "Natural History" could hardly have been made without such a hive in which he could observe their activities. Sir George Wheler brought the idea to England in 1682 when he published a description of the hive in his book "A Journey to Greece". He described also how half of the combs from each hive were removed each spring and placed in an empty hive. Wheler's news did spur efforts of English beekeepers to devise new hives but they did not manage to produce the "perfect" beehive.

Honey bees were brought to the Americas early in the 17th Century. The earliest American record of honey bees is 1638. When one reads stories of the hardships experienced by the pioneers who crossed the ocean in tiny ships, which took months to make the crossing, one has to admire as well the honey bees that shared their problems. No doubt many colonies were lost en route but some survived to begin to populate the huge North American continent. As honey was the only source of sweetening the settlers had, other than maple sugar which they learned to produce after being taught by the native peoples, survival of the bees was of paramount importance to them.

The father of modern beekeeping was not European but a citizen of the United States of America, the Reverend Lorenzo Lorraine Langstroth of Philadelphia. As a young man he became interested in honey bees and bought books and box-hives of bees and began experimenting with them. The problem of a satisfactory moveable frame hive occupied much of his time. Finally he solved the problem. He discovered the bee space, the space that the bees themselves maintained between their combs, 8 - 9 mm or 5/16 - 3/8 inch. He applied this to the making of frames which would be suspended close to the hive walls, leaving a space only as wide as the bee space. He found that the bees did respect this space and did not attach their combs to the side walls of the hive. He published his findings in 1851 and the era of modern beekeeping arrived. The news spread rapidly and the Langstroth hive is now used world-wide.

Once the modern hive came into use, other inventions and innovations soon followed. Beeswax foundation was invented by J. Mehring in Germany in 1857. This led directly to the use of honey supers above the brood chamber. As honey could now be taken from the bees rather easily, something was needed that would allow removal of the honey without destroying the combs. This was soon provided as Hruschka in Austria invented the centrifugal honey extractor in 1865. In the same year, in France, Abbe Collin perfected the queen excluder. In 1891, E.C. Porter, in the United States, developed the bee escape so that the bees in the honey supers would remove themselves to the brood chamber, thus leaving the honey supers free of bees.

Other improvements have been made since that time, such as the "shouldered" frame developed by Hoffmann, which effectively spaces the frames at the proper distance from each other. This was a distinct advantage over the "hand" spacing or "staple" spacing which had been used. Some other developments are discussed in the chapter on equipment. They are not historic and so are not included here.

The Subspecies or "Races" of Honey Bees

A subspecies is a population of a species which has become isolated from other populations of the same species and is an inbreeding group which develops characteristics which differ from those of the other populations.

The honey bee, *Apis mellifera* Linnaeus has developed a number of such geographically separated subspecies. The origin of the honey bee was probably in the "Near East" of Asia. It probably came from a common ancestor with *Apis indica* (or *cerana*), the Indian honey bee. The two species, *Apis mellifera* and *Apis indica* are regarded as sister species. They may interbreed but the progeny cannot produce offspring. The subspecies of *Apis mellifera* are able to interbreed if they are brought together. Our honey bee has spread over western Asia, Europe and all of Africa.

The subspecies of honey bees are indicated by adding a third Latin name to *Apis mellifera* as well as the name of the author who first described the subspecies. These subspecies differ from each other in a number of ways, so that each of them now has its own traits and characteristics. In Europe some northern subspecies are larger than others which occur in the south and all of them are larger than those found in Africa. Small bees build smaller cells in their honeycombs. However, the smaller bees generally have proportionally longer wings, longer legs and longer tongues.

There are also other morphological structures which vary in shape and size. The colour of the body varies; some are yellow, some are grey and some are nearly black. The colour pattern is also variable.

Some subspecies have disappeared or nearly so, even in the geographical areas where they originated. Beekeepers determined that they were inferior in some respects, usually in honey production but also in behavioural traits such as hostility, and replaced them with better producing colonies that were easier to manage. The Italian bee has displaced the Syrian bee, *Apis mellifera syriaca* and also *A. m. cypria* of Cyprus, so that both are less common than they used to be. A stronger, more dominant subspecies will usually displace a weaker one if they are competing with each other.

a) Black Bees

The first honey bee to be brought to North America was the "black" bee of northern Europe, mainly from populations from France and from the British Isles (the latter are now extinct or nearly so). This bee, *Apis mellifera mellifera*, is a large dark bee. It is mainly uniformly dark to black with yellow spots on the second and third abdominal terga. The abdomen is not banded. These are nervous bees, sometimes aggressive and they usually "run" on the comb, so that a beekeeper has some difficulty in examining the bees and the comb. The tongues of the workers are shorter than those of the Italian bees. They are not particularly good honey producers and they are quite susceptible to brood diseases. The European black bee does winter very well but does not build up population strength in the spring as quickly as Italian or Caucasian bees. I remember a beekeeper who still had some "German Black bees" but that was more than 30 years ago and even these are gone. It is doubtful that any black honey bees now exist in North America.

b) Italian Bees

Apis mellifera ligustica Spinola originated in the Italian peninsula and, because of its superior characteristics, has now become the "commercial" bee over most of the world. Italian queens came to North America in 1859, and their offspring, and that of other queens which followed them, have now entirely replaced the black bees. Italian bees are slender with more slender abdomens than the black bees and they have longer tongues. They have three or four golden yellow bands on their abdomens. The hairs on these bees are also golden. They are gentle bees, usually easy to manage, and they build up quickly in the spring. They have larger comb areas devoted to brood rearing than any of the other subspecies. They are less prone to swarming than most of the others. Only about 40 percent of neglected colonies of Italian bees will swarm under our conditions, a much lower proportion than for most of the other subspecies. They will winter well if the colonies are strong but use more stored food than the other subspecies which have been wintered under our conditions. They have some faults too - they are more likely to rob other colonies than any of the other subspecies. Their orientation sense is not as good as some of the others making drifting a greater problem than with Caucasian or Carniolan bees.

c) Caucasian Bees

Apis mellifera caucasica Gorbatschew originated in the Central Caucasus Mountains, which are now part of the Georgian S.S.R., U.S.S.R. They are dark bees, often called grey bees because of the grey colour of the hairs. Drones have black hairs on the thorax. The tongues of the workers are longer, up to 7.2 mm, exceeding the tongue length of the others which are found in our region. They are noted for their gentleness and calmness on the combs. They build up quickly to strong colonies, although not as rapidly as Italian bees. They are very little inclined to swarm. I have kept Caucasian bees off and on over a period exceeding 30 years and have yet to see a swarm from a Caucasian colony. The main drawback to keeping Caucasians is their excessive use of propolis which makes routine colony examinations quite difficult. They usually winter poorly as they are very susceptible to Nosema disease but this can be overcome by fall antibiotic feeding. Caucasians store somewhat less honey than Italians and like them are inclined to drifting and to robbing. Most of the Caucasian bees in North America are descended from stock imported from Russia from 1920 to 1939 but additional stock has been imported since that time.

d) Carniolan Bees

Apis mellifera carnica Pollman is a subspecies which originated along the border between Austria and Jugoslavia and is found along the valley of the Danube River in Hungary, Romania and Bulgaria. Carniolan bees are probably the quietest and most gentle of all the subspecies of honey bees. In appearance, they resemble Caucasian bees. They are slender, have long tongues (6.4-6.8 mm), and are grey in appearance due to the dense hairs of that colour. The second and third abdominal terga usually have brown spots or a brown band. Drones have grey to greyish brown pile rather than black like the Caucasians. Carniolans build up rapidly in the spring if the weather is good but will gauge the amount of brood reared to the quantity of stores being collected. Colony strength tends to be very much less than that of Italian bees during the winter, but they tend to winter very well even under harsh conditions. Their main fault is their tendency toward excessive swarming. Beekeepers who keep Carniolan bees must always consider swarm prevention as part of routine manipulations.

e) The African Bee

Apis mellifera scutellata normally lives in central Africa between the Sahara and Kalahari deserts. It resembles the Italian bee very closely but is slightly smaller. It is adapted to hot dry conditions. Colonies habitually abscond under poor conditions: the entire population leaves the old home and may migrate a long distance searching for better conditions and a new home. Colonies also usually produce several small swarms each year. This African bee is extremely aggressive, easily stimulated to sting. Once stinging behaviour is initiated it continues and is accelerated far beyond the stinging behaviour of any other subspecies of honey bee. Additional information on this bee and the problem in the Americas is found in a later chapter (Chapter 12).

f) The Cape Bee

Apis mellifera capensis lives in a small region of the Republic of South Africa on the coast near Cape Town. It is included here because of an unusual biological feature which does not occur to any extent in any other honey bees, although on very rare occasions reduction division failure may also occur in Italian bees. In queenless colonies, workers begin laying eggs, most of which develop into females, despite the fact that the workers do not mate and their spermathecas do not contain sperm. Thus colonies are able to rear queens from eggs laid by worker bees. The only way this can happen is that reduction-division in egg production, which normally reduces the chromosome number to half (haploid), fails to occur so that the eggs contain the full (diploid) chromosome complement. This is normally brought about by union of male and female gametes, each being haploid, to produce the diploid number and thus initiate development of a female individual.

g) Other Honey Bee Subspecies

It is very unlikely that other subspecies will be brought to this region. Present quarantine regulations prevent such importations except for scientific purposes and few of them exhibit characteristics which would make them likely candidates for a breeding program. Some are rather vicious, often stinging without provocation. Apparently *Apis mellifera cypria* from Cyprus and *Apis mellifera syriaca* from Syria were in this category. *Apis mellifera iberica* from North Africa and *Apis mellifera lamarkii* from the Nile valley of Egypt are more difficult to manage than Italian bees, as are the central African bees, *Apis mellifera adansonii* and *Apis mellifera scutellata*. The European Black bee, *Apis mellifera mellifera* is rather aggressive and, as previously stated, is a poorer honey producer than the Italian subspecies and is very susceptible to brood diseases.

Some of these subspecies, and probably others, have been imported into North America. Both *Apis mellifera cypria* and *Apis mellifera syriaca* were brought in about 75 to 100 years ago. Although they are very attractive looking bees, they were so hostile and difficult to manage that they were replaced by Italian bees. In recent years, lesser known subspecies have been used in Canada and in England in scientific breeding programs. The importation of new genetic material is very strictly regulated and such importations can be made only by scientific institutions.

The Honey Bee Colony

The honey bee is classed as a "social" species of insect. In the social insects castes have developed, which are groups of individuals that differ in size and structure and which perform different functions in the social organization. Honey bees have three castes: queen, workers and drones. Each of these is identifiable by size and shape (Fig. 1.5).

Worker honey bees are the smallest in size but are by far the most numerous bees in a colony. Although they are females, the ovaries of most workers do not develop and most do not lay eggs if a colony has an ac-

Fig 1.5: Castes of honey bees: top, queen; middle, worker; bottom, drone. (Photo by K. Lorenzen, Andromeda Productions, Elmira, New York).

Fig 1.6:
Pollen-carrying
bee on a comb.
Attention of the
other bees
indicates the
pollen carrier was

tive queen. A few workers may deposit a small number of eggs but these are infertile and develop only into drone bees. Worker bees are very well equipped to perform the work which is necessary to maintain the colony. They are required to do all of the work except for egg-laying. They have structures such as antenna cleaners, pollen brushes and pollen baskets on their legs (Fig. 1.6). They also have "honey stomachs" and it is in these stomachs that the process of manufacturing honey is carried out.

Worker bees have 12-segmented antennae. They also have wax and scent glands which do not occur in queens and drones. Worker bees have longer tongues than queens or drones. Each of their compound eyes has approximately 6300 facets. The sting is barbed and when a worker bee stings it cannot pull out the sting becasuse of the "harpoon-like" barbs near the tip. Instead the sting and the poison sac and associated glands and muscles are torn out of the body of the bee, which dies shortly afterward. Because a worker bee can sting only once, it stings only to protect the colony and the stores of food. Normally bees working in the field gathering nectar and pollen do not sting. They have nothing to protect but themselves and suicide is not an efficient method of protection. The bee attempts to get away and to carry its load back to the hive. It will sting if handled or sometimes if it accidently bumps into a person. Honey bees normally fly about 1-2 meters (5 feet) above the ground so collisions do occur occasionally. Wasps and bumble bees can sting repeatedly as their stings do not have barbs.

Queen honey bees are intermediate in size, larger than workers but smaller than drones. Their shape is different, the abdomen is cylindrical and nearly pointed at the tip. Like the workers, queens have antennae composed of 12 segments but unlike the workers, lack the corbiculae or pollen baskets on the hind legs. The eyes have fewer facets, approximately 3900 in each compound eye. A queen has a long sting which is slightly curved and has only very tiny barbs. The sting is used only to dispose of other queens, whether they are still in their cells, not quite ready to emerge, or in open combat with a sister queen on the face of the comb.

A virgin queen will commence making pre-mating orientation flights in less than a week if the weather is suitable. A mating flight takes place five days to three weeks after emergence. She leaves her home and searches for a congregation of drones, flies through it, and then climbs to a height of about 15 meters. The drones follow and only the strongest are able to catch her and mate with her. A queen mates with one to 11 drones (or perhaps as many as 18) in quick succession; the entire mating flight may not take more than half an hour. There is usually only one mating flight but there can be several, occuring over one or two days. The sperm becomes stored in her body and will fertilize her eggs throughout her life. The sperm from a single drone is not sufficient to allow her to deposit fertilized egs for the rest of her life and such a queen may become a 'drone layer', laying unfertilized eggs in worker cells, which develop into undersized drones. It is important that there are plenty of drones when queens leave the hives for their mating flights. In eastern Canada in early spring this can be a real problem; queens can be raised but we seldom have enough drones to ensure adequate mating until late in May.

If a queen fails to be mated within the three week period, she will make no more flights but begins laying unfertilized eggs. Queens can be induced to begin laying at one week of age, even though they are not mated, by exposing them to carbon dioxide gas. An older queen, one more than three weeks of age, can still be made fertile by artificial insemination.

After mating, the queen returns to the hive and soon afterward will begin to deposit eggs in the wax cells prepared by the workers. When she is laying eggs her abdomen becomes swollen and heavy so that she cannot fly well. Her primary function in the colony is to lay eggs to produce more bees. She also produces a pheromone which has a great deal to do with colony activity and behaviour. This is discussed later. She deposits fertilized eggs in the smaller cells which develop into females, workers or queens, depending upon the diet which is fed to the larvae. She can also lay unfertilized eggs, usually in the larger, deeper cells. These develop into the males, the drones.

Drones are the largest members of the honey bee colony. They have only one function to perform, mating virgin queens. Their entire body is adapted for this function. The senses of sight and smell of a drone are more acute than those of the other castes. The antennae, which are 13-segmented (in contrast to the 12 segments ofthe workers or queens), are provided with many thousands of sensory receptors. These enable the drone to detect the scent (pheromone) of a virgin queen as she leaves the hive. The eye of a drone contains about 13000 facets and meet at the top of the head. Thus vision is excellent, enabling the drone to see and to follow the queen. A drone is large with a squarish body. The flight muscles are strong so that a normal drone can fly faster than a queen so that he can catch her in flight. Proportional to body size, the drone bee has the largest genital organs of any animal. In mating the entire penial structure turns inside out so that the sperm is on the outside. The drone dies following mating as the entire organ is torn out of his body. The queen returns to the hive with the genitalia of the drones with which she mated protruding from her vaginal opening. These are retained for a time until the sperm is stored in the spermatheca of the queen. She may remove the remains herself but usually is assisted by worker bees. In eastern Canada drones may be found in a colony from early May until fall. As the days grow short and blooming plants become scarce, worker bees drag the drones out of the hive and do not allow them to re-enter. They soon die of exposure or starvation. This is the usual case although I have seen drones in colonies early in spring which undoubtedly had wintered with the worker bees.

The life cycle of the bees differs in the different castes. All eggs hatch in 3 days but the duration of the succeeding stages differs. The following table indicates the life cycles as a beekeeper would see them.

	Worker	Queen	Drone
Egg hatches (days)	3rd	3rd	3rd
Cell is capped (days)	8th	8th	10th
Adult emerges(days)	21st	16th	24th

Some queens have been known to emerge in 15 days. The beekeeper does not see the pupal stage, the great transformation from a legless white worm to the completed adult; this takes place inside the capped cell. He is able to observe the tremendous rate of growth of the larva, which is tiny when it hatches but in 5 days has grown to fill the cell. He knows when he sees capped brood cells that an adult bee will emerge from each cell in less than two weeks. If he sees a capped queen cell, he knows that there will be a new queen in the colony within a week. If there are "swarm" queen cells, he knows that the colony can swarm very soon, possibly within two or three days, and in any case in less than a week.

The life span of worker bees in summer is about six weeks, but in periods of light activity is somewhat longer. It is less, probably no more than 35 days, during the "honey flow". Worker bees normally spend three weeks inside the hive and the remainder as "forager" or field bees. In the fall, the worker bees are physiologically different due to the protein reserves stored in the hypopharyngeal glands and fat bodies. These extend to maximum capacity due to the large quantities of pollen which the workers consume. This seems to retard aging so that many of the bees are still alive in the spring.

Queens can live for several years and can continue to produce fertilized eggs. There is a record of a queen living at least eight years (Betts, 1946). The average is much less,

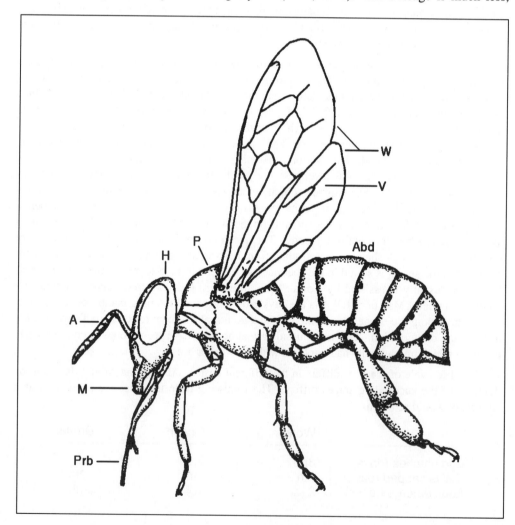

Fig 1.7:
External structure of a worker bee: A, antenna; Abd, abdomen; H, head; m, mandible; p, prothorax; Prb, proboscis; v, wing vein; w, wings. (Adapted from Villeneuve and Vickery, 1980).

perhaps three years, although most commercial beekeepers change the queens at least every two years.

Drones are not sexually mature when they emerge from the cells and are not ready to mate until about 13 days later. The average life span of the drones in summer is about 60 days, providing a period of 46 to 47 days that any individual drone can successfully mate with a queen. The drones referred to previously, that had lived over winter, obviously had a much longer life. It is not known whether these drones were still capable of mating queens.

The External Structure of the Honey Bee   *(External structure* Fig. 1.7)

Snodgrass (1975) has provided a very complete work on the morphology (structure) of the honey bee (see also Villeneuve and Vickery, 1980). Like other insects, the honey bee has a body made up of three regions, head, thorax and abdomen, with three pairs of legs and two pairs of wings borne on the thorax. In young bees, the dense coat of hairs may make these divisions difficult to see. Most of the hairs on the honey bees are branched, making them ideal for pollen transfer from one flower to another. On the head are found the compound eyes, the antennae and the organs of feeding. The thorax is made up of four segments, rather than the three usually found in insects. The fourth segment, the propodeum, is actually part of the abdomen which has become a functional part of the thorax. The segments are the prothorax, mesothorax, and metathorax and the propodeum. Each of the first three segments bears a pair of legs; the middle two segments each also bear a pair of wings. The thorax is the center of locomotion of the insect and is filled with strong muscles.

The abdomen is divided into segments, which appear as rings around the body. The abdomen carries most of the spiracles (the openings through which the bee breathes), the wax glands, scent glands and the sting (in workers), the sting and female reproductive organs (in queens) or the male reproductive organs (in drones), as well as enclosing other essential organs of the insect.

a) The Head

In frontal view, the head is triangular. The dorsal part is rather flat while the rear is concave next to the thorax, to which it is joined by a narrow neck. The compound eyes are the most prominent features. Each compound eye is made up of many facets, each of which is actually a complete eye. The structure is different than in the eyes of mammals, being made up of rods and cones and each eye facet has its own nerve leading to the brain. On the top of the head are three simple eyes or ocelli.

The antennae, which are freely movable appendages, arise close together near the center of the face, set into sockets in membraneous areas of the head wall. Each antenna is geniculate (L-shaped). Antennae are important sensory organs as they are covered with thousands of several kinds of tiny receptors which are linked to a large double nerve from the brain. These sensory receptors are efficient chemical receptors so they detect odours and are also responsive to touch.

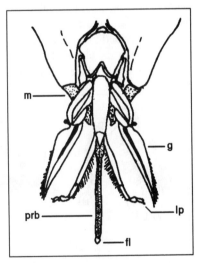

Fig 1.8: Mouthparts of a worker bee: fl, flabellum; g, galea (part of maxilla); lp, labial palp; m, mandible; prb, proboscis. (Adapted from Villeneuve and Vickery, 1980).

The mouthparts are made up of several structures (Fig.1.8). The mandibles are attached to the sides of the head. Many insects, like beetles, use the mandibles as the primary organs for eating food. Honeybees use them mainly for working and shaping wax in building combs, or capping cells and as grasping instruments, but also for feeding on pollen. The mandibles are very strong due to a double articulation and strong muscle attachment. The main feeding apparatus is the long tongue or proboscis, which is inserted into flower nectaries to siphon up the nectar. Inside the proboscis is a food canal which leads to the esophagus and thence to the honey stomach. In the head there is a sucking pump consisting of the cibarium and the associated muscles which enable the bee to suck up nectar or honey or water and also to regurgitate it upon return to the hive. Associated with the probocis are salivary glands; the saliva is conducted to the tip of the proboscis where it mixes with the food materials. It may be used also as a solvent to liquify sugar or granulated honey.

Inside the head and part of the thorax of a worker bee there are "hypopharyngeal glands" which produce "royal jelly", a food rich in proteins and fats. This is fed to all larvae for three days after they hatch from the eggs. Queen larvae are fed entirely upon this substance. Worker bees also have mandibular glands located near the hypopharyngeal glands. These secrete an "alarm pheromone" if the bees detect a source of danger to the colony. Queens have mandibular glands in similar position but their function is quite different; they produce the "queen substance".

b) The Thorax

The four segments of the thorax are strongly ridged internally, these appearing on the outside as slightly sunken lines called sulci. The internal ridging is necessary for the attachment of the muscles which operate the legs and wings. The hairy coat of the bees usually obscures these sulci.

The legs, on close examination, are found to differ somewhat from each other, but the basic structure is essentially the same as in most insects. There are six principal parts or segments (Fig. 1.9), moveable on each other at flexible joints. The segments, beginning at the attachment to the body, are the coxa, trochanter, femur, tibia, tarsus and pretarsus. The tarsus is divided into small segments called tarsomeres. The pretarsus carries a pair of claws and, between the claws, a flexible pad called the arolium. The joints in an insect leg move only in a single plane. There is no mobility or freedom of movement like in the human

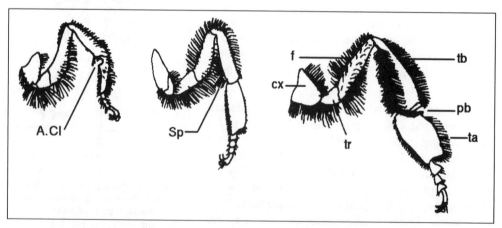

Fig 1.9: Structure of the legs of a worker bee: left, foreleg; A.Cl, antenna cleaner; middle, middle leg; Sp, spine; right, hind leg; cx, coxa; f, femur; pb, pollen basket or corbiculum; ta, tarsus; tb, tibia; tr, trochanter. (Adapted from Villneuve and Vickery, 1980).

wrist, elbow or shoulder, but there is some compensation in that not all of the joints move in the same plane.

The legs of honey bees are used for locomotion but they have also become modified or speciallized, especially in worker bees, to perform special functions. The tarsi of the fore and middle legs have brushes of stiff hairs on their inner surfaces. Those on the front legs are used to clean pollen or other particles from the head, eyes and mouthparts, while those of the middle legs are used in cleaning the thorax. The fore legs also have a notch which can be closed over the antennae in order to remove debris from the sensory organs. The tibiae of the middle legs each have a long spine for loosening and removing pollen pellets from the pollen baskets on the hind legs.

The smooth, concave, outer surfaces of the broad hind tibiae and basitarsi of worker bees are fringed with long curved hairs. The space thus enclosed forms the pollen basket or corbiculum. Pollen is first collected from the body by the fore and middle legs and is deposited on the large flat brushes on the inner surface of the broad basal segments of the hind tarsi. The deep notch between the tibia and the basal tarsal segment is used to transfer the pollen from the tarsal brushes of the leg on either side to the corbiculum on the opposite leg. The pollen has been mixed with a small quantity of nectar so that it adheres to the floor of the pollen basket.

The wings are strengthened by veins. To ensure that both wings on either side work together each hind wing has a coupling apparatus consisting of about 20 upturned hooks which catch automatically in a curved fold on the rear margin of the fore wing when the wings are extended. When not in use the wings are held horizontally against the dorsal surface of the abdomen.

Honey bees fly very well. Their top speed is about 27 kilometres per hour (15 mph). They have some difficulty in flying against strong wind. Wing movements are complicated, up and down, forward and backward and with a partial rotary movement. Honey bees can fly backward, sideways, upward and downward and can hover in one place in addition to forward flight.

c) The Abdomen

The abdomen has nine segments, besides the propodeum which has transferred to the thorax. In workers and queens only six segments are visible. The others are reduced in size and are concealed beneath the visible segments. The principal external features are the wax glands, scent glands, the sting and the spiracles. On the underside of the worker abdomen there are paired, smooth, glistening, oval areas on four of the segments. These are the wax mirrors. Wax is secreted onto these surfaces from internal glands and hardens into flakes. These are removed by the bee and are used wherever wax is required in the hive. The scent gland, or Nassanoff gland, is internal on the dorsal part of the abdomen near the tip. When it is functioning to attract other bees the abdominal tip is bent downward so that the gland is exposed, appearing externally as a slight elevation, with a smooth, slightly concave surface, on the rear edge of the next to last visible segment. The sting is enclosed in a chamber at the tip of the abdomen with only the tip of the sharp tapered shaft protruding. The shaft appears to be a simple structure, but is, in fact, composed of three parts, a stylet above, with three pairs of teeth on its sides, and two lancets beneath, each with nine or ten recurved barbs on the outer edges near the end. The spiracles are breathing pores. Each spiracle leads to an internal tracheal trunk. The tracheae send branches to all parts of the insect body. In insects, oxygen is not carried in the blood but is supplied to the various tissues through the closed tracheal system.

Internal anatomy and physiology

a) Digestion

The food tract (Fig 1.10) begins at the mouth which opens into the cavity of the sucking pump. A small tube, the oesophagous, leads from the pump to a thin-walled sac, the honey stomach, which is located in the anterior part of the abdomen. The honey stomach serves as a storage tank for food, a place to carry nectar from the field back to the hive, and is the place where chemical conversion of nectar to honey takes place. Enough food for nourishment of the bee is passed from the honey stomach to a narrow tube, the proventriculus, which acts as a valve to prevent food, such as the nectar to be used in making honey, being passed to the looped intestine or ventriculus, the true stomach where digestion takes place. Following the ventriculus is a coiled anterior intestine and a pear-shaped posterior intestine or rectum. The tapered end of the rectum opens through the anus into the cavity which encloses the sting.

The structures which function as kidneys in insects, the Malpighian tubules, are attached at the junction between the ventriculus and the anterior intestine.

b) Circulation

The body of an insect is enclosed by its external skeleton. Inside the skeleton are the muscles and organs. The spaces around these structures are filled with blood, an amber-coloured liquid called haemolymph. The blood system is not enclosed in

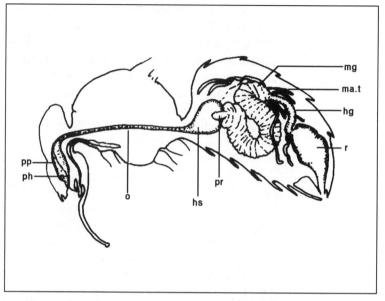

Fig 1.10: Digestive tract of a worker bee: hg, hindgut; hs, honey stomach; ma.t, Malpighian tubules; mg, midgut; o, oesophagous; ph, pharynx; pp, pharyngeal pump; pr, proventriculous or crop; r, rectum. (Adapted from Villeneuve and Vickery, 1980).

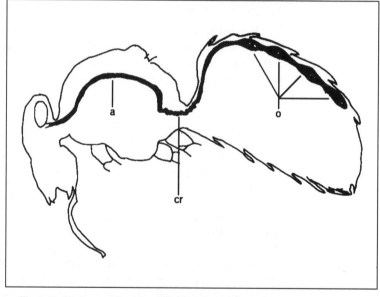

Fig 1.11: Diagram of the blood circulating system of a worker bee: a, aorta; c.r., convoluted region; o, ostia.

arteries and veins, as in mammals, but bathes the tissues directly. Very little oxygen is carried in the haemolymph, which carries mainly digested food that is absorbed into the tissues. The single blood vessel (Fig. 1.11) is a long slender tube extending forward from the middle of the abdomen to the head, where it opens beneath the brain. The part of the vessel in the abdomen is called the heart. On the sides are five pairs of slits, the ostia, through which the blood enters the heart. Rhythmic pulsation pushes the blood forward through the thoracic part of the vessel, the

16   **INTRODUCING THE HONEY BEE**

aorta, and is discharged from this organ to bathe the brain and other organs in the head, then flows through the body cavity back through the thorax and abdomen. Dorsal and ventral membranes, called diaphragms, pulsate to push blood forward and backward, respectively, to ensuring that the blood circulates throughout the body.

Insects do not have a true liver, but they do possess a food storage organ, the fat body, which stores fat, glycogen and protein granules until these food materials are required. Honey bees also store proteins in their hypopharyngeal glands.

c) Respiration

The chemical changes inside the body of an animal require oxygen for consumption and produce carbon dioxide which must be eliminated. In insects the food materials are carried to the cells by the blood but oxygen is supplied directly in a closed system. Ten pairs of spiracles in the body wall (in the sides of the thorax and abdomen) open internally into tracheal trunks (Fig. 1.12). Branches (tracheae) from the paired trunks subdivide again and again into very fine tubes called tracheoles, which go to practically all of the cells of the body. With the exception of the tiny second thoracic spiracle all of the spiracles have closing mechanisms which operate to prevent airloss. Air is sucked in by contractions and expansions of the abdomen. The tracheal trunks are thin-walled and can expand and contract in volume. The tracheae and tracheoles have rigid walls. A liquid in the tips of the tracheoles absorbs oxygen and passes it through the wall to the nearest cell. Carbon dioxide, which is produced in the cell by oxidation of the food materials (metabolism) is not discharged into the tracheoles but into the blood and eventually diffuses through the tracheae or softer parts of the insect skeleton. Metabolism in all animals produces heat and raises body temperature. It is well known that honey bees are able to maintain the temperature of the brood nest when brood is being reared and also to raise the temperature during the winter. Sustained action by the large wing muscles increases the rate of metabolism in these tissues, producing heat.

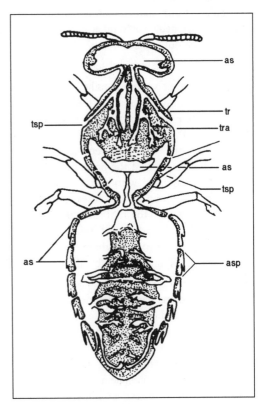

d) Protection

The sting is at the posterior end of the abdomen. Many female insects possess an ovipositor, a tube-like mechanism for depositing eggs. In honey bees, this has become modified for another purpose, protection of the hive colony and its stores of food. Normally the sting is enclosed within the body. The shaft is composed of three separate parts, a stylet above and two lancets beneath. These slender rods fit closely together, and between them enclose a channel, the poison canal. The canal is joined to the poison sac which is a reservoir for the venom. This is connected to the poison

Fig 1.12: Respiratory system of a worker bee: as, air sacs; asp, abdominal spiracles; tr, tracheae; tra, tracheole; tsp, thoracic spiracles. (Adapted from Villeneuve and Vickery, 1980).

gland, where the poison is secreted. A second gland is connected to the canal below the entrance of the poison sac. Since the lancets and stylet can slide upon each other, the sting is capable of penetrating deeper once the barbs have been inserted. The poison sac is equipped with muscles, which contract to force the venom into the wound made by the sting.

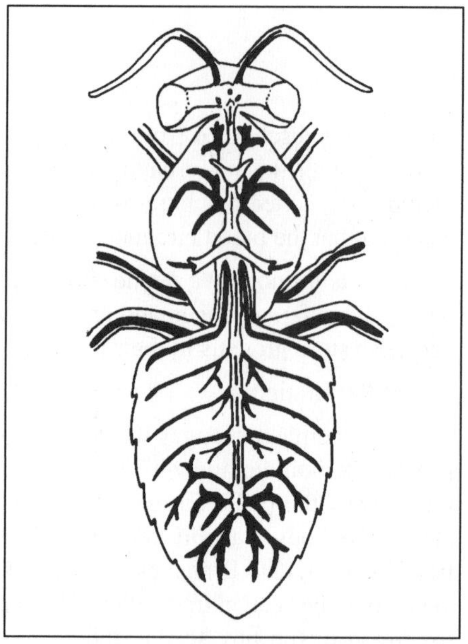

When a worker honey bee stings the entire stinging apparatus is torn out of its body and the bee dies. The muscles of the poison sac continue to work and, if the sting is not removed, will pump the entire contents of the sac into the wound. Never use the thumb and forefinger or forceps to remove a sting. This will squeeze the contents of the poison sac into the wound. Drag the sting out sideways using a fingernail.

Although honey bees can sting, they nearly always do so in protection of the hive. It is not normal for Caucasian, Italian and Carniolan honey bees to attack unless they feel that their hive is threatened. Some other subspecies of bees are notorious for aggressiveness and unprovoked attack but this has not usually been a problem here.

Fig 1.13: Nerve cord, the nervous system of a worker bee. (Adapted from Villeneuve and Vickery, 1980).

e) Nervous system and sensory organs

The nervous system is rather simple, a brain in the head and a ventral nerve cord extending from the brain to the tip of the abdomen (Fig.1.13). In most segments there is a nerve centre, a ganglion (which actually is two ganglia that are nearly fused together). In the lower part of the head three of these ganglia have come together to form a large suboesophageal ganglion (sometimes called the second brain). This structure provides nerves to the feeding apparatus. The ganglion of the prothorax, the first thoracic segment, supplies nerves to all of the structures associated with that segment. The second thoracic ganglion in the honey bee is made up of a group of four fused ganglia and supplies nerves to the remaining thoracic segments as well as to the first segment (the true second segment) of the abdomen. There are five ganglia in the abdomen supplying nerves to all of the abdominal segments.

The brain and ganglia are masses of nerve cells and nerve fibers. There is more independence of the nerve centres in insects than in most other animals. The brain receives the sensory nerves from the antennae and eyes. If the head of an insect is removed, these senses and the ability to eat are lost but the insect can still walk or fly, and a headless bee can still sting. The sensory structures associated with the nervous system are many and varied.

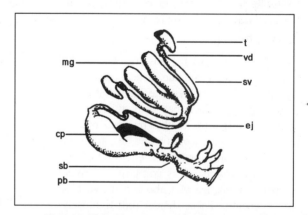

Fig 1.14: Male (drone) reproductive system: cp, chitinous plate; ej, ejaculatory duct; mg, mucus gland; pb, penis bulb; sb, spiral band; svc, seminal vesicle; t, testis; vd, vas deferens. (Adapted from Villeneuve and Vickery, 1980).

Eyes: The essential parts of the eyes are the external lens and the retina, a light-sensitive structure connected by nerves to the brain. Each of the three simple eyes, or ocelli, has but one lens and one retina. A compound eye has thousands of lenses and a single retina which is divided into parts corresponding to the lenses. Although it is thought that insects see mosaic pictures, it is impossible to determine the final effect upon the brain and the actual picture that they see. It is known that honey bees can distinguish certain shapes and that they can detect and respond to moving objects. It appears that honey bees are particularly responsive to a "flickering" motion,which is what they would see when flying over plants being moved by wind. Honey bees see certain colours, yellow, blue-green, blue, violet, and ultraviolet. They do not see red.

Antennae: The antennae are covered with sensory receptors. Many of these are in the form of hairs which connect at their bases with nerve cells. The nerve cells lead to the large double nerve trunks which extends from each antenna to the brain. The hair-like receptors are organs of touch. Other receptors are peg-like and are probably stimulated by odours or particles in liquids. They are organs of smell or taste. Some of these receptors occur in sunken cavities. Still others, the most numerous of all on the antennae, appear as tiny oval discs or plates. They are called plate organs and are thought to be the principal organs of smell in honey bees. The antennae of queen bees have 2,000 to 3,000 of these plate organs while worker bees have 5,000 to 6,000 and drones have nearly 30,000. The sense of smell of drones must be very acute in order to detect and pursue virgin queens leaving hives on mating flights.

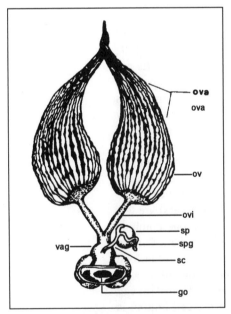

Fig 1.15: Female (queen) reproductive system: go, genital opening; ova, ovary; ovi, oviduct; ov, ovum (an egg); sc, spermathecal canal; sp, spermatheca; spg, spermathecal gland; v, vagina. (Adapted from Villeneuve and Vickery, 1980).

Reproductive structures

Males (Fig. 1.14): The testes of drone bees are paired flattened organs inside the abdomen. These are connected by ducts to seminal vescicles which open into two large mucous glands. A common duct from these glands leads to a penis which discharges sperm during mating. The penis is normally held inverted inside the abdomen of the drone. Sperm are stored in the seminal vesicles until shortly before mating, when they move along the ducts and fill the bulb of the penis. When a drone mates with a queen the penis is everted (at least the end of the penis structure is turned inside out) and is inserted into the vaginal opening of the queen. The penis is then torn from the drone, breaking at its weakest point leaving the penis bulb and the sperm with the queen. The drone then tumbles to the ground and dies.

Females (Fig. 1.15): The ovaries of queen bees are two pear-shaped masses of small, closely packed tubules called ovarioles. At the posterior end, the ovarioles of each ovary unite as a lateral oviduct and these two unite as a common oviduct. On the dorsal wall of the vagina is a duct leading to a spherical pouch, the spermatheca, in which the sperm is stored.

Insemination and Fertilization

A virgin queen makes a single mating flight or successive flights over a period of one or two days. Drones follow her to an altitude of about 15 metres (50 feet). She may, and usually does, mate with

Fig 1.16: Worker bee producing wax scales.
(Photo by K. Lorenzen, Andromeda
Productions, Elmira, New York).

several drones in succession on the same mating flight, usually between 10 a.m. and 2 p.m. on a fine day. After the mating flight or flights a queen never mates again.

When the penis of a drone is everted and inserted into the vagina of a queen, sperm which were inside the penis bulb before eversion of the penis, are discharged directly into the vagina. They are stored temporarily in lateral vaginal pouches. When the queen has returned to the hive worker bees assist her in removing the genital remains of the drones. The sperm is then forced into the spermathecal duct and into the spermatheca by muscular contractions. Within the spermatheca the sperm retain their vitality and viability throughout the reproductive life of the queen.

When the queen is ready to deposit eggs in the cells, the lower end of an ovarian follicle opens and an egg passes down into the vagina. The vacated follicle shrivels and its place is taken by the next follicle above. Since there is a tremendous number of such follicles, eggs can be matured continuously and move to the vagina one after another in quick succession. During the descent from the follicle to the vagina, an egg completes its maturation process. Its nucleus divides twice, one of the new nuclei peristing while the other three are absorbed. In the cell nucleus of the female honeybee there are 32 chromosomes. The chromosomes carry the hereditary directives which determine the structure, behaviour, etc., of the new individual. During the first division, each new cell receives only half of the number of chromosomes (16). During the second division, each chromosome splits so that each new cell also has 16 chromosomes. The egg, with only half the total chromosome complement, is now ready to be fertilized by sperm which are discharged from the spermatheca. Drones have only 16 chromosomes, so no reduction in number occurs in formation of the sperm. Only eggs which are destined to produce female bees (queens or workers) are fertilized. The two nuclei, the egg from the queen and the sperm from the drone combine and the total number of 32 chromosomes is restored. The resuting bee will be a female. Whether the fertilized egg becomes a queen or a worker depends entirely upon the food given to the larva. The queen can also lay unfertilized eggs. Since these contain only 16 chromosomes, they develop into drones. The queen has to reach deeper to deposit an egg on the bottom of the deeper drone cell. The extra stretching to reach the cell bottom is said to cause constriction of the duct from the spermatheca and prevents the descent of sperm to fertilize the egg.

A queen can lay a tremendous number of eggs in a short time, up to 3000 in a 24 hour period, but usually no more than 2000 and an average perhaps of only about 1500. Even at that she lays at a rate of an egg in less than a minute.

Glands and pheromones

Glands:

There are glands in larvae and pupae of honey bees which produce hormones governing development of these immature stages to the adult stage. These hormones function within the bodies of the insects. The salivary glands of honey bees contain enzymes, one of which is invertase which brings about the conversion of sucrose and other complex sugars to glucose and fructose, the simple sugars of honey.

The hypopharyngeal glands of worker bees secrete royal jelly, the protein-rich food which is fed to young worker larvae and to larvae of queens and drones. When producing royal jelly, young nurse bees five to twelve days old eat large quantities of pollen. At the age of 12 or 13 days, they cease eating pollen and these glands cease functioning. Wax glands of worker bees, 12 or 13 to 18 days of age secrete the wax used in building combs and capping cells (Fig. 1.16).

Pheromones:

Another group of chemical substances, produced by glands of honey bee adults, and probably also by larvae, function in a very different way. These chemical substances, called pheromones, are chemical messengers by which the bees communicate with each other. Most pheromones are volatile, producing odours which are detected by sensory receptors of other individuals, most of which are on the antennae and mouthparts. They evoke very definite responses in other individual honey bees.

The term "pheromone" was coined by Karlson and Butenandt (1959) to describe the "substances" that are produced in glands in insects and other animals, which do not affect the individual that produces them but which do affect other individuals of the same species. The term is a combination of two Greek words, 'pherein' (to carry) and 'horman' (to excite or stimulate) (Karlson and Butenandt,1959).

a) Queen pheromone.

Butler (1954) recognized that something connected with the queen produced a profound effect upon the behaviour and activities of the worker bees in a colony. He referred to this as the "queen substance", a term which is still useful as it is now known that this pheromone is a combination of compounds, some of which act together and others which act alone. It is produced in the mandibular glands of the queen. These glands exude the "substance" near the mandibles and it is then spread by the queen over her body. Several times I have noticed queens stretching and turning their bodies and passing their legs along the sides of their bodies, first the first pair of legs, then the second pair, followed by the third pair in rapid succession. I noted this behaviour but was not conscious of its significance until I became aware of the work of Butler (1954, 1960a,1960b, 1961).

Karlson and Butenandt (1959) listed two ways in which pheromones could elicit a response, those which are olfactory as airborne scents and those which are oral and cause reaction when ingested. The queen substance acts both ways.

Adler *et al.* (1973) studied the chemical composition of the queen substance and isolated a major component, trans-9-oxo-2-decenoic acid. This compound is a sex attractant for drones (Gary, 1962) and also inhibits ovary development and queen rearing in worker bees (Butler *et al.*, 1961). It has been shown that a response to this compound is triggered by cells in the specialized pore-plates on the antennae of all three castes of bees (Kaissling and Renner, 1968). It would appear that this fraction of the queen substance is of the olfactory type. It certainly works in an olfactory way to attract drones in flight and requires only a very small amount to be effective. This pheromone does not attract drones inside the hive, probably because the substance is present in such a large quantity that the attractant pore-plates of the drones are overpowered and so do not function to elicit a response. Worker bees were found not to be affected by the tiny quantities which affected drones but required much higher levels. The results obtained by Adler *et al.* (1973) corroborated the very similar results obtained by Blum *et al.* (1971).

Judging from observations of the bees as they were attending the queen and their subsequent behaviour, the queen substance also affects the worker bees by oral dosage. Many of these bees stroked the queen with their antennae and some appeared to "lick" the abdomen of the queen. Few attendant bees remained near the queen more than a few minutes. Nearly all of those bees which have been marked and observed became food-sharers and continued to share food with worker bees engaged in other tasks for up to 35 minutes. During food sharing, two bees continuously tap each others antennae but, as worker bees require a higher level of the pheromone than drones (1.0 mg for workers as compared to 0.025 mg for drones (Adler *et al.* (1973)) it is doubtful that antennal tapping is the sole method of transfer from one bee to the other. The transfer takes place, is rapid and is continuous, judging by the quick response of nearly all bees in a colony when the queen is removed. They become aggressive and agitated and the number of guard bees is greatly increased in a very short time.

The effect of the queen substance on the colony as a whole is to maintain "morale", if the bees can be thought of as recognizing well being. As previously mentioned, they recognize when the queen is missing through the lack of the "share" of the pheromone to each of them.

Queen substance acts on the worker bees to inhibit development of their ovaries. Ovaries of most worker bees will develop only in the absence of the pheromone, when the queen is missing or has failed. In some cases of rapid colony buildup, distribution of the pheromone to all worker bees in a colony may be affected and if the amount of the pheromone secreted by the queen does not increase to match the rise in colony population, then the amount given to each worker may be insufficient to inhibit ovary development. It is probable that a small number of laying workers exist in nearly all very strong colonies.

The pheromone also normally inhibits queen cell building (Butler, 1960a). If the share of each worker drops below a certain level, this inhibition is removed. This appears to be the basic reason for the building of queen cells so that the colony can swarm.

Drones react to very minute amounts of airborne chemical which, when a virgin queen leaves the hive, acts as a very powerful drone attractant. The drones are able to follow the scent until they are close to the queen, then follow her by visual means. At close range the pheromone acts as an aphrodisiac, stimulating the drones to mate.

Worker bees outside the hive are able to detect the odour of the airborne pheromone so that when a swarm leaves the hive, the cluster forms around the queen which has alighted on a nearby object. It also serves to

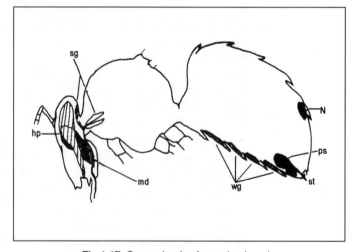

Fig 1.17: Some glands of a worker bee: hp, hypopharyngeal gland (produces Royal Jelly); md, mandibular gland (produces alarm pheromone); N, Nasonov gland (produces attractant phromone); ps, poison sac; sg, salivary glands; st, sting gland; wg, wax glands.

maintain the cluster. If the queen is not able to fly, when a swarm leaves the hive, the bees do not form a cluster but return to the hive.

Shearer *et al.* (1970) found that queens of *Apis dorsata* (Fabr.) and *Apis cerana [= indica],* the honey bees of India, also possess queen substance and that it is chemically identical to that of *Apis mellifera.*

b) Pheromones of Worker Bees

i) Attractant Pheromone.

McIndoo (1914) studied the "scent-producing organ" of the honey bee and described its structure. Many authors before 1914 had mentioned the "organ" and recognized that it produced an attractant substance. The "organ", the plate on the seventh abdominal tergum, together with its underlying gland, is now widely known as the Nasanov (or Nassonoff) gland. Figure 1.17 shows the location of the pheromone-producing glands of a worker bee. Boch and Shearer (1962) studied the chemical composition of the Nasanov pheromone and found that it contained free geraniol. The gland also produces other compounds; seven are known including geraniol, geranic acid, nerolic acid, (E) citral, (Z) citral, (E,E) farnesol and nerol (Pickett, *et al.*, 1980)

To attract the bees of a colony into the hive, worker bees elevate their abdomens and bend the tip downward so that the Nasonov gland bearing the chemicals is exposed. They then fan with their wings sending the odour outward from the hive. The reaction to this stimulus is most noticeable when bees are placed in a new home, such as hiving a captured swarm. When the workers are satisfied that the new home is acceptable and that the queen is present, they will use the attractant to bring in the bees that are still flying around outside.

Bees can often be seen "scent-fanning" at the hive entrance (Fig. 1.18), apparently to attract young bees on orientation flights as well as heavily laden foraging bees returning from the field. The scent from the Nasanov gland of worker bees does not differ from colony to colony but there appears to be superimposed upon it an odour which is specific to a colony and which does differ from colony to colony. This tends to ensure that bees in flight will re-

Fig 1.18:
Bees "scent fanning" at hive entrance to attract nectar or pollen laden hive mates and young bees from the hive on orientation flights. (Photo by K. Lorenzen, Andromeda Productions, Elmira, New York).

turn to the correct hive. This may be derived from floral scents or other sources as well as from the bees in the colony, to produce the isolating identifying factor. It probably is olfactory, transmitted by touch or by sensing a volatile com ponent that seems to be effective only at short range.

ii) Alarm Pheromones

Worker bees produce two "alarm" pheromones, one associated with the sting chamber and the other with the mandibular glands. The mandibular gland pheromone has been identified as 2-heptanone. This compound causes an immediate aggressive reaction by the bees guarding the entrance. Many of them assume the pose which is characteristic of guard bees, either standing with head and front legs raised and antennae testing the air, or running in a rather jerky manner, but in either case, ready for flight and attack as soon as an intruder comes into view. This pheromone is released by the first guard bees to identify a possible problem. Generally they do not sting unless the problem is a moving intruder. This pheromone is repellent to other bees and one of its functions may be to repel potential robber bees (Butler, 1966; Simpson, 1966; Winston, 1987).

The second alarm pheromone, iso-amyl acetate, is produced by a gland within the sting chamber (Boch *et al.*, 1962). It is not released until the sting, which is usually retracted entirely within the abdomen, is everted to the stinging position. This pheromone produces a much stronger response than the pheromone of the mandibular glands. Even then, the pheromone does not exert its maximum influence until the bee has stung and the sting, together with the glands, poison sac and muscles are torn out of the body of the bee. The pheromone then acts to "mark" the place where the bee has stung as a target for other bees. This is the reason that a sting in any exposed part of the beekeeper is usually followed very quickly by other bees which sting or attempt to sting in or near the same place.

Blum (1969) stated that the mandibular gland pheromone, 2-heptanone, was present in *Apis mellifera* and not in *Apis indica*. This is proof that the two are distinct, separate species, not the same species as had been suggested by some earlier workers. The pheromone secreted by the mandibular gland, 2-heptanone, appears to have more than one function. It acts on the bees themselves as a repellent and may be the substance used by foraging bees to mark the flowers from which they have taken the nectar. Other bees are repelled and do not visit those flowers. By the time the pheromone has dissipated the nectaries are again full of nectar (Simpson, 1966). Another pheromone, the so-called "Footprint" pheromone may be produced either in the apical segment of each tarsus, or may be 2-heptanone that is transferred to the tarsi. This pheromone may be entirely or partly responsible for marking flowers in the field from which nectar has been extracted. It may also be used to mark the entrance of the hive.

It is interesting to note that the mandibular glands of workers are homologous with the mandibular glands of queens but the pheromonal secretions and the effect of these secretions are very different. Those of the queens produce the "queen substance" but the mandibular glands of workers have two age-related functions. When the bees are young the glands produce the enriched food for the growing larvae; later they produce 2-heptanone, the alarm pheromone.

c) Other Honey Bee Pheromones

There have been opinions expressed regarding other pheromones which possibly or probably affect bee behaviour. One such opinion is that newly hatched larvae produce a pheromone which induces workers to feed them. When they require food worker bees may produce a pheromone to cause other workers to feed them.

Diploid drones can develop from fertilized eggs if a queen mates with a drone that shares a sex allele with her (Currie, 1987). Production of drones from fertilized eggs was reported earlier by Woyke (1965a). However, diploid drone larvae are eaten by worker bees within a few hours after the eggs hatch (Currie, 1987). Woyke (1965b) found the these larvae were not eaten because they were in worker cells but that some other factor was responsible. Dietz and Lovins 1975) reported that diploid drone larvae produce a pheromone that causes feeding response in worker bees. The pheromone is not produced by normal haploid drone larvae.

In an isolated area, where no new bees are added, inbreeding can cause production of many diploid drones. The size of a breeding population is important. Populations of honey bees have between 6 and 19 sex alleles on their chromosomes. A smaller population will produce more diploid drones than a larger population, even as many as 25 to 50 percent of the total (Page and Laidlaw, 1985).

Pain (1973) listed 31 pheromones, of which only 13 had been identified. The queen substance has been synthesized and has been successfully tested as a drone attractant and to prevent the construction of queen cells in a queenless colony. It is to be expected that additional work on honey bee pheromones will reveal the composition of the various pheromonal compounds which they produce and clarify their roles in honeybee behaviour. Winston (1987) has excellent coverage of current knowledge of the honey bee pheromones. ❏

REFERENCES

Adler, V.E., R.E. Dolittle, H. Shimanuki and M. Jacobson. 1973. Electrophysiological Screening of Queen Substance and Analogues for Attraction to Drone, Queen and Worker Honey Bees. J. econ. Ent. 66 : 33-36.

Betts, A.D. 1946. Longevity of queens. Bee World 27: 26.

Boch, R. and D.A. Shearer. 1962. Identification of Geraniol as the Active Component in the Nassanoff Pheromone of the Honey Bee. Nature 194 : 704-706.

Blum, M. 1969. Alarm Pheromones. Ann Rev. Ent. 14 : 57-80.

Blum,M.S., R.Boch, R.E. Doolittle, M.T. Tribble, and J.G. Traynham. 1971. Honey bee sex attractants; conformation analysis, structural specificity and lack of masking activity of congeners. J. Ins. Physiol. 17: 349-364.

Butler, C.G. 1954. The method and importance of recognition by a colony of honeybees (*A. mellifera*) of the presence of its queen. Bee World 35 (9) : 169-176. [Also in Trans, R. ent. Soc. London 105 (2) : 11-19].

Butler, C.G. 1960a. The significance of queen substance in swarming and supersedure in honeybee (*Apis mellifera* L.) colonies. Proc. R. ent. Soc. London A : 35 : 129.

Butler, C.G. 1960b. Queen recognition by worker honeybees (*Apis mellifera* L.). Experentia 16 : 424.

Butler, C.G. 1961. The scent of queen honeybees (*A. mellifera* L.) that causes partial inhibition of queen rearing. J. Insect. Physiol. 7 : 258.

Butler, C.G. 1966. Mandibular gland pheromone of honeybees. Nature 212:530.

Butler, C.G., R.J. Callow, A.W. Greenway and J. Simpson. 1974. Movement of the pheromone, 9-oxodec-2-enioc acid, applied to the body surfaces of honeybees (*Apis mellifera*). Entomologia exp. et appl. 17: 112.

Crane, E. 1975. The World's Beekeeping - Past and Present. Chapter 1, pp. 1-18 in Dadant and Sons (Eds.) *The Hive and the Honey Bee*, Hamilton, Illinois, U.S.A. Dadant and Sons.

Currie, R.W. 1987. The Biology and Behaviour of Drones. Bee World 68: 129-143.

Dietz, A. and R.W. Lovins., 1975. Studies on "Cannibalism Sub stance" of Diploid Drone Honey Bee Larvae. J. Georgia ent. Soc. 10 : 314-315.

Gary, N.E. 1962. Chemical Mating Attractants in the Queen Honey Bee. Science 136 (3518) : 773-774.

Kaissling, K.E. and M. Renner. 1968. Antennale Rezeptoren fur Queen Substance und Sterzelduft bei der Honigbiene. Z. vergl. Physiol. 59 : 357-361.

Karlson, P. and A. Butenandt. 1959. Pheromones (Ectohormones) in Insects. Ann. Rev. Ent. 4 : 39-58.

Levin, M. 1983. Value of Bee Pollination to U.S. Agriculture. Bull. ent. Soc. Amer. (Winter, 1983), pp. 50-51.

McIndoo, N.E. 1914. The scent-producing organ of the honey bee. Proc. Acad. nat. Sci. Philad. pp 542-545.

Page, R.E. and H.H. Laidlaw. 1985. Closed population honeybee breeding. Bee World 66: 63-72.

Pain, J. 1973. Pheromones and Hymenoptera. Bee World 54 : 11-24.

Pickett, J.A., I.H. Williams, A.P. Martin, and M.C. Smith. 1980. Nasonov pheromone of the honeybee *Apis mellifera* (Hymenoptera: Apidae), I. Chemical characterization. J. Chem. Ecol. 6: 425-434.

Robacker, D.C. 1988. Intelligence : Man, Bee, and Boojum. Bull. ent. Soc. Amer. (Winter, 1988), pp. 177-183.

Scott Standard Postage Stamp Catalogue. 1983. Countries of the World, G - O. 139th Ed., 1983 - Vol. 3, p. 531, no 1147. Scott Publ. Co., New York.

Shearer, D.A., R. Boch, R.A. Morse and F.M. Laigo. 1970. Occurrence of 9-oxodec-trans-2 enoic acid in queens of *Apis dorsata, Apis cerana*, and *Apis mellifera*. J. Insect Physiol. 16 : 1437-1441.

Simpson, J. 1966. Repellency of the mandibular gland scent of worker honey bees. Nature 209 : 531-532.

Snodgrass, R.E. 1975. The anatomy of the honey bee. Chapter 4, pp. 75-124, in Dadant and Sons (Eds.) *The Hive and the Honey Bee*. Hamilton, Illinois, U.S.A. Dadant and Sons.

Villeneuve, J.-L. and V. Vickery. 1980. Biologie de l'abeille. Québec Min. Agr., Cons. Prod. Veget. Québec. (Agdex 616) 25 pp.

Wigglesworth, Sir V.B. 1987. Is the honey-bee conscious ? Antenna 11 (4): 130.

Winston, M.L. 1987. *The Biology of the Honey Bee.* Cambridge, Mass. and London, England. Harvard Univ. Press. 281 pp.

Woyke, J. 1965a. Genetic proof of the origin of drones from fertilized eggs of the honeybee. J. apic. Research 4:7-11.

Woyke, J. 1965b. Do honeybees eat diploid drone larvae because they are in worker cells ? J. apic. Research 4:65-70.

2

APIARY EQUIPMENT

The only beehives that are legal for housing honey bees in Canada and in bordering states of the United States are those in which combs can be removed for inspection. Comb removal is essential for inspection for disease or merely to determine the stage of progress of the colony, as well as the removal of the combs of honey when the "honey flow" is finished. Other types of hives are to be found in other parts of the world, especially in less well developed countries and particularly in Africa. Even in Europe, straw skeps can be seen at roadside stands or as displays in parks and other such establishments (Fig.2.1).

The Langstroth type hive is nearly universal in Canada. This "modern" hive has changed somewhat since Langstroth's day but the changes are only cosmetic and utilitarian. Fig. 2.2 shows the hive we use today. The modern hive preserves the bee space and generally uses Hoffmann type frames so that colony manipulations are made easier. Several bee supply companies manufacture equipment for beekeeping and they all use nearly the same measurements so that the equipment from several sources will be interchangeable.

If bee equipment is made in a home workshop, special care must be taken to ensure that the dimensions of the home-made equipment are the same as those of factory-built equipment. In general, it is best to leave construction of most bee equipment to the companies that are

Fig 2.1: Straw skeps, Leiden, Holland. (Photo by Dr. Linda Gilkeson)

Fig 2.2: Modern beehive. Note "short" bottom board and modified hive stand.

specialists. They can usually manufacture the equipment better and cheaper than can be done in a home workshop. Anyone who is reasonably good with tools, and who has the use of a circular table saw, can make hive covers, inner covers and bottom boards. If one has access to a source of good quality pine lumber, one might also make shallow supers. In my experience, the deeper, brood-chamber size supers are cheaper to buy than to make at home. This was not always the case and I have some home made supers that have been in use more than 30 years (and some that are probably 50 or more years old) and they are still serviceable and will be so for years to come. The home work-shop may turn out quite serviceable feeders of the tray type although the construction of leak-proof feeders requires more skill than making covers or bottom boards.

Parts of a Bee Hive

The parts of a hive (Fig. 2.3) are as follows: a bottom board (or floor of the hive), usually with an entrance reducer; full depth hive bodies, one or more, usually two, which serve as the broodnest or brood chamber; an inner cover and a cover. For honey storage a number of hive bodies or supers are added above the brood chamber, either full depth (same size as those used for brood) or of either of two sizes of shallower supers or any combination of these. Use of a queen excluder, a wire grid which confines the queen and thus determines that brood will be reared only in the lower supers (brood chamber) is growing in popularity. The queen excluder is placed on top of the brood super or supers and the honey supers are placed above it.

A hive stand or a suitable substitute is required beneath the bottom board to keep it clear of the ground. If the bottom board is placed directly on the ground, it will become cold and perhaps wet and the colony will suffer. Ants, which may become the scourge of the apiary, will find easier access if the bottom board is in contact with the ground. Some beekeepers purchase or construct hive stands with alighting boards, as shown in Figure 2.4. The bees should have some place to land in front of the hive entrance but the method of supplying this is left to the individual beekeeper. Hive stands can be made out of old scrap lumber, spruce or fir will do, but they must be strong enough to bear the weight of the hive with a full crop of surplus honey. Treatment of all parts of the stands, except the alighting board, with a wood preservative such as pentachlorophenol, will ensure that they will last for years. Do not treat them with creosote.

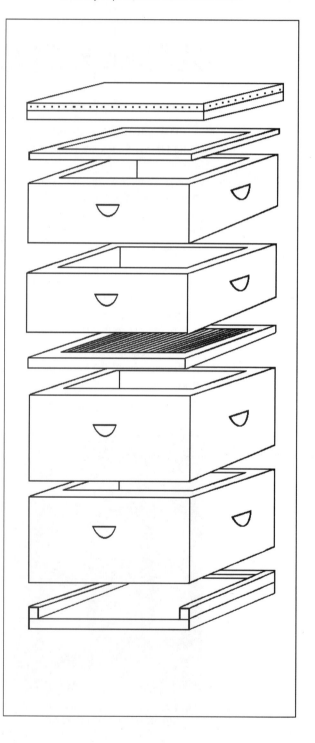

Fig. 2.3: Parts of a beehive, from the bottom up are: bottom board, 2 brood boxes, queen excluder, 2 honey supers, inner cover and cover.

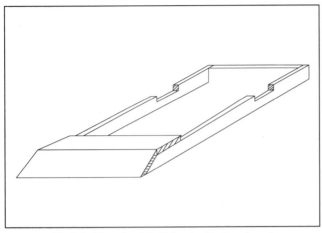

Fig 2.4: Hive stand, built for short bottom board with front alighting area.

Bottom Boards

Commercial bottom boards are reversible so that one side will provide an entrance 3/4" (1.9 cm) deep and the other a depth of entrance of 3/8" (0.94 cm). The beekeeper is supposed to unload the hive in the fall and again in the spring to reverse the bottom board. Over the past 15 or 20 years I have not found a beekeeper, other than a hobbyist with two colonies, who does this. The double-sided board adds to the cost at no benefit to the bees or to the beekeeper, who almost universally uses an entrance reducer to limit the size of the entrance. This simple, easy to make, reducer serves the purpose better and cheaper and is much easier for the beekeeper to install and remove. Single sided bottom boards are easy to manufacture at home. The bottom consists of 1/2" (1.2 cm) or 5/8" (1.6 cm) waterproof plywood cut to the size of a super. I treat the cut edge of the plywood with boiled linseed oil. The side rails (on three sides, as shown) are made from scrap wood, usually spruce, cut to 3/4" by 3/4" (1.9 by 1.9 cm). All exterior surfaces are painted with aluminum paint. This will last for some time and also makes an excellent base coat for a single coat of good quality alkyd-base paint.

The flat side of this type of bottom board is very useful as a base (or a cover) for stacking empty supers in the apiary where they will be close by when needed. They help to make the stacks "bee-tight" and help to protect against the ravages of the wax moth.

An entrance reducer is easy to make. All that is required is a piece of wood 3/4 by 3/4 " (1.9 by 1.9 cm) long enough to fit in the hive entrance. A slot, 5/16" by 2" (0.8 by 5.1 cm) is cut out of one side, the bottom, which will be the restricted hive entrance. The entrance re-

Fig 2.5:
An ingenious entrance reducer made of mud. El Minya, Egypt.

ducers sold by dealers usually have two entrances, one small, the other larger. The reducer is rotated through 90 degrees to change the opening. I have not found it necessary to have more than one size of restricted entrance. Figure 2.5 shows a mud reducer that I saw in Egypt.

The length of the bottom board that I use is the same length as a super and it does not protrude when in use. This "short" bottom board is gaining in popularity (Fig. 2.6). Although I first saw this type in use by Endel Karmo, then Provincial Apiarist in Nova Scotia, I have seen it also in such distant places as Australia. If the "multiple-colony wintering pack" is used in winter, the short bottom board is essential. It is usually necessary to provide a place in front of the bottom board for the bees to land on. I use a modified hive stand with the alighting board built in (Fig. 2.4), or at least a board laid in front of the hive.

Hive Bodies or Supers

You should notice that I use the term super for all of the boxes containing frames though some people religiously use 'hive body' for the lower brood chamber boxes and 'super' for any boxes used above the brood chamber. In many cases the boxes used above the brood chamber are identical to those used for the brood chamber so the separate definitions are really not very useful. When I mean brood chamber I say brood chamber.

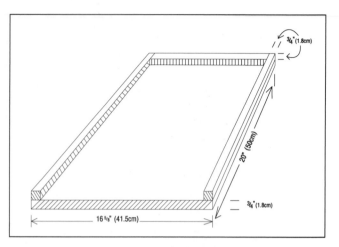

Fig. 2.6: Short or single-sided bottom board

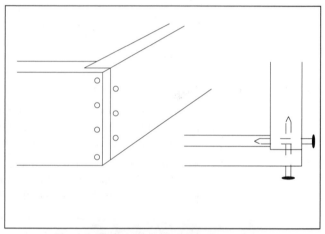

Fig. 2.7: Super with butt-end corners, showing nail placement for strength.

The standard brood chamber super is, if constructed of 7/8 inch (2.22 cm) lumber, 9 1/2"deep, 16 5/8" (42.9 cm) wide and 20" (50.8 cm)long. If the lumber is 3/4" (1.9 cm) thick the outside width of the super will be 16 1/2" (41.9cm). The inner top edges of the ends of the supers are rabbeted to support the ends of the top bars of the frames. The bees will propolize the frame ends, making them difficult to remove so the rabbet is generally cut to depth of 3/4" (1.9 cm) by 3/8" (0.95 cm) of the thickness of the wood and a metal frame rest is nailed into place.

Shallow supers are made in the same way but are shallower, 5 5/8" (14.3 cm) for the "regular" shallow, or 6 5/8" (16.8 cm) for the deep shallow super. Commercially manufactured supers are made with dovetailed corners and are usually sold in cartons of five. When assembling supers, one should not mix the contents of several cartons. The cuts in different lots may be slightly different so that it may be difficult to fit them together. I have seen discrepencies so great that putting the pieces together was impossible and both cartons came from the same manufacturer.

The dovetailed corners can be made at home if you are expert enough but a corner such as that shown in Figure 2.7 is just as satifactory and the super should last for many years. I have some "butt-end" supers that were in use long before I bought them more than 35 years ago.

Commercially produced supers have "hand-holds" cut into all four sides to make lifting the super easier. It would be more appropriate to call these finger-holds as only the tips of the fingers will fit into them. Hand holds should be cut into all home built supers. It is quite easy to do if you have a bench saw or radial arm saw. A full-depth super full of honey may weigh up to 90 lbs. (40.8kg) and is awkward to carry even with the hand-holds. I do not recommend nailing hand grips on the outside of the supers. These get in the way and in any case are not usually as easy to grip as the cut in hand-holds.

Frames

Self-spacing Hoffman type frames are generally the best to use. Hoffman frames are self-spacing because the "shoulders" on the end bars (Fig. 2.8, left) are of such a width that only 10 frames will fit in a super. When new frames are put into a super they will appear to leave empty space but this is only as it appears. The frames, or at least the finished drawn combs, will be spaced a proper bee space apart but the beekeeper must provide the bee space between outside frames and the side walls of the hive by pushing the frames away from the walls. If this is not done, there will be only half a bee space and the combs built in these frames will either not be built on the outsides or may be attached to the wall. End bars are 9 1/8" (23.2 cm) long, 13/8" (3.5 cm) wide at the top and 1 1/8" (2.9 cm) at the bottom. They are notched 7/8"

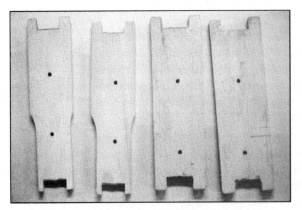

Fig. 2.8: Two types of frame end bars for shallow supers: left, with shoulders, right, closed type.

Fig. 2.9: Frames with grooved bottom bars. The frames shown also have grooved top bars and closed end bars. They are designed for use only in honey supers.

(2.22 cm) at the top and with two 3/16" (0.5 cm) slots at the bottom to take the top and bottom bars respectively. Four 1/8" (0.3 cm) equidistant holes are drilled through the end bars to take eyelets and the horizontal supporting wires for the wax foundation when it is installed.

Staple-spaced frames used to be common but were never as satisfactory as the Hoffman type frames. Bottom bars used to be either solid or in two pieces but both of these types have largely been superceded by the grooved bottom bar (Fig. 2.9). Bottom bars are 17 5/8" (44.7 cm) long and 3/8" (0.95 cm) thick and 3/4" (1.90 cm) wide with a central groove into which the wax foundation is to be inserted later.

Top bars are 19" (48.3 cm) long, cut so as to lock with the end bars. A piece on the underside is deep cut two ways but is left in place. This piece is to be removed by the person assembling the frame and is nailed in place to hold the sheet of wax foundation firmly.

Frames must be nailed together securely. Nailing through the top bar into the end bar and also through the end bar into the top bar from the end ensures that top bars are not pulled off when prying the frame loose.

The shapes and cuts required are rather difficult but they must be precise. It is better to purchase Hoffman type frames than to try to make them unless you are a "whiz" with wood and have the proper tools to do the job. Hoffman type frames for use in shallow supers are precisely the same as those for the full-depth supers except in the length (depth) of the end bars. For standard shallow supers the end bar is 5 3/8" (13.7 cm) and for the deep shallow 6 1/4" (15.9 cm) in length.

Comb Foundation

When purchasing comb foundation, be sure you get the correct size for your frames. The size for the deep frames is 16 3/4" x 8 1/2 (42.5 x 21.6 cm). It can be obtained with or without vertical support wires embedded in the wax. I prefer the wired foundation but one should be sure that the wires are "crimped" rather than straight. Straight wires do not add as much support as crimped wires do. If you use plain (unwired) foundation, you should use four horizontal wires in the frame; if the foundation has vertical wires, two horizontal wires in the frame are enough to provide the necessary support. The horizontal wires are necessary because the bees maintain a high inside temperature, 34 to 36 degrees C, and at this temperature the wax becomes soft and can sag or twist or even become "accordion-pleated" before the bees have built the cells. Once the bees have "drawn" the cells the comb should be good for a number of years - if it is well built; if not, you may have to "cull" it before the end of the first season.

Always wire the frames before inserting the foundation. The end bars are cut from pine, usually white pine in the eastern part of North America. White pine is a soft wood and the support wires will cut completely through it unless the holes the wires go through are reinforced with metal eyelets. When purchasing eyelets, get an eyelet punch too. Embed the eyelets into the holes to be used for wiring, two or four on each end bar, depending upon how many wires you need for the foundation you have on hand.

The wires must be tight in order to give the proper support. I use a gadget which puts pressure on the centres of the two end bars. Pull the wire through the desired holes then twist it around a small nail driven into the edge of the end bar and set the nail to hold. Pull the wire tight and wind the other end around another nail, cut the wire and set the nail. Be careful that you don't leave wire ends protruding. If you do they will "get" your fingers sooner or later. When the pressure on the end bars is released, the wire is tightened.

Before installing the foundation make up a support board with an upper piece that will fit inside the frame and support the foundation. Break out the nailing slat from the frame top bar. Check the sheet of foundation. There is usually one side with more wax covering the vertical wires. Place this side next to the horizontal wires with the frame top bar open slot upward. Insert the foundation into the groove in the bottom bar. Then nail the nailing slat in place to hold the foundation securely. It is not necessary to drive the nails through the foundation. It is better to drive them at an angle so that they are pointed at the rear corner of the top bar, through the thickest possible part of the top bar. This will ensure that you will not have nail points protruding. Turn the frame over so that the wires now lie above the foundation which is supported firmly from beneath. The wire has to be embedded into the wax. Some people use a spur embedder which is run along the wire while exerting pressure. This method is usually satisfactory but results are not as good as with the electric embedder. The electric embedder runs an electric current through the wire, heating it and melting the wax around it. Pressure on the bar pushes the wire into the wax. The operator must be careful as leaving the current on too long can melt through the foundation. Little more than one second is usually enough to embed the wire. After releasing the switch, hold the embedder in place for a few more seconds until the wax solidifies around the wire. Now the frame is ready for the hive. The rest is up to the bees.

Some comb foundation is now manufactured with a thin sheet of plastic between layers of beeswax. This type is somewhat stronger and is readily accepted by bees (Dadant, 1975).

Frames for the shallow supers can be of the same style as those used in the deep supers except that the end bars are shorter, 6 1/4" (15.9 cm)for the deep type shallow and 5 3/8" (13.7 cm) for the ordinary shallow supers. Obviously the foundation must be the proper size to fit your frames.

You can extract about 30 lbs (13.5 kg) from a shallow super and about 40 lbs (18 kg) from a deep shallow. It is obvious then that three deep shallows will hold as much honey as four of the ordinary shallows. From an economic standpoint the deep shallows are a "better buy" than the ordinary shallows. If lifting and carrying the weight is a problem, you may decide to use ordinary shallows anyway.

If you use ordinary shoulder-type frames in the honey supers yoou should use only nine (9) frames spaced equidistantly. In brood supers the bees build cells of the proper depth for rearing brood. Consequently when these are filled with honey the combs will be "thin" and somewhat difficult to uncap. In an area where brood cannot be raised, such as honey supers, and only nine combs are used, the bees will build the cells deeper and the result is thick combs containing plenty of honey. In order to space the combs the proper distance from each other the use of frame spacers is recommended. Frame spacers are metal frame rests with slots for the ends of the top bars.

Some manufacturers of bee equipment make a different type of frame for the honey supers. These "closed end bar" frames have wide end bars without "shoulders" . A frame of this type that I have used extensively is easy to make in a home workshop (Fig. 2.8). Both top and bottom bars are 7/8 " (2.2 cm) wide and 3/8 " (0.95 cm) thick. Both are grooved. The only difference is that bottom bars are 18 " (45.7 cm) long and top bars are 19 " (48.2 cm) in length, providing 1/2 " (1.1 cm) hangers, without a bee space between the end bars and the ends of the hive. The end bars are 1 5/8 " (3.5 cm) wide and each has two 1/8 " (0.3 cm) holes equidistant from the ends so that split pins or wire can be used for extra support for the foundation. The length of the end bars is 5 3/8 " (13.7 cm) or 6 1/4 " (15.9 cm) depending upon the super in which they are to be used. The width of the end bars spaces the frames nine to a super.

The wax foundation must be cut to fit the frames, 4 7/8 " (12.3 cm) for the shallow super, 6 " (15.2 cm) for the deeper super. To instal the foundation insert one edge in a groove (either top or bottom) and bow the foundation so that the other edge can can be inserted in the opposite groove.

Queen excluder

Do not attempt to make queen excluders. Any dealer in bee supplies has them and once purchased they will last many years. A good queen excluder is made up of round wires placed parallel to each other and welded in place. The excluder is made with outside dimensions the same as a super. It is placed on top of the upper brood chamber super. Worker bees can pass through but queens and drones are larger and so are confined to the brood chamber area. If you ever, for any reason, place brood combs above the queen excluder remember that any drones that emerge from these combs will be trapped above the excluder.

These queen excluders can be "metal bound" or "wood bound", these terms referring to the outside rim of the excluder. Either type is satisfactory. The wood bound excluders may require new rims after 15 to 20 years of use. You may also be offered queen excluders made of perforated zinc or perforated plastic. If so, run your hand across the stamped out openings. The edges of the perforations are rough and abrasive and will wear upon the wings of any bee passing through. I do not recommend this type of excluder. Other beekeepers must have the same opinion as zinc queen excluders are no longer available from many dealers.

Inner cover

A standard commercial inner cover is made of 1/4" (0.3 cm) plywood, or masonite. It has a rim 3/8" (0.95 cm) deep and about 3/4" (1.91 cm) wide - on one or both sides. It may have an elongated rounded hole cut in the centre or two such holes located near the sides and toward opposite ends. These holes are to take "Porter bee escapes" when the board is used beneath honey supers that are to be removed. The escapes provide "one-way streets" for the bees; they go down to the super below and cannot return. The holes can also be used at feeding time if you plan to feed with cans. Inverted one gallon (4 litre) cans with finely perforated friction-top lids or plastic feeder pails are placed over the holes. The holes provide access so the bees can gather the syrup at the can lid. This type of inner cover is satisfactory but I use tray feeders rather than cans and a different type of "bee escape" so I use an inner cover which is, in fact, a multi-purpose unit (Fig 2.10). I cut 1/4" (0.3 cm) plywood into 4" (10 cm) strips, then cut these into lengths of 16" (40.5 cm) and 12 5/8" (32.1 cm). Two of each of these make the sides and ends, and a rim of 5/16" (0.80 cm) high x 3/4" (1.91 cm) wide is nailed (or stapled) on each side. Screen of 1/8" (0.125 cm) mesh is placed over the open centre of the board on each side and is stapled into place. Protruding staples are clinched over. In one end (and usually also in a side) I cut a 2" (5 cm.) slot. The two pieces are readily removable but are left lightly tacked in place until needed.

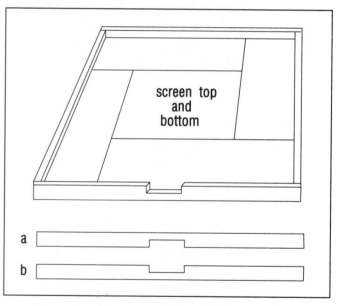

Fig. 2.10: Double-screened inner cover with rim-slot entrance. Can be used a) with slot downward for upper entrance in winter, or b) with slot upward as entrance for upper colony in double queening

I use these as inner covers with the rim slots closed during summer, or with the slots facing upward so the bees cannot use them. In hot weather, I place 2" (5 cm) thick blocks on top of the inner cover. This raises the cover and makes it possible for the bees to vent excess moisture through the top and I do not have to stagger the supers as some beekeepers do, or to elevate the bottom super above the bottom board. I dislike both of these practices and, as well, both involve extra labour.

I also use the screen boards when splitting colonies or using the double queen system, as I carry out both of the practices about the end of April when the weather is cool. The screen board is placed above the parent colony with one slot open and facing upward. This becomes the entrance for the upper colony, which is heated from below through the screens. The screens are far enough apart so that the bees from one side cannot reach the bees on the other side.

As winter approaches, and after the bees have been fed, the screen board inner covers are placed with one of the rim slots downward. The slot becomes the upper entrance for the bees during the winter.

Hive Cover

Telescoping hive covers are the most popular type in the east and appear to be the only type available from most dealers in bee supplies. These covers have sheet metal tops. The inside dimensions of this type of cover should be at least 1/4" (0.64cm) greater than the dimensions of a super. If you have supers made from 7/8" (2.22 cm) lumber, be careful when purchasing covers. Some manufacturers use only 3/4" (1.91 cm) thick lumber and they make covers to fit their supers which are 16 1/2" (41.9 cm) wide rather than 16 5/8" (42.2 cm). These covers will go on the wider supers but they may stick and be quite difficult to remove.

Covers are easy to make. The tops can be cut from 1/4" (0.64 cm) poor grade plywood. I cut mine 17 1/4" (43.8 cm) by 20 7/8" (53.0 cm) so they will fit over the supers made by any manufacturer. The telescoping side pieces are cut 3" (7.6 cm) wide and are nailed on through the top. I generally use spruce or whatever I have in 3/4" (1.91 cm) thick lumber for the side pieces. The top can be covered with metal if desired. Originally the metal was put on to prevent water getting inside as the top piece was made of boards, sometimes tongued and grooved, but would not be leakproof. As we now use plywood there is no danger of leakage and the metal top is not really necessary. If a metal top is not used the wood should receive at least two coats of good quality paint, preferably white paint, to protect the wood. Covers without metal tops are rather light in weight and must be weighted down with rocks or bricks to prevent their being blown off. I have covers like these that have been in use for 14 years and they appear to be good for several more years. Other types of covers can also be made easily in a home workshop.

Feeders

In northeastern North America bees should be fed twice during a year, early in the spring and near the end of September before the onset of winter-like conditions. The times will vary somewhat in other parts of Canada and the northern United States. I always feed at these times whether the colonies are in dire need of food or not, in order to feed fumagillin to protect the bees against Nosema. There are a number of ways and variations of these ways in which bees can be fed.

a) Boardman Feeder

The Boardman or entrance feeder consists of a wooden or plastic insert for the hive entrance which will hold an inverted container of sugar syrup, and will allow the bees access to the perforated lid of the container (Fig. 2.11). The container is usually a glass jar with a "Mason Jar" lid. I have not found these feeders to be very useful if the weather is cold and the capacity of the jar is only about a litre. It is useful if a beekeeper wishes to simulate a honey flow during queen introduction or queen rearing. I do not use them at any other time.

b) Division Board or "Frame" Feeders

This feeder is made in the shape of a frame and is intended to replace a frame during feeding (Fig. 2.12). The sides are made of Masonite with the smooth side facing inward. A stick floats in the syrup so that the bees will be able to cling to it when taking up the syrup. I have found that many bees invariably drown in the syrup in these feeders, and also in the plastic counterparts for the same reason. The smooth inner face is too smooth for the bees to climb easily and many fall into the syrup and are unable to extricate themselves. When I use this type of feeder, usually when introducing queens at times other than when the honey flow

Fig 2.11: Boardman entrance feeder

Fig 2.12: Division board feeder in place in a hive

is on, I throw away the float stick, cut a piece of screen about the height of the feeder and place it upright inside for the bees to climb on.

c) Cans or Pails

The cans and pails which are designed for feeding bees have either many tiny holes perforating the lid or a section of very fine stainless steel screen, through which the bees can take the syrup. The containers are inverted over the combs, or over a hole in an inner cover. The syrup does not leak out through the screen or the perforations. Cans or pails must be surrounded by an empty super and the cover is placed on top. This is an efficient method of feeding bees. The drawbacks are that the containers must be stored when not in use and an empty super is required for each colony to be fed. If you don't have spare empty supers you will have to remove and store the combs for each super required. I had problems with the number of combs that had to be put somewhere and always some of them would be broken. It is illegal in Quebec to leave combs outside and uncovered so finally I discarded my pails and switched to using tray feeders.

d) Tray Feeders

Any type of tray feeder has an advantage in that the syrup is located directly over the cluster of bees and is kept warm by the heat escaping from the cluster. Tray feeders usually hold a gallon or two gallons (4.2 to 8.4 litres) of syrup so the feeding operation can usually be done at one time and repeat visits for feeding are not necessary. The commercially built feeder generally available in eastern North America has a box-like structure (Fig.2.13) in the centre which allows the bees to come up and take syrup and return to the hive below. The centre structure is covered over by a box with metal top and sides and with wooden ends. Unless this box is weighted to hold it down, it will rise somewhat because the wood floats in the syrup. When the syrup level is low, bees can escape under the edges of the metal sides and become stuck in the syrup. I have seen thousands of bees dead in feeders of this type (see Fig. 13.3). I feed bees to keep them alive, not to kill them, so I have discarded the metal and wooden boxes and have replaced them with a box made entirely of 1/8" (0.3 cm) screen. This cannot float and no bees are lost. I have used them for years with no trouble. Another modification, if it can be called that, is to just throw away the metal covers, sprinkle handfuls of dead grass in the syrup, and allow the bees free access. Jack Arnott has told me that the bees take the syrup very rapidly using this method. He has also used a tray feeder in this way beneath the brood supers in very cold weather. It worked for him but I won't try it.

Most beehives are tipped slightly toward the front so that if rain beats in at the entrance it will run out again, not run to the back of the bottom board and remain as a serious problem to the bees. In feeders with the transverse box, some syrup runs to the front end of the feeder and is not available to the bees. I had heard of a feeder with the feeding area at the front, called a Collins type feeder. I had not seen one but proceeded to build a few which usually worked

Fig. 2.13: Tray feeder, the type sold commercially.

Fig. 2.14: Tray feeder, a new design.

very well, except that "package" colonies in cool weather did not move forward to follow the path to the syrup. These feeders also had the food access covered by screen to prevent the bees getting stuck in the syrup. I was surprised that the package colonies did not use this feeder more readily as I have had excellent feeding success with the same type of feeder designed to feed small colonies in 4-frame nucleus hives.

I tried another approach. The result is shown in Figure 2.14. The access for the bees runs from the centre of the box to the front end. It is covered by screen. There has been no difficulty at all for the bees to reach the syrup and to get all of it. I did not patent this feeder. I have shown it to others and there are many now in use.

Slatted Bottom Boards

These slatted boards are placed between the bottom board and the bottom brood super. Extra room is provided for the bees and the slats discourage the building of burr comb below the bottom bars of the combs. The boards are supposed to help to prevent swarming. I have not tested them for this aspect but colonies in hives with the slatted boards built up in the spring more quickly than similar colonies without them. They may be of some use in outside wintering. The slatted boards I have used are deeper (3" =7.5 cm) than standard slatted boards. The cross slats are near, but not at the top.

Koover (1989) found that he did not need double brood chambers when he started using slatted boards and still had strong colonies and excellent honey yields when he used the slatted boards with single brood chambers.

Solar Wax Melter

Although many beekeepers do not use a solar wax melter, it is a useful piece of equipment in an apiary. Established beekeepers continually find burr comb on frames and scrape it off with a hive tool. Over a season the amount of wax builds up. Then there are those combs that are to be culled. Too many drone cells, sagged combs, broken combs, etc., or even very old combs all should be set aside. Queen excluders collect quite a lot of wax over a period of time. This wax can be removed very effeciently by placing the excluders in a solar wax melter.

A solar wax melter allows a beekeeper to salvage all of the wax and at no cost for energy. All he has to do is to throw the scrap combs, etc., into the melter. The sun does the rest.

The melter consists of a box, insulated at one end and on sides and bottom, with a double-glazed tight fitting top. The rear end of the box is raised about 30 degrees so as to catch the sun's rays. Heat from the sun melts the wax which runs into a container while the "slum gum" residue is trapped. Any honey in the combs will melt and run to the container where it remains under the wax.

Personal Equipment and Tools

a) Hive tool

Two types of hive tools are currently available to the beekeeper, the old standby L-shaped tool which has been used for many years and the tool with the hook at one end (Fig.2.15), which has been available in North America only during the past few years. I like the old style tool for prying apart supers, for separating frames in a super, and for scraping hive parts, but for getting combs out of a super, the hook type is definitely superior. I keep both types on hand in the apiary.

b) Bee Veil

I can't recall how many times I have been stung on the end of the nose and a sting there is more painful (for me anyway) than a sting anywhere else. If I had worn a veil this might not have happened. I dislike wearing a veil unless I have to and much of the time I can work without it, but I always have one nearby when I am in the apiary.

A veil should be part of any beekeepers list of essentials. There are many styles. I use a folding wire screen veil and I am careful to fold it flat after use. I learned to do that after leaving hat and veil in the trunk of my car and piling a load on top. The veil was not completely ruined but the hat was a complete loss. There are veils which are fastened to a coverall by a zipper. This is certainly a bee proof arrangement but I have a lot of trouble to get the veil (with hat) zipped on after I have put on the coverall. With this it is either wear the veil or forget the veil. I like to keep my options open, that is to put on the veil in a hurry if I have to. Many veils tie on with the cords crossing over then around the body. They do work loose in time and it is always possible for bees to crawl up inside. Some of my nose stings were acquired while wearing a veil. Most of the time I manage to release or "otherwise dispose of" bees that get inside my veil, without being stung.

A newer type of veil has a plexiglass front panel and is said to allow better visibility. I have not tried one but it seems to me that it would fog up, and would then be a hindrance rather than a help. An ordinary mosquito veil is satisfactory and no hat is required. Visibility is not quite as good with the mosquito veil as with other types but it keeps out black flies too in areas where these are a problem. A bee-hood and veil zipped to a bee suit, eliminates the use of a hat and will allow much better head movement. This is the one I recommend as it is probably the answer for people who are rather afraid of bees or those who are sensitive to bee stings. This type will probably be essential for working Africanized bees or hybrids.

Most veils require a hat and are fitted over the crown of the hat. The "bee hats" sold for use with veils are fine, especially those with a mesh weave which allows passage of air. Don't wear a felt hat. Bees do not like animal products like fur, hides, leather or felt. Even woolens are on their hate list. Once a few stings are placed in a felt hat, the hat becomes an immediate target on the next visit to the apiary. The marker pheromone which accompanies a sting is apparently retained in felt for some time.

c) The Smoker

Every beekeeper requires a smoker (Fig. 2.16) and a supply of fuel to keep the smoker going during the apiary operations. I strongly recommend that a prospective beekeeper should

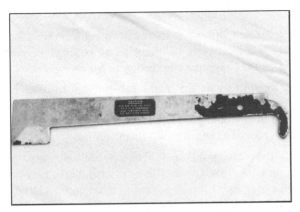

Fig 2.15: Hive tool, hook type.

buy a smoker with a protective shield. An unshielded smoker can give a very bad burn as the fire-pot becomes very hot. I like to have both hands free when working the bees so I usually keep the smoker between my knees. You can see why I need a shielded smoker.

Do not use a great deal of smoke on the bees. This is not a situation where a lot is better than a little. A couple of quick puffs at the entrance is usually enough. Be ready to give more when you remove the inner cover. After that use smoke only when there are so many bees that what you want to see is hidden. Too much smoke may cause the bees to "run" on the combs making it difficult to see what is in the cells.

Fig 2.16:
Bee smoker with shield

d) Gloves

Bee-proof gloves may be useful once in a while and may seem to be essential to beginning beekeepers. Experienced beekeepers rarely use them unless they happen to be very sensitive to bee venom. I do not wear them unless the bees are so excited that it seems necessary, and that is very infrequent. Gloves make it more difficult to get a proper grip on a super or a frame. I would rather take a few stings on the fingers than risk dropping a comb. If you buy gloves, get those that have ventilation screen at the wrists; otherwise the gloves are very hot to wear.

Marking Equipment

Bee hives and other equipment are often marked with some means of identification. If it is stolen, the item can be identified readily if it is marked. Without such marking, proof of ownership is nearly impossible even though the beekeeper can recognize his own property.

Marking with paint is not always satisfactory as the marks can be painted over, but paint is better than no marks at all. If the owners name or initials are painted clearly on the outside of supers, covers, etc., a would-be thief would probably leave them alone unless the hives (and perhaps also the bees) are to be moved a long distance in a short time.

Some beekeepers use rubber stamps and marking ink to mark equipment with the name and address of the owner, even on the top bars of the frames. In time such marks may become obscured but the ink penetrates the wood and positive identification can usually be made. Stamped marks are not visible very long on painted surfaces.

The best method of marking bee equipment is to burn the marks into the wood with a branding iron. Brands can be made up which attach to a blowtorch and can be used to brand a large stock of bee equipment in a short time. A 3/8" (1.6 cm) brand can be used even on the top bars of frames. There is no way that these branded marks can be removed. Even deep planing may not remove the traces as the wood fibres not only are burned but deeper in the wood are bent. Planed areas can be treated to reproduce the brand marks.

REFERENCES

Dadant, C.C. 1975. Beekeeping Equipment. Chapter 10, pp. 303-328, *in* Dadant and Sons (Eds.), *The Hive and the Honey Bee.* Dadant and Sons, Hamilton, Illinois.

Gagnon, M. 1978. Equipment apicole. Publ. Québec Agr, Cons. Prod. Veget. Québec, (Agdex 616). 10 pp.

Karmo, E.A. 1974. Instructions for Home Construction of Beehives. Circ. Nova Scotia Dept. Agr. Mkting 110; 9 pp.

Koover, C. 1989. What size brood chamber ? Gleanings Bee Cult. 117: 222-223.

Townsend G.F. and P.W. Burke. 1972. Beekeeping in Ontario. Publ. Ont. Ministry Agr. Food. no. 490; 387 pp.

ACTIVITIES OF WORKER HONEY BEES

3

A honey bee colony must be considered as a unit and any individual bee only a temporary member of the unit. A single bee has a short life span. In isolation the life span of this bee is much shorter than when in association with other bees. Stray bees always tend to join other bees and a group of 75 or more worker bees, in the absence of a queen, will always form a cluster.

Inside a hive many activities and many behavioural patterns occur at all times, by individual bees as well as by groups of bees. Each pattern is a function of factors, some of which are internal and others which are external to the bees. Some internal factors are physiological age, genetic makeup, and hormones. External stimuli, such as sound, sight, touch, odours and pheromones, all cause behavioural responses.

Some sequences of behaviour are apparently programmed. If the pollen pellets are gently removed from a pollen-carrying bee when it arrives at the hive, the bee will still go through the motions of pellet removal and may attempt to pack pollen in a cell, even though there is no longer any pollen to take care of. Humans do such things by force of habit but do honey bees form habits independent of programmed responses ? We don't know the answer, but it is possible. Consciousness is a state which is usually found only in higher animals but Wigglesworth says that as the bees have "the components of personality and memory, at least the potential for consciousness can be seen to exist for the bee" (Wigglesworth,1987).

Programmed and Learned Responses

Bees react to stimuli instinctively. They may not be able to reason or think but they can learn. The honey bee is the shining example of learning in the insect world. Some of her relatives, wasps, bumble bees and solitary bees also exhibit learning but to a lesser degree and most insects do not learn at all. Honey bees can follow circadian (24 hour) rhythm when foraging; they can be trained to visit food sources at considerable distances from the hive, and to visit them at certain times; they learn landmarks in the general vicinity of their home hive; they associate certain colours and scents with specific food sources; they can navigate around obstacles and can even follow extremely circuitous routes from the hive to a food source and back in order to take advantage of any artifact which offers some protection from wind.

The bee dances convey information on direction and distance of a food source (or of a new home). The dance may be programmed but the dancing bee first had to learn the information which the dance conveys. Bees are able to assess the comparative quality of food sources and will select the nectar which has the highest concentration of sugar, if other factors, such as distance from the hive and ease of obtaining the nectar are equal.

It has been said that bees invariably respond to a given stimulus in the same fixed manner. There are so many variables in stimuli, many of which we are unable to assess adequately, that such a statement is difficult to prove or disprove. If it is true, bees could well be called biological robots, but there are many facets of bee behaviour which contradict this point of view.

Activities Inside the Hive

A honey bee colony is a well integrated and cohesive unit. The worker bees perform all of the essential functions in the hive except producing eggs. This task normally is performed only by the queen. There is a well defined division of labour among the worker bees in a colony. This was recognized nearly two thousand years ago but more recent observation has brought this phenomenon into much clearer focus.

It is well known that newly emerged bees confine their activities to household chores within the hive and begin field duties at approximately three weeks after emergence. Young adult worker bees, newly emerged from cells, first look for food. Older bees patrolling the brood area provide this food. Many new bees are fed before they are completely free of the cell in which they passed their immature stages.

a) Cleaning the Hive and Feeding the Brood

Under normal circumstances, the "house" duties performed by newly emerged bees follow a well defined sequence. First they clean cells, removing any debris (such as bits of pollen or loose wax) and smoothing and repairing the rims of the cells, which are usually in a somewhat ragged state after bees emerge from them.

Several house duties are dependent on development and functioning of certain glands in the bodies of the bees. Until these begin to function, a bee is unable to perform duties other than house-cleaning and feeding older larvae. Feeding older larvae usually starts when the bees are three days old. Older larvae are fed a mixture of pollen and diluted honey which has been thoroughly mixed by the nurse bee. At the age of six to seven days, the mandibular glands become functional and the nurse bee produces "Royal Jelly", the "brood food", which she feeds to younger larvae. The time taken in feeding a larva varies. Some visits are very short, taking only two or three seconds, but may last up to two or three minutes. The extended time is due to the examination of the larva before feeding. The nurse bee, using her antennae, apparently determines the health and stage of development of the larva before adding food in the base of the cell. The larva literally floats in its food supply. It has been observed that an individual larva is visited about 1300 times a day or has more than 10,000 visits during its larval life (Lineburg in Nelson et al., 1924). Lindauer (1953) determined the time expended in rearing one larva and the number of bees involved: 2785 bees spent 10 hours, 16 minutes and 8 seconds. Multiply that by 1500 new eggs each day and you will have an idea of what the term "busy as a bee" really means.

Another large gland in the head of a young worker bee, the hypopharyngeal gland, produces proteins, lipids and vitamins. Later the gland produces the enzyme invertase, that is so important in producing honey from nectar.

When the larva is about six days old, it has grown so that in its coiled form it fills the cell. At this stage the cell is capped over with wax by the house bees.

b) Wax Production and Comb Construction

Honey bees produce wax in wax glands on the underside of the abdomen. The hypopharyngeal glands cease to function as a bee reaches the age of about 13 days. At the same time, her wax glands become functional. Bees consume honey and pollen before they secrete wax. It is estimated that it takes about eight kilograms or more of honey for each one kilogram of wax produced. Pollen is also essential. The amount of wax produced is directly proportional to the supply of pollen in the hive. Wax production can be carried on only at high temperatures, 33 to 36 degrees C. inside the hive.

When bees secrete wax scales, they hang very quietly by the fore-legs, often in a great festoon of bees hanging together. As the scales are produced they are dislodged from the wax pockets by means of spines on the hind tarsi. The scales are then transferred to the forelegs where they can be grasped by the mandibles. The wax is chewed thoroughly and is mixed with a secretion from the mandibular glands before it is used in comb-building. A bee which produces wax usually places a wax ball near where it will be used. Other bees carry out the actual construction. Honey bees which have been hived following swarming, and also during a honey flow, will draw foundation and build new combs very quickly. At other times they will build only enough comb to supply their immediate requirements.

The cell of the honeycomb is a hexagonal-shaped tube. Each of the six walls forms part of the wall of another cell (Fig. 3.1). The comb is built vertically with cells on both sides of a common base and they are not built at right angles to the base, but are sloped slightly upward. The slope helps to prevent a larva or honey falling out of the cell. This type of construction is recognized by engineers to be the strongest type possible.

Worker sized cells average 8.57 per square centimetre (55.3 per square inch) in combs constructed by Italian and Caucasian bees. Drone cells are larger in diameter and each square centimetre contains about 5.20 cells (33.5 per square inch). Bees wax foundation is made on rolling dies which emboss or press into the sheet the bases of the correct size for worker cells. Both worker and drone cells are permanent cells and both are used for brood rearing and for storage of honey and pollen. Queen cells are temporary cells, produced only when a new queen is required, in an emergency where a queen has been injured or killed, in cases where a queen is failing and supercedure is essential to colony survival, or when a colony is preparing to swarm. A queen cell is much larger, and is built on the comb face or near the bottom bar of the frame with the tip pointing downward (Fig. 3.2).

Fig. 3.1
Cells in a honeycomb.

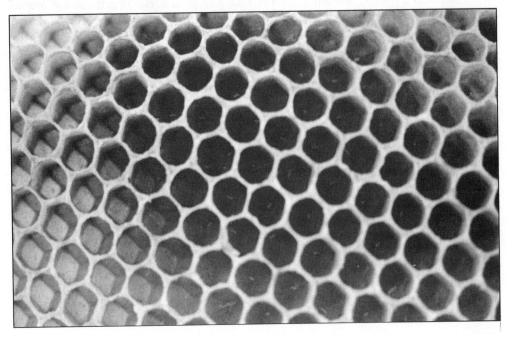

c) The Honey Makers

Storing and ripening honey are activities which are directly related to feeding the brood since the food must be processed before it can be used.

Ripening honey involves two distinct processes, a chemical change in the sugar and elimination of surplus water. After a house bee has received a load of nectar, that is composed mainly of the disaccharide sugar sucrose and water, from a field bee she performs a series of movements of the proboscis, raising and lowering it and at the same time regurgitating and swallowing small drops. This is part of the ripening process. Then she searches for a cell in which to deposit the drop of nectar. Using her mouthparts as a brush, she paints the nectar on the upper wall of the cell. This is to increase the surface area so that excess water can be evaporated. Sometimes, workers hang drops of nectar in cells, also to increase surface area for evaporation. Later the nectar is collected and it may be worked over by many bees before it is "ripened" and stored in the cells. The bees add an enzyme to the nectar: this enzyme, invertase, causes inversion of the sugars changing them from complex to simple sugars. Most of the process is completed in a few hours, although inversion continues to take place even after the honey has been packed. The sucrose must be reduced to less than 5 percent and the water content to 20 percent or less before the product can be called 'honey' under the Pure Food Laws of Canada. The honey may ripen in three to five days if the original concentration of sugar was high. The rate of evaporation depends to some extent on outside conditions of temperature and humidity. When the moisture content of most of most honey has been reduced to 17.6 per cent. or less, the cells are capped with beeswax. Heather honey usually is capped when the moisture content is greater than 20 per cent., but this is a special case. Heather honey forms a gel and does not ferment or granulate at this moisture level. Prior to capping, honey may increase in moisture level if humidity is high and further evaporation may be necessary. Honey does not lose or gain moisture to the same extent after the cells are capped.

d) Orientation Flights and Guarding the Hive

When the young bee is about thirteen days old she makes a short flight outside the hive for the purpose of orientation or defecation. Then she returns to begin other work in the hive. These duties may include cleaning the hive, carrying out dead bees and debris, packing pollen, taking nectar from field bees and storing it, ripening honey, producing wax, building comb, capping cells and applying propolis. When house bees are 18 to 20 days old they may also do guard duty at the hive entrance to prevent the entrance of intruders. At 20 to 21 days of age the bees begin field work, bringing nectar, pollen, water and propolis back to the hive. On the average, the field workers die between the thirtieth and thirty-fifth day, although exceptional circumstances can shorten or prolong this period.

This outline of duties is in general correct, but the duration of any type of duty is very flexible. It is known that worker bees in the hive do not work all the time. They do not sleep, in the same sense that we know sleep, but they do spend time doing nothing and a great deal of time "patrolling", moving about the hive with no readily discernible purpose. These two activities, "loafing" and "patrolling" may take up as much as 70 percent of the time spent by bees on household duties. Bees which appear to be wandering aimlessly will take on any task if they find one that requires attention. Most of the bees perform many different duties during their tour of duty in the hive. Only a very few bees actually perform guard duty and only a few bees attend the queen. Most bees produce wax, though perhaps not all of them do. If they produce wax, it is at age 12 to 18 days, as it is at this time that their wax glands are at full development.

The life of a colony proceeds without any need for direction for the bees to perform the essential tasks. Patrolling bees are able to determine what is required and to begin work at these tasks immediately.

e) Environmental Control - Air Conditioning

Environmental control in the hive consists of removing foreign objects (debris, invading animals), cleaning, propolizing, heating and ventilation. Any foreign object, even a dead bee, is removed from the hive as soon as possible. When nectar gathering is at its peak, field bees may be dying at the rate of one thousand or more each day. Many of these bees may be affected by a poisonous substance or a disease. Others may be worn out. Most of them die in the field; those which die in the hive are removed immediately. If possible they are carried well away from the hive so it is unusual to find more than a few dead bees near the entrance. If there are many dead bees, something is obviously wrong and requires checking by the beekeeper. Immediate removal of dead bees protects the remaining bees from infectious diseases or poisons which they might be carrying. Should an object or animal get into the hive which is too heavy for the bees to remove, they kill it by stinging, then cover it completely with propolis. They almost always try to remove it by chewing it. When they fail the propolis is added often covering the skeleton of the animal. I have found field mice and snakes completely covered with propolis on the floor of a hive.

The bees keep their hives scrupulously clean, although when they use a great deal of propolis, it may not appear to us to be clean. The propolis seals spaces and fills cracks and crevices that might harbor bacteria, moulds or small insects. Propolis has a bactericidal effect due to the presence of galangin, caffeic acid and ferulic acid (Cizmarik and Matel, 1973). It also appears to protect the inside of the hive against water and it stops air draughts.

Bees consume honey and produce heat by vigorous muscular activity with the flight muscles. Coupled with heating is ventilation, which is very important in colony sanitation and well being. Excessive moisture is a major problem in the hive.. The bees must evaporate water to produce honey and this adds to the moisture problem. Honey bees ventilate (Fig. 3.3) by fanning to cause air to move through the hive and to carry moisture out of the hive. Alternatively, when the weather is hot they bring in quantities of water and evaporate it inside the hive while ventilating, to keep the hive temperature relatively constant. Honey bees are very efficient at maintaining the proper balance of temperature and humidity inside the hive.

Fig 3.3: Ventilation: bees are fanning at the entrance. Wing beats are so fast that wings appear to be missing. Note the bee carrying pollen.

When brood is being reared the area surrounding the cells containing brood is maintained at a relatively constant temperature of 34 to 35.5 degrees C. (93 to 96 degrees F.). During the winter the interior of the cluster remains at about 26 degrees C. (79 degrees F.), at about 14 degrees C. (57 degrees F.) in the shell of the cluster, and at about 6 to 8 degrees C. (43 to 46 degrees F.) on the outside of the cluster. When brood is present during the winter, the centre of the cluster is kept at the brood-rearing temperature, even though ambient temperature may be very cold. The winter cluster is a spherical grouping of the bees formed of an outer insulating layer 2.5 to 8 cm (1 to 3 inches) thick. Inside the shell other bees generate heat through movement. As outside temperature rises and falls, the cluster expands and contracts in size. Only the food which is stored in the area within the cluster is available to the bees during most of the winter.

As a house bee reaches 17 to 18 days old, the wax glands cease functioning and the poison sac has become filled with venom. A newly emerged bee has very little venom but this increases with age. No additional venom is produced once this level (about 0.3 mg) is reached.

Honey bee venom does not vary in bees from different geographical areas. This indicates that venom is synthesized by the bees and is independent of the proteins in varying local sources. The venom of honey bees is more toxic than the venom produced by wasps (Benton and Heckman, 1969) but, as wasps have smooth stings and can sting repeatedly, the total effect of stings by a wasp can be greater than the sting of a honey bee. Venom contains at least eight proteins, including: histamine, dopamine, mellitin, apamin, MCD-peptide (Mast Cell Destroying), minimine, and the enzymes phospholipase A and hyaluronidase.

Some individuals may be hypersensitive to honey bee venom and for these people one sting could be fatal. Death can occur in about half an hour. Prompt treatment with injections of adrenalin and antihistamines, together with ice packs, are required in such cases. Non-sensitive individuals would probably survive a hundred stings. I have personally received more than 250 stings in two minutes and obviously I survived. I felt rather dizzy for a time and my pulse rate increased but this did not last long. There was very little swelling in the areas where the stings were concentrated.

The sequence of activities of house bees correlated with age is usually as outlined but this sequence can change greatly in response to the needs of the colony. Usually, nurse bees are 3 to 12 days of age but, if an artificial colony is made up of bees of the same age group, bees up to 75 days old can become nurse bees. A colony made up entirely of newly emerged bees can send out forager bees which are only 4 or 5 days old. The behaviour pattern is very flexible and responds to take care of whatever requirements the colony may have.

Field Activities of Honey Bees

Flight outside the hive normally begins at the age of about three weeks, although some bees will make foraging trips at an earlier age if they are not required for inside duties. When a bee first ventures outside the hive, she makes short flights, then returns. These flights, which last only a few minutes, are orientation flights during which the bee learns the position of the hive in relation to other nearby objects. Often, especially on a windy day, bees may return to the wrong hive. This phenomenon, known as drifting, may be rather great in apiaries where there are no good orientation markers, but is much less in yards which have prominent distinguishing objects. If hives are painted in different colours the bees have less trouble in finding their own hives. Once orientation is established and the bees begin foraging, drifting is reduced. It may still be a problem where hives are placed close together.

The bees in a colony fan an identifying scent from the hive entrance in order to direct the bees from that hive to their home. When ventilating the hive, bees fan with their abdomens bent downward. When they are "orientation fanning" or "scent fanning", the abdomens are raised with only the tip segment bent downward to expose the Nasanov gland (Fig. 3.4).

Worker bees which have just begun foraging duty usually are directed by scout bees or other foraging bees to certain sources of supplies. About seven to ten percent of the field bees may be engaged in scouting duties. They report the sources which they have found to other bees in the hive and give directions to the sources by means of the "bee language".

In the field, honey bees on foraging trips follow the directions they have received. They use sight to locate groups of plants in the area where the source is supposed to be. Presumably they are attracted by the colour and the flickering motion of the flowers, either as the

Fig 3.4:
Bees scent-fanning at the entrance (photo by K. Lorenzen, Andromeda Productions, Elmira, New York).

flowers are moved by wind or as they appear to flicker as the bee flies above them. As they get closer to the flowers, the odour of the nectar or pollen is detected and compared with the sample obtained from the dancing scout bee in the hive.

Scout Bees

When a colony is moved to a new location, all of the field force must perform orientation flights. Some of them, the scout bees, soon extend their flight range in search of nectar and pollen. Such a colony will restrict its flight range to about 50 metres during the first day if they find suitable food sources. After this the rate of extension of flight range will be determined by the availibility of nectar and pollen, up to 150 metres if sources are good and up to 1 km if sources are sparse. Honey bees may fly as far as 12.5 km (8 miles) to gather nectar from a particularly attractive source, but their effective working range is 2.5 km (1.5 miles). The speed of flight of honeybees is about 21 to 26 km per hour (13 to 16 mph) but this speed can be maintained only with very light wind conditions. The time taken to gather nectar from a distant source is great and results in small yield for the time and effort. A bee with a load flies quite slowly.

Fidelity to plant species

Honey bees are noted for their fidelity to blossoms of a plant species. Once a bee begins to harvest nectar from the flowers of a certain kind of plant she will return to the same plant species as long as the supply of nectar and/or pollen is available. Other bees from the same colony may be working other kinds of plants, each bee showing the same constancy to the species she is working. Pollen gatherers are not quite so constant and a bee which is gathering pollen may return to the hive with pollen from more than one species. Normally, however, about 75 percent of the bees will gather pollen from only one plant species on any trip to the field and they tend to return to the same plant species as long as they can obtain pollen.

An interesting fact concerning identification of particular plants, given by Kevan (1987), is that the bees use hairs on their antennae to feel microscopic "bumps and ridges" on the petals, much like a blind person reads braille.

An individual bee works in a rather small area, returning to the same spot repeatedly. The area is variable, depending upon the density of plants. In the case of apple trees in full bloom, the area may be only one side of a single tree or the adjacent sides of two trees. In a clover field the area may be only about four or five square metres.

The speed at which a bee works flowers depends upon the amount of nectar and pollen present in the flowers and the ease at which the bee can collect these products. A bee can collect the nectar from one apple blossom in about 34 seconds; some other flowers require much more time. Pollen gatherers can collect a load in about half the time taken to collect a load of nectar. The speed of field work is influenced by temperature. The best range is between 16 and 32 degrees C. (61- 90 degrees F.),with reduction in activity below and above the optimal range. At very high temperature, 34 to 39 degrees C.(93 to 102 degrees F.), foraging activity increases markedly but this consists mainly of collecting water to cool the interior of the hive.

What the Bees Collect

a) Pollen

Pollen is essential to the colony since it makes up part of the diet of worker larvae as well as the adult bees. It provides the only source of protein, fats, minerals and vitamins. A populous colony will gather about 34 kg (75 lbs.) of pollen in a season. In collecting pollen, a bee crawls over the flowers, then begins to brush the pollen from the head, body and mouthparts with the front legs. This can be done while the bee is resting or while she is hovering in the air. The second pair of legs collects pollen from the thorax and also receives the pollen from the front legs, then transfers it to the corbiculae or pollen baskets on the hind legs. A bee may visit 8 to 100 flowers over a period varying from six to ten minutes up to three hours in order to gather a load of pollen. Pollen loads may weigh 12 to 29 milligrams, a heavy load for an insect weighing only about 82 milligrams.

When gathering both nectar and pollen, 25 percent of the bees may gather only pollen, about 58 percent only nectar, and 17 percent may collect both pollen and nectar.

When a bee returns to the hive with a load of pollen she searches for an empty cell or one which already has pollen in it. She kicks off the pollen pellets into the cell, but may not always pack it in the cell. This may be done later by house bees.

Pollen is rich in protein but the proportions of various proteins in pollen is not uniform. The amount of protein is also variable, from about 7 per cent. to more than 35 per cent. It follows that the food value of various pollens varies widely, so that a mixture of pollens from a number of sources is necessary to provide proper nutritional level for the bees. As bees do not seem to be able to select pollen for nutritional value, but apparently are guided primarily by the odours of the pollens, collections from a number of plant species are necessary. Dandelion pollen lacks some essential elements but is the only pollen available in large quantity early in spring.

Colonies that lack pollen will gather some very unlikely substitutes, such as sawdust, coal dust or *Lycopodium* spores (which have little or no nutritive value) and other odd substances.

In addition to proteins, pollen contains lipids, free amino acids, carbohydrates, minerals, enzymes, sterols and pigments. The carbohydrates are made up of sugar, starch and cellulose. The minerals are calcium, magnesium, phosphorous, copper, iron, sodium, potassium, aluminum manganese and sulphur. The copper content is especially important. Vitamins include pantethenic acid, nicotinic acid, thiamine, riboflavine, ascorbic acid and traces of Vitamins D and E.

b) Nectar

Honey is also essential for survival of the colony as it is the main source of the carbohydrates that are necessary in the maintenance of brood-nest temperature. It is produced by the bees from nectar gathered from the nectaries of flowers. When very close to or on a flower the bee is guided to the nectaries by the odour. She probes with her proboscis and sucks up all of the nectar that she can reach, then moves to another floret or to another flower. If the nectar is present in copious quantity and if the sugar concentration of the nectar is high, a bee may gather a load by visiting about 100 blossoms or less. This would permit numerous trips per day by each field bee. Each blossom she visits she marks with a pheromone which will indicate to other foraging bees that the nectar has been taken. Observations indicate that field bees average about 10 trips per day when gathering nectar, about half as many as when gathering pollen, although the number can vary between 1 and 24 trips, depending upon conditions. A heavy load of nectar can weigh up to 70 mg although average loads probably weigh about 40 mg. Some of the nectar gathered by a bee may be used as food by that bee. Sugar concentration of the nectar also affects the size of the load carried by bees: the greater the concentration, the greater the load. Temperature also has an effect; within the optimum range (16 to 32 degrees C) the higher the temperature, the greater will be the load collected and carried back to the hive.

When a field bee returns to the hive she regurgitates the nectar which is then taken up by a house bee. The forager bee may pause to take food and to clean herself, but this pause is short, about two to four minutes.

c) Water

Water is required by nurse bees when it is necessary to dilute ripe honey for feeding to the brood. It is essential in using granulated honey as the bees are unable to melt more than very small quantities unless they have access to water. Water is also essential in cooling the hive. Large quantities of water may be evaporated within the hive on hot days. Unlike honey and pollen, water is not stored in the hive for long periods, but short-term storage does occur. Water may be found on the top bars of the frames in enclosures made of wax and propolis. It may also be found in indentations in the cappings of capped brood and occasionally also in open cells which contain brood. Another method of storing water for short periods is rather unusual. Some bees fill their honey stomachs with water until their abdomens are quite distended. The water is regurgitated and spread to a very thin film by the unfolding of their probosces. As the water evaporates, it is replaced to maintain the cooling effect. These water-storage bees may retain enough water to last several days.

Water-gathering worker bees may continue to collect water even after the colony requirement for water has been met. Then the house bees refuse to take the water from them. If the field bee cannnot dispose of its load quickly she will not go to the field to collect more water.

When a hive is short of water, the sugar concentration in the honey stomachs of the house bees rises. At a certain point, the housebees will refuse to accept nectar from the field bees unless it is very dilute. This appears to be the signal to the field bees that water is required.

d) Propolis

Propolis is a sticky resinous substance which is gathered from flower buds. Honey bees will also gather unusual substances such as pitch, paint and asphalt. They frequently gather sticky materials from coniferous trees. It is used to seal up cracks. Small quantities may be mixed with wax used to build brood combs. Any space which is too small for a bee to crawl through is sealed. This serves as protection from enemies of the bees, ants and other insects seeking to rob honey, and from wax moths which could destroy the combs. Propolis also prevents entry of water and allows control of air movement within the hive.

Propolis has a very complex chemical structure, and varies chemically between collections. The colour may vary as well from brownish red to greenish. Cizmarik and Matel (1970) gave the following as being representative of an average sample of propolis: waxes 30 per cent., resins (including balsams) 55 per cent., aromatic oils 10 per cent. and pollen 5 per cent. Propolis has a bactericidal effect due to the presence of compounds such as galangin, caffeic acid and ferrulic acid (Cizmarik and Matel, 1970, 1973).

The total number of propolis-gathering worker bees in a hive is small but these bees continue to gather only propolis throughout their lives as field bees. Caucasian bees gather and use more propolis than Italian bees and this is the main reason that they are not as popular as the Italian bees in this part of North America. The extensive use of propolis makes frame removal for inspection quite difficult.

When a worker bee finds a source of propolis, she bites it with her mandibles and, using the mandibles and front legs, tears off a small piece. This is kneaded with the mandibles then transferred to the pollen basket on one hind leg. The next piece is placed on the other hind leg. When fully loaded she flies back to the hive. If a bee has difficulty in obtaining a load she may fly to the hive to obtain food, then return to the source to continue loading. In the hive the bee goes immediately to a place where propolis is needed. She does not remove the propolis herself. This is done by a "cementing" bee, which tears off small pieces with her mandibles and applies it where it is needed. Removal of the load of propolis may take an hour or several hours, depending upon the requirement for propolis within the hive.

Robber Bees

Honey bees will collect honey from any source, even if this source is a weak colony in the same apiary. They will not rob during a heavy nectar flow, but when the flow is over and the bees are forced to become idle, any source of honey will be investigated and taken by force unless guard bees of the attacked colony can drive off the invaders. Italian bees are more prone to robbing than are any other subspecies of honey bees.

Robber bees do not at first fly directly into the hive being robbed but dart to and fro at the entrance as though trying to get in unnoticed by the guard bees of the colony. These movements, however, alert the guard bees and the robbers are attacked. Additional recognition by the guards is provided by the different odour of the robbers. Each colony has its own distinctive odour. If robber bees attack in numbers, the guards sting them but soon may be overcome as each one can sting only once. Then the robbers enter the hive and begin to carry the honey back to their own hives. Other colonies soon follow the example. Soon the honey is gone and the colony is left in a badly disorganized state, or without any surviving population. When the hive has been cleaned out, the robbing bees may attack other hives. Any weak colonies, or those in hives with more than one entrance, may not be able to provide adequate defense. Once bees begin robbing, the entire apiary will be in an uproar which will last until the only remaining colonies are those which can defend themselves against attack. Small nucleus colonies are very prone to attacks by robber bees and all nuclei in an apiary may be destroyed.

Robbing can be prevented or at least kept to a minimum by ensuring that all entrances of nucleus or weak colonies are small, at any time except during a nectar flow. All cracks should be sealed. A beekeeper can sometimes stop robbing by use of heavy dense smoke from a smoker, or by installing entrance reducers on all of the hives. Piling fresh green grass in front of the entrances forces all of the bees, robbers as well as defenders, to crawl laboriously through it, while still allowing ventilation.

Communication

Animals in which solitary existence is the usual state, have no need for communication. Honey bees are social animals and in any type of social or community structure, communication is essential.

The role of pheromones in the behaviour of a honey bee colony has been discussed in the first chapter. Pheromonal communication is involuntary.

Honey bees also have methods of direct communication which are used in response to certain conditions. The dance language of honey bees has received considerable attention in recent years following the decoding of the language by Karl von Frish (1920, 1953). He was not the first to focus efforts on this phenomenon. More than 100 years earlier Spitzner (1788) called attention to the dances and described them as the method the bees used to pass information to other bees about the location of nectar-producing flowers. His work was largely ignored until Karl von Frisch began his work about 1914. For his work on the dance language, von Frisch shared a Nobel prize in 1973. He is the only worker in apiculture who has received this prestigious award.

We can see the bees dancing on a comb and tend to overlook the fact that the bees in the dark hive cannot see a dancing bee. There is little doubt but that the movements of the dancing bee are accompanied by other stimuli, such as odour and sounds. Bees have no organs of hearing but apparently they can detect the vibration of sound through the substrate (the comb) on which they stand, or through anything that they touch with their antennae.

When a scout bee has discovered a source of nectar or pollen, she conveys the information to recruit other bees to go to the same source. Samples of pollen or nectar are shared with other nearby bees. Close examination of a dancing bee reveals that other bees may tap her abdomen with their antennae. This procedure conveys the following information to the other bees: the type of food that is available, the abundance of the supply, the direction with respect to the hive and the sun and the distance a bee must fly to reach the food.

The type of food is given by the odour of the flowers that the scout bee had visited. This odour is carried on the body hairs of the bee. Samples of nectar that are given to the recruits reinforce this information.

The richness or abundance of the food at the source is conveyed by the duration of the dance. Dances normally continue for a few seconds to about three minutes. A dance of short duration indicates a sparse stand of plants or nectar that is low in sugar concentration. A rich or abundant source will cause prolonged dancing on the comb, after which the bee moves to another comb and repeats the procedure.

a) Directional and Distance Information (Bee Dances)

The location of the food, particularly the direction in which the recruit bees must travel to reach the source, is given by the angle of deviation of the food source from the position of the sun. In the dark hive the sun position is translated to the vertical by means of sensitivity to gravity.

Von Frisch (1953) found, while observing Carniolan bees, that there were two types of dances. One was a "round dance" (Fig. 3.5) that indicates a food source close to the hive, that is, within 100 metres. The dancing bee covers a circular pattern then, at the completion of the circle, turns and travels the same circular path in reverse direction. This is repeated again and again, with the bee always reversing at the same point on the circle. It is unlikely that direction is indicated by this dance. At one time I thought direction might be shown by the place where the bee changes direction but I have not been able to confirm this.

It is interesting to note that, like people, honey bees that are geographically isolated from others tend to have dialects so that their languages differ. A dance does not necessarily convey the same information to Carniolan and to Italian bees. Carniolan bees dance and read the round dance as signifying a source within 100 metres of the hive (von Frisch and Lindauer, 1956). Italian bees on the other hand, would search only close to the hive when reacting to this dance. For distances greater than about 20 to 50 metres, Italian bees perform a sickle dance (Fig. 3.6). I have observed the change from round to sickle dances at about 50 metres many times. I am certain that the bees were not pure strains, though all of the dancing bees that were observed were consistent. The sickle dance gives an approximation of direction. It is shown by bisecting the open space between the sides of the sickle.

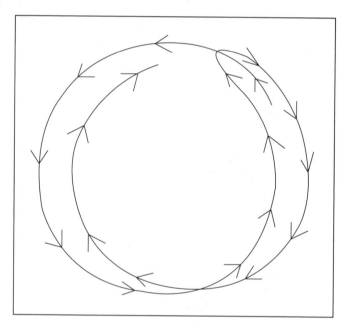

Fig 3.5: Diagram of honeybee 'Round Dance'.

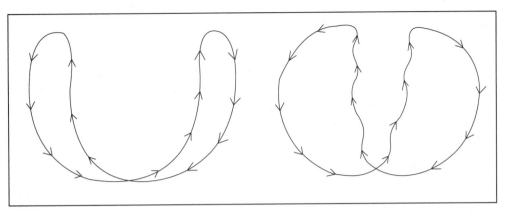

Fig 3.6:
Diagrams of "Sickle Dance": left, distance of about 60 m; right, distance of about 80 - 85 m.

3

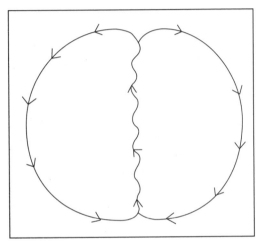

Fig 3.7: Diagram of "Wagtail Dance'.

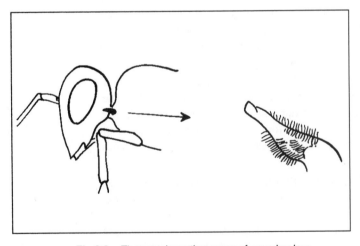

Fig 3.8: The proprioceptive organ of a worker bee

The sickle dance changes as the distance changes. Near 100 metres the two sides of the sickle close and meet. Along the path of the now confluent sides the bee vibrates rapidly as she progresses, thus forming the wagtail dance" (Fig.3.7). The direction of the "waggling" run indicates the direction of the food source in relation to the position of the sun. Sun position is always directly upward in a vertical line on the comb.

Most insects are believed to lack a direct response to gravity, but the honey bees are able to use it to translate sun position. Above and below the junction between the head and thorax on each side, a bee has groups of hairs that form a proprioceptive organ (Fig. 3.8) (Alcock, 1976). The head of a worker bee, because its attachment to the thorax is unequally weighted in its upper and lower halves, the lower half being much heavier. Thus, if a bee is moving directly upward on the comb, the heavier lower half of the head causes the head to tip downward between the front legs. This distorts the hairs of the proprioceptive organ, but the distortion is equal on each side. If the bee moves straight downward, the head falls away from the legs. Once again the hairs are distorted, and again the distortion is equal on each side. When the bee has to indicate an angle of deviation away from the sun, the distortion of the sensory hairs is unequal. The degree of inequality of the distortion produces the required angle of deviation.

Lindauer (1953) glued tiny weights to the tops of bees' heads and as a result the bees indicated a source opposite to the actual position, that is they move downward rather than upward to indicate a source lying directly in line with the sun. Figure 3.9 shows normal bee dances in response to food at the location shown.

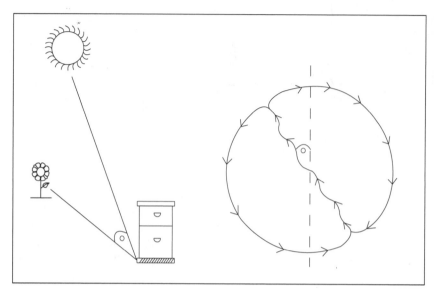

Fig. 3.9: Diagram of wagtail dance and route to source of nectar or pollen.

Lindauer (1967) found slight inaccuracies in the angle portrayed by dancing bees that were greatest at 45 degrees from vertical and horizontal and least at vertical and horizontal. The error seems to be because of a lack of precision of the proprioceptor organ at the greatest angle. The inaccuracies were deviations from the expected angles to the provided food sources. Strangely enough, the imprecision did not affect accurate location of the source as there apparently is some mechanism compensating for the error.

Lindauer stated that the "waggling run" is the most important source of information in the dance and that it also has a sound component (Lindauer, 1967). Pulses of vibration of about one-fifteenth millisecond are repeated at a frequency of 30 cycles per second, which registers a frequency of 250 cycles per second. These sounds are produced by the flight muscles. Esch (1963, reported in Lindauer, 1967) proposed a relationship between sound and the quality of the food source, as poor food sources caused silent dances. Bees attending the dancer do not hear the sounds but they are able to detect the vibration of the sound.

Wenner (1967) challenged the "theories" of von Frisch and stated that recruitment of new foraging bees was entirely due to the odour of the flowers the dancing bee had visited. The controversy was settled by Gould (1975), who pointed out that both von Frisch and Wenner were partly right. The dances, reinforced by the odour information, are the usual means of communicating information, but the bees are able to function reasonably well on either dances or odours if the second stimulus is absent.

In order for a dancing bee to convey information on distance, the bee must first have measured the distance accurately. This is measured by energy expended in flying from the hive to the source (Lindauer, 1967). It is not measured visually - bees have fixed focus eyes and cannot see objects at long distances. It is not measured by flight time as the bee will use more energy if it encounters a headwind, or has to fly over or around obstacles but the distance given is actual distance, not the distance the bee had to fly.

There is also a correlation between the distance to the food source and the place in the hive where the dancing takes place (Lindauer, 1967). The more distant sources induced dancing farther removed from the entrance than did closer sources. Dancing sites also revolve counter clockwise during the day synchronizing with the rotation of the waggling line indicating sun position in the dance.

There are several parameters that can be measured in observing dances and calculating distance; total number of circuits per unit time; duration of waggling per waggle run; and the number of waggling runs per unit time. A time span of 15 seconds is commonly used and it appears to give the most accurate determination of the distance. This is because the dancing bee dances quickly to indicate a nearby source and dances progressively more slowly as the distance from the hive increases. Lindauer (1967) found small variations from dance to dance if several bees were reporting on the same food source. Older, more experienced forager bees tended to dance more slowly than younger bees. Amazingly enough, bees which have not foraged before apparently are able to average the information given by several dancers and to orient themselves to the source more accurately than the messages conveyed by individual dancers would allow.

Very often the route from the hive to the food source is not linear, that is, not in a straight line. The recruited bees may have to deviate from the "bee line" and detour around large buildings, groves or rows of trees, rocky outcroppings or other obstacles. The actual route may be two sides of a triangle or even a very circuitous route. Experimental work carried out by von Frisch and by Lindauer (reported by Lindauer, 1967), provide conclusive evidence on the calculation of distance by the bees.

The following table shows the distance indicated by the waggle of a dancing bee, based upon the number of waggle runs in 15 seconds. The time can be checked with a stop watch.

Straight runs in 15 seconds	Distance (metres)
9-10	100
7	600
4	1000
2	6000

It is apparent that a distant source produces a slow dance, one that will not attract as many recruits as another, faster dance at the same time. It is an advantage to the bees to respond more readily to nearby sources than to distant ones. This is shown clearly in Figure 3.10 from von Frisch (1953).

b) Communication of Height

A great deal of research on the language of honey bees has shown that bees convey information and distance. No work was done for some time on height of a food source since von Frisch (1953) stated that the bees were unable to assess and convey this type of information. Wellington and Cmiralova (1979), working with Italian bees in British Columbia, provided food sources at different heights but in the same direction and at the same distance. They marked bees at each feeding site and also the recruits that came to the sites. Although the difference in height was only 170 cm, there was scarcely any mixing of the foragers visiting the two sites. There tended to be a few bees from the lower site that were attracted to the upper site because of the activity above them.

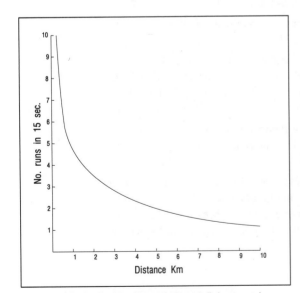

Fig 3.10: Graph of speed of wagtail dance and distance to source of nectar or pollen. (Adapted from von Frisch, 1953).

Although they did not observe differences in the dances of the bees which apparently conveyed the information on height of the food sources, they stated that a bee could "determine and communicate the height of a food source as accurately as it can determine the distance and more accurately than it can estimate the direction". They suggested that any examination of the dances to determine how height information is passed on should include acoustical measurements and recordings to examine the response of bees recruited by the sounds.

c) Dancing on Swarms

Before a colony swarms, scout bees that will accompany the swarm actively search for suitable new homes for the swarm to live in. This activity continues while the swarm remains clustered near the apiary. Returning scout bees dance on the surface of the cluster indicating the direction and distance of the place they have found. The dances are the same as those used inside the hive to indicate food sources, but with this difference. Instead of using gravity and a vertical line to indicate sun position, they orient using the sun directly and the position of the new home is at a direct angle of deviation from the sun. Bees dancing on combs in the hive will alter their dances if the hive is opened and the sun becomes visible.

Very recently German and Danish scientists have used a computer controlled "robot bee" that has been able to mimic a dancing bee, to provide samples of flavoured sugar syrup and to mimic the sound produced by a dancing bee. The robot bee was able to persuade foraging bees to search for nectar at the places it designated with fairly good success, but was less successful than when a living bee gave the directions (Moffett, 1989). It is rather remarkable that the bees accepted the directions given by the robot bee.

d) Other Dances of Honey Bees

The bees also need to communicate information other than food sources and they have dances to serve this purpose. The "Alarm" dance is used when a source of contamination is brought into the hive. This could be nectar or pollen which is poisonous as a result of insecticide applications to the flowers the bees are working. If the contaminant is detected (some are not) the bees respond by running in rapid zig-zag or spiral patterns while shaking their abdomens vigorously from side to side. Other disturbances in the hive may also cause alarm reactions.

Other dances, such as "cleaning", "dvav"(dorsal-ventral abdominal vibration), or "joy" and "massage" dances have been described by Haydak (1954).

The cleaning dance is the response of a bee to foreign matter in its hair-coat. It stamps its legs and swings its body from side to side. At the same time it cleans around its wing bases with its middle legs. This usually attracts other bees which then clean the bee, which becomes immobile as soon as it is touched.

The "dvav" dance occurs when older field bees place their front legs on another bee, accompanied by up and down movements of the abdomen. This dance most often occurs when a virgin queen emerges from her cell.

A "massage" dance occurs when a bee begins to bend its head in peculiar fashion. Other bees investigate the bee and massage various parts while the first bee, which is thought to be sick, cleans its tongue. Eventually the sick bee recovers and the other bees leave her or she may be removed from the hive. This phenomenon is seen usually in spring and fall when the treatment is applied to bees that have been chilled.

Vision of Honey Bees

Each compound eye of a honey bee contains a large number of facets. The eye of a worker bee has about 6,300, the queen only 3,900, and the large eyes of the drone have 13,000 or more facets. Each facet is a complete eye. The outer part is chitin, which corresponds to the cornea in higher animals. Internally the structure is different from that of mammals as each facet has a crystalline cone and a retinal rod, together called an ommatidium. The retinal rods of the thousands of ommatidia together form the retina. Each ommatidium is positioned at a slight angle from all the others and each of them is surrounded by a light excluding substance, so that each one passes a discrete image to the retina. The image is not inverted as it is by a lens, as there is no lens in the eye of an insect.

An eye without a lens lacks a focusing device. The eye of a bee has "fixed focus"; it is not able to see clearly at a distance. The different angles of the ommatidia are such that a bee is able to see separate points as separate points if they are situated one degree apart. The human eye allows us to focus on close objects as well as those that are far away and can see separate points which are only one-sixteenth of a degree apart (von Frisch, 1953).

The eyesight of a bee is far less acute than ours. It is difficult to determine what and how well the bees actually see. They can differentiate between some shapes but not others. This was shown clearly by the training methods and shape trials conducted by von Frisch (1953). Figure 3.11 shows the shapes, upper row, that the bees could differentiate. Bees were not able to distinguish between the shapes in either the middle or lower row, but have no difficulty in distinguishing any of the shapes in the middle row from any of those in the lower row.

Gould (1985) made an in-depth study of the ability of honey bees to see images. He concluded that bees are able to detect and distinguish between similar complex patterns. Contrary to previous beliefs, the bees are able to learn, store and remember flower patterns as low resolution images. The limiting factor is not the ability of a bee to see and remember but is the storage capacity of its brain. The patterns used by Gould were much more complex than those used by von Frisch.

Honey bees do see moving objects very well, probably because in flight the images received by a single ommatidium or group of ommatidia change very rapidly. Thus, they can detect repeated small movements such as flowers and leaves which are moved forward and backward by wind or as they enter and leave the visual range as the bee flies over them.

Fig 3.11: Shapes. Bees can distinguish between shapes in the upper and lower rows but not between shapes in rows. (Adapted from von Frisch, 1953).

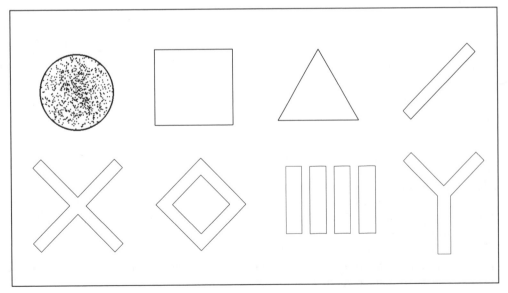

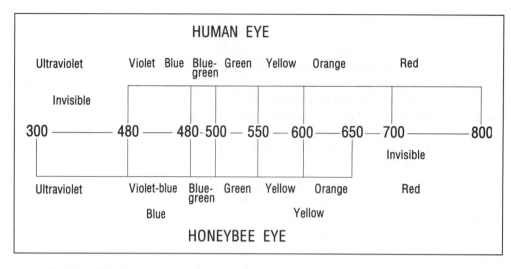

HUMAN EYE

Ultraviolet		Violet	Blue	Blue-green	Green	Yellow	Orange		Red	

Invisible

300 ———— 480 —— 480-500 — 550 — 600 —— 650 — 700 ———— 800

Invisible

Ultraviolet		Violet-blue	Blue-green	Green	Yellow	Orange		Red	

Blue   Yellow

HONEYBEE EYE

Fig 3.12: Diagram, colour vision of bees compared with mankind. We do not see ultraviolet - bees do, but they cannot see red.

a) Polarized Light

Honey bees are able to see the plane of vibration of polarized light. They are able to analyze polarized light and, if the sun is not visible, to determine its precise position if they are able to see a small area of open sky. Mankind is unable to see polarized light without special lenses, but these insects do see it and use it to their advantage (von Frisch, 1950, 1953). If the sky is completely overcast, bees can still perceive the exact location of the sun because they are able to see the ultraviolet light which penetrates the cloud directly in front of the sun (von Frisch, 1958).

b) Colour Sense in Bees

The pioneering work of von Frisch proved conclusively that honey bees can distinguish between colours. He trained bees to visit certain colours by placing food on those colours. In order to prove that the bees actually have colour sense and were not perceiving the colours as shades of grey, as a totally colour-blind human would do, he provided as alternate colours, many shades of grey. There was no confusion. The bees never failed to distinguish between the colours and the greys. One might expect them to confuse shades of blue with shades of grey but they did not, proving conclusively that the bees have a true colour sense.

Additional experiments by von Frisch (1950, 1971) and Weiss *et al.* (1973) showed conclusively that bees see four colours, yellow, blue-green, blue-violet, and ultraviolet. They do not see red; apparently to the bees red is black. We do not see ultraviolet, but the bees see this very well (Fig. 3.12). People often ask how it is that bees cannot see the colour red

Fig 3.13: Diagram of flower to show an ultraviolet 'nectar guide'.

and yet are able to visit red flowers without any difficulty. The answer is that these red flowers, and also flowers of many other colours, reflect light with a strong ultraviolet component, which the bees see very well. In many cases a bee probably does not see the entire flower but only the parts reflecting ultraviolet. These parts usually act as a "nectar guide" (Fig. 3.13) to the bees to indicate where the nectar is located. The flower appears to the bees as a shape quite different to what we see.

The Internal "Time-clock" of the Bees

Honey bees are able to account for the passing of time. Feeding experiments have shown this very clearly (von Frisch, 1953). Marked bees were trained to visit a feeding station for a two hour period each day. On a test day no food was supplied at the station but during the usual two-hour period 38 marked bees arrived looking for food. Only six bees arrived at other times, two of which were a half hour early and two were a half hour late. The other two bees were 12 hours out of phase with the feeding time. Later, von Frisch repeated the experiment using three feeding periods each day. When tested, most of the marked bees arrived at the appointed times. The experiments showed that the bees possess time-sense and also proved that they have relatively efficient memory capacity.

Additional proof of time-sense was found by Lindauer (1954). He observed bees dancing at night and indicating the correct position of the sun at the time of dancing. The dancing bees would not have been able to do this unless they were able to calculate the correct sun position without being able to see it through the passing of time.

A bee must be able to change the bearing about 15 degrees per hour as this is the average rate of change in the azimuth of the sun (direction from the observer) during the day.

Bees are quick to learn the time of day that each species of nectar-yielding flower opens and will visit punctually at that time, day after day.

Renner (1966) trained bees to visit a food station on Long Island, New York, from 12:54 to 2:54 p.m., E.S.T. The colony then was flown to California, and was tested on three successive days. The time difference between the two locations is three hours, fifteen minutes. The bees would be expected to visit a feeding station 24 hours after the last feeding, in this case between 9:54 and 11.54 a.m., P.S.T. Many bees did visit then, but the peak of activity occurred about half an hour earlier than expected. Visits then declined but peaked again an hour and a half later. On the second day also there were two peaks of visits, one at the expected time (9:54 to 11:24) and the other an hour and a half later. Both peaks occurred one and one half hours later than on the first day. On the third day the first peak was the same as on the second day but the second peak was in the period 12:54 to 2:54 p.m., P.S.T., the same sun time as the training period in New York.

Gould (1980a) trained 20 to 30 individually marked bees to visit feeding stations. When the marked bees had returned to the hive, it was closed and moved to a new location several miles away. This was done so that none of the foraging bees would find familiar territory and navigate using landmarks. Feeding stations were established at the same distances, in the same directions from the hive and with the same food as before. Before the move the bees were visiting the feeding stations in the morning; after the move they were allowed to fly only in the afternoon. In all of the six experiments, the bees extrapolated to allow for the passing of time and flew directly to the feeding stations. Gould found that honey bees in their calculation of time, actually lagged behind the actual time by about 20 minutes. He suggested that the time lag is "simply manifestations of a general time averaging processing strategy for orientation and that the extrapolation rate measured here represents a similar 40 minute average which is, of necessity 20 minutes slow". In other words, the lag is present only when the time-averaging process is on-going and the discrepancy is soon overcome.

Navigation

As previously mentioned, bees can see the plane of polarization of light. They are able to see this on cloudy days if a small amount of sky is visible, to ascertain the actual position of the sun and so navigate by means of their built- in sun compass. If the sun is visible, they use it as a direct reference. Under complete overcast, they can detect the sun by the ultraviolet light which passes through the cloud at the sun position. Dyer and Gould (1983) gave a very extensive account of the complex orientations of the bees.

Although the bees appear to be very efficient users of the sun compass, they do not rely upon it entirely. They are also able to memorize landmarks, such as trees, roads, rivers or other topographical features, even very small ones. This is apparent when a hive is moved to a new location out of bee range from the original site. The bees search out the area near the hive and only gradually extend their range.

Gould (1980a) noted that nature often has built in "backup systems for critical behavioural tasks". This was first discovered in the bees (von Frisch, 1967).

Magnetic Effects

Very few animals appear to detect the magnetic field of the earth and to respond to it, especially to changes. Gould (1980b) stated that the sensitivity of honey bees to magnetic direction is quite clear. Although Lindauer (1977) doubted the presence of "magnetoreceptors" in honey bees, Gould postulated that honey bees should have small permanent magnets, and then was able to show that magnetism in the bees is due to a large number of small magnetite crystals. These must be synthesized in the body of the bee as they do not appear until late in the pupa stage, several days after the larva has been fed its last meal and has been sealed in its cell. He found a constant alignment of magnetism in the horizontal plane and across the body axis, as the crystals are located at the anterior end of the abdomen.

The bees also have uniformly sized, much smaller crystals of superparamagnetic grains of magnetite. The complete story of crystalline magnetite in honey bees and its role in bee navigation is far from clear at this time. No doubt further research will reveal these facts and the use made of them by the bees. ❑

REFERENCES

Alcock, J. 1976. Perceptual Systems, pp 139-141 *in* Alcock, J.,*Animal Behavior, an Evolutionary Approach*. Sunderland, Mass., U.S.A. Sinauer Associates Inc.

Benton, A.W. and R.A. Heckman. 1969. Facts concerning stinging insects, their venoms, and human reactions to stings. Amer. Bee J. 109 (6) : 222-223; (7) : 262-263.

Cizmarik, J. and I. Matel. 1970. Examination of the chemical composition of propolis. I. Isolation and identification of the 3,4 dihydroxycinnamic acid (caffeic acid) from propolis. Experentia 26 : 713.

Cizmarik, J. and I. Matel. 1973. Examination of the chemical composition of propolis. 2. Isolation and identification of 4-hydroxy-3 methoxycinnamic acid (ferulic acid) from propolis. J. apic. Res. 12 (1) : 63-65.

Dyer, F.C. and J.L. Gould. 1983. Honey Bee Navigation. Amer. Scientist 71 : 587-597.

Frisch, K. von. 1920. Über die "Sprache" der Bienen. Munchen Med. Wschr. (1920) : 566-569.

Frisch, K. von. 1950. Die Sonne als Kompass im Leben der Bienen. Experientia 6 : 210-221.

Frisch, K. von. 1953. The Dancing Bees. Harcourt, Brace and World, Inc.

Frisch, K. von. 1958. The sun compass as the basis of communication in the colony. Amer. Bee J. 98 : 100-101.

Frisch, K. von. 1967. The Dance Language and Orientation of Bees. Belknap Press of Harvard Univ. Press, Cambridge, Mass., U.S.A. (Translated from German by L.F. Chadwick).

Frisch, K. von. 1971. Bees: their vision, chemical senses and language. Cornell Univ. Press, Ithaca, New York and London.

Gary, N. 1975. Activities and Behavior of Honey Bees. Chapter 7, pp. 185-264 in Dadant and Sons (Eds), The Hive and the Honey bee. Dadant and Sons, Hamilton, Illinois.

Gould, J.L. 1975. Honey Bee Recruitment: The Dance-Language Controversy. Science 189 : 685-693.

Gould, J.,L. 1980a. Sun compensation by bees. Science 207 : 545-547.

Gould, J.L. 1980b. The evidence for magnetic field sensitivity in birds and bees (such as it is). Amer. Scientist. 68 : 256-2657.

Haydak, M.H. 1954. Ventilation in a bee-hive during summer. J. econ. Ent. 28 : 657-660.

Kevan, P.G. 1987. Bees use 'braille' to tell flowers apart: researcher. The Gazette, Montreal, January 10, 1987, p. J-8.

Lindauer, M. 1953. Division of labour in the honeybee colony. Bee World 34 : 63-73, 85-90.

Lindauer, M. 1954. Dauertänze im Bienenstock und ihre Beziehung zur Sonnenbahn. Naturwiss. 41 : 506-507.

Lindauer. M. 1967. Recent Advances in Bee Communication and Orientation. Ann. Rev. Ent. 12 : 439-470.

Lindauer, M. 1977. Recent Advances in the Orientation and Learning of Honey Bees. Proc. Int. Congr. Ent., Washington, D.C., 1976. 15 : 450-460.

Moffett, M.W. 1990 [1989]. Dance of the Electronic Bee. National Geographic. [Jan., 1990 issued in Dec., 1989].- 177 (1): 135-140.

Nelson, J.A., A.P. Sturtevant and B. Lineburg. 1924. Growth and Feeding of Honeybee Larvae. Bull. U.S. Dept. Agr. 1222 : 1-38.

Southwick, E.E. and G. Heldmaier. 1987. Temperature Control in Honey Bee Colonies. BioScience 37 : 395-399.

Spitzner, M.J.E. 1788. Ausführliche Beschreibung der Koebbienen zucht im sächsischen Churkreis, ihrer Daver und ihres Nutzens, ohne künstliche Vermehrung nach den Gruden der Naturgeschichte und nach eigener langer Erfahrung. Leipzig.

Weiss, K., D.A., Hurd and A. Deitz. 1973. Color-time association studies in honey bees. J. Georgia ent. Soc. 8 (2) ; 111-114.

Wellington, W.G. and D. Cmiralova. 1979. Communication of Height by Foraging Honey Bees, *Apis mellifera ligustica* (Hymenoptera, Apidae). Ann. ent. Soc. Amer. 72 : 167-170.

Wenner, A.M. 1967. Honeybees: do they use the distance information contained in the dance maneuver ? Science 155 : 847-849.

Wigglesworth, Sir V.B. 1987. Is the honey-bee conscious ? Antenna 11 (4) : 130.

THE APIARY SITE

4

Requirements of an Apiary Site

The selection of a proper site for an apiary will determine, to a large extent, the yield of honey that a beekeeper can obtain from his colonies. It is seldom possible to locate an ideal site but there are certain requirements which should be met.

a) Wind Protection

The topography of the site is important. Wind probably causes a greater problem for bees than any other factor except flower abundance. There should be good wind protection near the hives in the direction from which the prevailing wind blows. This is usually the west side but a good wind-break, trees or shrubs or other barrier, should ideally offer protection on both west and north sides (Fig. 4.1). A slope from the northwest to southeast is useful so that cold air in Spring or Fall will drain away. Don't ever place colonies of bees in the North in hollows: these become frost-pockets in the spring and invariably result in chilled brood and slow colony buildup.

b) Water

A source of water nearby is essential. If there is no natural source, such as a stream or pond, water should be provided at or near the apiary site. A half-drum (a 45 gallon drum

Fig 4.1:
An apiary in a sheltered location.

halved lengthwise) is useful. Large chips or larger pieces of wood should be placed to float on the surface of the water. The bees need something to cling to while taking water, otherwise they are likely to fall into the water and drown. The beekeeper should ensure that clean water is available to the bees at all times during the active season. Bees will collect dirty water if that is all they can find. They have also been known to take water from swimming pools located at some distance from the apiary and when this happens, someone usually steps on a bee which then stings. Water near the apiary usually eliminates this problem. Do not place bee hives too close to a river, brook or stream. Flooding in the spring could cause heavy loss.

c) Exposure

The apiary should be open and exposed to sunlight on the south and east sides. The ideal placement is to have them facing southeast. The morning sun shines into the entrances and the bees begin work earlier than if they face other directions.

d) Access for the Beekeeper

There should be easy access to the apiary for a vehicle. Ideally, one should be able to drive a truck behind the hives so as to unload supers and other equipment, syrup when feeding, and to take away the surplus honey when it is ready. Carrying heavy supers (and they are heavy when full of honey, about 39 kg (85 lbs) for deep super (24 cm or 9 1/2 inches), nearly 20.5 kg (45 lbs.) for a 16 cm (6 3/4 inch) super and nearly 16 kg or more (35 or more lbs.) for a 13.6 cm (5 3/8 inch) super, across ditches, over fences, or for long distances, takes the joy out of keeping bees. You may have to do these tasks yourself as it is often difficult to persuade the uninitiated to approach the apiary.

e) Protected Site - Vandals

If an apiary is to be located where it can be seen from the dwelling of the beekeeper, the next piece of advice can be ignored. If it beyond the range of sight, it is a good idea to make sure that it is also out of sight of passers-by and the public in general. Damage from vandals is not only very annoying but can be very serious, and there is no point in advertising the presence of vulnerable bee hives. I have had to put colonies back together several times and I did not enjoy it. On two occasions I found evidence that the bees themselves had taught the vandals a lesson. On another occasion I was called upon to remove a hive of bees from a corridor on the second floor of a student residence. The students would not leave their rooms until I had removed the hive and taken care of the "knots" of bees on the walls and windows. I was able to scoop up and salvage most of the bees and return them to the hive, but some had to be destroyed. This was on Graduation Day so you can imagine the furor that the incident caused.

f) Flowers - Sources of Nectar and Pollen

The last, but very important requirement for an apiary site is that there must be an abundance of flowers for the bees to work to collect nectar and pollen. The floral sources should be within the effective working range of the bees, that is, within 2.5 km (1.5 miles) of the apiary. The bees will travel beyond their effective working range if flowers are scarce closer to the apiary or if the more distant source provides more and/or higher quality nectar. The quantity that a bee delivers to the hive decreases with distance so the best apiary sites are those which provide good floral sources nearby.

The flora that the bees will work should be available throughout the season, one plant species or a group of plant species blooming, one after another in succession, from early spring until frosts bring the end of the foraging season.

The first sources of pollen early in spring begin with alder (*Alnus* species) followed by poplar (*Populus* species), willows (*Salix* species), elm (*Elmus* species), and red maple (*Acer rubrum* L.). Later dandelion (*Taraxacum* species), followed by wild fruit trees and shrubs and orchard trees (cherry, plum, pear and apple) provide plenty of pollen. On calcium-rich soils, coltsfoot (*Tussilago farfara* L.) provides a very abundant, very early source of pollen.

Some early blooming garden plants supply both pollen and nectar. These include snowdrop (*Galanthus nivalis*), Crocus, glory of the grass (*Chionodoxa luciliae*), grape hyacinth (*Muscari botryoides*), and *Scilla siberica*, that produces bright blue pollen.

The first common plant to provide both pollen and nectar is a willow (*Salix capria*). Other willows bloom somewhat later, some even after dandelion bloom.

A common plant which provides both nectar and pollen in quantity is the common dandelion (*Taraxacum officinale* Weber) (Fig. 4.2). Most householders have been persuaded (I was about to say brain-washed) into believing that this plant is such a terrible weed that they go to great lengths to exterminate it, at least from their own lawns. The use of herbicides does remove this plant from many places in cities and towns, but still in many areas, is able to produce enough blooms to make it a valuable source of nectar and pollen. We seldom see dandelion honey advertised because most beekeepers prefer to allow their colonies to use it to rear more bees for the major 'honey flow' which is still to come. The pollen from dandelion is deficient of some of the amino acids required by the bees, and is not the best source of nutrients for them, but it does provide a valuable source when no pollen from other sources is available.

Fruit bloom, that is, the bloom of apple, pear, plum, etc., both cultivated and wild, begins before the dandelion bloom is finished and allows the colonies to continue building in strength. This is also the time when many colonies may be required for pollination of fruit crops.

As the petals fall from the fruit trees, the buds of some small fruits are opening. The strawberry (*Fragaria* species), both cultivated and wild varieties, continue the sequence of flowers which provide food for the bees. They are soon followed by the brambles, raspberry and blackberry (*Rubus* species, mainly the common wild raspberry, *R. strigosus Michx.* and *R. allegheniensis* Porter, the common blackberry). A short time later the wild blueberry (*Vaccinium angustifolium* Ait. and its various forms) begins to bloom. Bees obtain abundant nectar

Fig 4.2:
A honey bee on
dandelion bloom.

from the blueberry but they are not as adept as bumblebees in removing pollen from this plant. The pollen that they manage to remove is quite acid. It has a much lower pH than the pollen from most of the plants that the bees visit. If a colony has an urgent requirement for pollen the bees may forsake the blueberry in favour of good pollen producing plants, even though these may be much further away. The situation with high-bush blueberry and its cultivated varieties is much the same. *Rhodora* and other ericaceous plants blooming at the same time provide adequate alternate sources of pollen. The wild cranberry, another *Vaccinium*, also produces sour pollen in small quantity. Both blueberry and cranberry are important commercial crops and honey bees can be "persuaded" to work the flowers and bring about cross pollination.

Early in June many other plants begin to bloom. There is hardly a single plant species which predominates but many species, such as yellow rocket (*Barvaria vulgaris* R.Br.) and the mustards (*Brassica* species), followed by sumac (*Rhus* species) and species of cucurbits, lead to the "summer honey flow" which in eastern Canada begins about the 10th to 15th of June. The onset of this "flow" is slightly later in the Atlantic provinces, and is slightly earlier in the northeastern United States.

In many areas, knapweed (*Centaurea nigra* L.) is a very dependable source. It blooms shortly after raspberry. The honey made from knapweed nectar has a yellowish-greenish tinge. Cappings on combs are snow-white and finished combs are very attractive. Unfortunately, however, the honey tastes rather bitter and would not sell well as comb honey. The bitter taste disappears when it is blended with other honey.

Another plant that produces bitter honey is fall dandelion (*Leontodon autumnale* L.) that blooms in August. In dry summers, when there are few other nectar sources available at that time, the honey produced from this source, when mixed with other honey, may render the lot distasteful. It is amber in colour and when mixed with white honey will make the lot amber.

Legumes predominate in the host of plants making up the base for the summer honey crop. Clovers, including red, alsike, wild white and white dutch (all *Trifolium* species) and white and yellow sweet clovers (*Melilotus alba* Desr. and *M. officinalis* (L.) Lam., respectively), make up the bulk of the nectar producing plants. Wild white clover can be the main nectar source, especially where it occurs in rotated pastures in dairy and beef cattle districts. It appears to be less important than it used to be, probably due to increased use of herbicides. Alsike clover can be important where it occurs. Red clover is not visited extensively when the first blooms appear, mainly because the flower heads are large, the florets are long and the tongues of the honey bees are too short to reach the nectar. Later in the summer, when red clover may bloom again, there is less rainfall. Consequently the flower heads are smaller and honey bees can work them very well for both pollen and nectar.

The sweet clovers, where they occur, may provide most of the nectar which becomes the white summer honey which is prized by beekeepers. I have had yards of 30 colonies which gave me a surplus averaging 100 kilograms (220 lbs.) several years in succession, derived mainly from the sweet clovers. It is unfortunate that farmers look at these clovers as weed plants for they are very useful as soil builders and stabilizers and will grow well under drier conditions than other clovers will tolerate. Alfalfa (*Medicago sativa* L.) will produce nectar in copious quantities, which in turn becomes an excellent light honey with good flavour. Unfortunately most farmers cut the alfalfa crop for silage just before bloom so that the bees are robbed of this potentially excellent nectar source. Honey bees are not good pollinators of alfalfa because they have difficulty in tripping the floral mechanism but they are able to take the nectar without disturbing the tripping mechanism. The plant will bloom repeatedly after each of the successive cuttings. I noted on one occasion, in late summer, when an alfalfa field bloomed for ten days before it was cut, that nearby colonies of honey bees worked it very well and increased in weight by an average of 40 kilograms (about 88 lbs.).

Other plants which bloom in summer and which may help to swell the surplus honey crop are basswood (*Tilia americana* L.); bindweed (*Convolvulus* species); milkweed (*Asclepias* species - bees work milkweed very well but some of them become trapped in the intricate flower parts and eventually die still attached to the flower); mint (*Mentha* species - where this plant occurs in quantity a delightful minty flavour is imparted to honey from mixed plant species); smartweed (*Polygonum* species); thistles of various kinds; sunflowers (*Helianthus* species); Spanish needle (*Bidens bipinnata* L. and related species); Blueweed, sometimes called "Blue Burr", is an excellent source from late June to the end of July. The honey produced from nectar from this source, combined with sweet clover and basswood, has been a consistent prize winner at the Royal Winter Fair (Arnott, pers. corres. 1989). This plant is found in a belt along the Precambrian Shield in Ontario and northern New York State. There are many other plants that are good nectar sources, varying from one geographical area to another.

Later the bees may work wild carrot, often called "Queen Anne's Lace", (*Daucus carota* L.), if they cannot find blossoms of other plants. During some seasons they work this plant very well and in other seasons they visit it not at all.

In some eastern areas the bees will manage to produce a good crop of honey in the fall, from mid-August until killing frosts curtail their activity. Two groups of plants, the goldenrods (*Solidago* species) and the asters (*Aster* species) provide most of the nectar although boneset (*Eupatorium* species) and to a lesser extent ironweed (*Vernonia fasciculata*) may add to the total. Some kinds of goldenrods are better nectar producers than others. In general the 'flat-topped' species are better than the 'plume-topped' species. An exception is the plume-topped *Solidago bicolor* L., the so-called white goldenrod, which has a single stem without side branches. There are many species of asters, nearly all of which produce pollen in great abundance. Honey bees are frequently seen late in summer with their bodies covered with pollen from asters. This pollen source is important as the bees require pollen in large quantity during late winter and early spring in order to feed brood to produce new bees. The honey produced from aster nectar tends to granulate quickly owing to its high dextrose component. A beekeeper has to take care that the honey does not granulate in the cells before it is extracted. Honey which has granulated (crystallized) in the cells is very difficult for the bees to use during winter and colonies can starve while full combs of granulated fall honey are all around them.

A plant which is a good nectar source in parts of Great Britain, Heather (*Calluna vulgaris*, has been introduced but has not done well in North America. Heather honey does not granulate but forms a gel.

Plant lice (aphids) produce a sticky substance which can be seen on the leaves of the plants on which the aphids occur. Honey bees will gather the honeydew and will convert it into a darkish, strong honey. In Europe and the Middle East a considerable quantity of the honey comes from this source but we have very little of it in eastern Canada or the northeastern United States. Honey bees, and other bees, may collect nectar from extrafloral nectaries (nectar producing areas on plants which are not associated with the flowers).

There are some other plants that should be mentioned. Buckwheat *(Fogopyrum esculentum* Moench) is one of them. The honey made from buckwheat nectar is very dark with a strong aroma and taste. It is so strong that the colour and taste will dominate in a blend where buckwheat makes up no more than one-sixth of the total. Many people object to the flavour but others prefer it to all other honey, and will pay premium prices to get it. The plant appears to secrete nectar very slowly so that hardly more than a single bee visit per day per blossom will yield nectar. This is probably the reason why the bees often appear reluctant to visit buckwheat and, after a short time, will desert it to visit other food sources.

Fireweed (*Epilobium angustifolium* L.) is an excellent nectar producing plant and, where it occurs in dense stands in open woods, will provide excellent crops of very high quality water-white honey. The plant springs up in good stands following forest fires, hence its name, but it cannot long stand competition from other vegetation.

Canola flowers produce two drops of nectar that sometimes are so large as to make a complete load of nectar for an individual bee. The drops are so large that they are visible to the naked eye. The sugar content of the nectar is usually high, up to 60 percent. It is unfortunate that the honey is so high in dextrose sugar that causes it to granulate very quickly.

Some plants produce nectar that is toxic or poisonous to bees. We are fortunate that very few of these plants are found in our region. There is one such plant which may be troublesome where it occurs, this is Mountain Laurel (*Kalmia latifolia* L.). The nectar of this plant is toxic to bees and the honey produced from it can cause illness of humans. In this region (eastern Canada and northeastern United States) other species of *Kalmia* such as Sheep Laurel or Lambkill (*K. angustifolia*) and Pale Laurel (*K. polifolia* Wang) are relatively common weeds in lowbush blueberry fields, but they do not appear to be toxic to bees. Rhodora (*Rhodora canadense* (L.) Torr.) is another common heath plant that has been accused of being toxic to bees but this has not been verified.

Lovell (1966) and the revised edition edited by Goltz (1977) are useful references on nectar producing plants. Ramsay (1987) covers the plants useful to bees in Canada and the northern United States of America.

Arrangement of Hives in an Apiary - Drifting

Young bees, before they become foragers, usually take short orientation flights near the hives. They need to learn the home hive location in relation to its surroundings. If the hives are close together, and particularly if they are in "a nice straight row" as some beekeepers like to see them, many of these young bees become confused and enter the wrong hives. They pose no threat to the colony in the hive so they are not challenged by the guard bees and are allowed to enter. If there is a problem of prevailing wind blowing across the apiary yard, the bees will tend to drift with the wind, so that the colonies at one end become stronger at the expense of the colonies at the other end. Both wind direction and wind speed are important factors in drifting. Heavily loaded foraging bees may also 'drift' and enter the wrong hive, especially under windy conditions. These bees are carrying honey or pollen that the colony can use so the guards allow them to enter.

The distance of the bee hives from an effective wind break is also important. Bees tend to drift more if the hives are on a steep slope than if they are on level ground or on a slight slope. The time of year from May to August makes little if any difference in the rate of drifting. In the absence of wind, bees tend to drift from the centre of a row to hives at the ends of the row (Jay, 1965).

It is a good idea to have all of the colonies in an apiary of about equal strength so that robbing does not become a problem. This is particularly true of Italian bees. They are notorious robbers, far more so than other honey bee subspecies, and are sometimes referred to as the "Mafia" of the honey bee world.

Robbing can be serious but is not a problem of the same magnitude as the problem of disease organisms being carried from hive to hive by drifting bees. If one colony becomes diseased, all of the colonies in the apiary may become infected in a relatively short time.

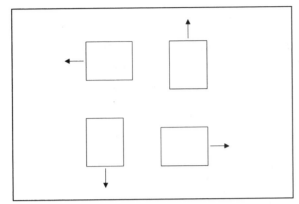

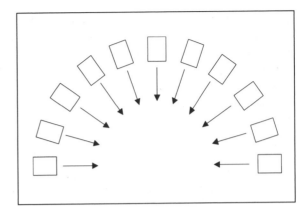

Fig 4.3: Diagram, apiary in groups of 4, to prevent excessive drifting.

Fig 4.4: Diagram, apiary with U- or V-shaped arrangement of hives to prevent excessive drifting.

Colonies in rows experience considerably more drifting along the rows than between rows (Jay, 1966a). Colonies at the ends of rows increase in strength and require more attention during the active season. These colonies are more prone to swarming and usually require more room than those in the centre of the row. Taranov (see Jay, 1966a) has shown that there can be a con siderable reduction in honey yield in apiaries where considerable drifting takes place.

Jay (1966a, 1966b, 1968) recommends the following apiary layouts to minimize drifting. Any type of irregular placement close to a wind-break is better than hives placed in a row, close to a wind-break or not. The layout shown in Figure 4.3, with hives placed in groups of four, each facing in a different direction, is effective and can be improved by placing different coloured boards above the entrances.

Another arangement, with hives placed in U- or V-shaped arrangement, with all entrances facing inward, as in Figure 4.4 is also efficient in reducing drifting. Less drifting will occur if hives are placed close to a wind-break than if they are at a distance from it (Jay, 1969).

In a U-shaped arrangement the hives in the centre of the U are best placed no more than three metres from the wind-break. Closer would be better, but this would prevent vehicle access behind the hives for crop removal. If hives are set in a U shaped arrangement about two metres apart, especially if hives are provided with different coloured boards above the entrances, drifting is reduced to a minimum. In the square arrangement, groups of four, the hives should be set two metres apart in all directions, as shown in Figure 4.3. Either of these plans is recommended for Quebec (Beauchesne, 1977) and will be useful in any apiary. ❑

REFERENCES

Beauchesne, F. 1977. Emplacement du rucher et dérive. Publ. Qué. Agr. C.V.P.Q, (Agdex 616), 4 pp.

Jay, S.C. 1965. Drifting of honeybees in commercial apiaries. I. Effect of various environmental factors. J. apic. Res. 4 (3): 167-175.

Jay, S.C. 1966a. Drifting of honeybees in commercial apiaries. II. Effect of various factors when hives are arranged in rows. J. apic. Res. 5 (2): 103-112.

Jay, S.C. 1966b. Drifting of honeybees in commercial apiaries. III. Effect of apiary layout. J. apic. Res. 5 (3): 137-148.

Jay, S.C. 1968. Drifting of honeybees in commercial spiaries. IV. Further studies of the effect of apiary layout. J. apic. Res. 7 (1): 37-44.

Jay, S.C. 1969. Drifting of honeybees in commercial apiaries. V. Effect of drifting on honey production. J. apic. Res. 8 (1): 13-17.

Lovell, H.B. 1966. *Honey Plants Manual.* Medina Ohio, U.S.A. A.I. Root Co.

Lovell, H.B. 1977. *Honey Plants.* Revised and edited by L.R. Goltz. Medina, Ohio, U.S.A. A.I. Root Co.

Ramsay, J. 1987. *Plants for Beekeeping in Canada and the northern U.S.A.* London, England. International Bee Research Association.

THE FIRST STEPS IN BEEKEEPING

The Venom of the Honey Bee

Sooner or later a beekeeper will be stung by a honey bee. When that happens, he or she will learn whether or not he or she is highly allergic to the venom, merely sensitive, or will suffer no prolonged reaction. Highly allergic individuals may die within half an hour due to paralysis of the thoracic muscles, which inhibits breathing. Sensitive people may experience some moderate to severe swelling and perhaps also some dizziness and/or shortness of breath. Non-sensitive people feel only the pain of the sting (as do the others) and this is temporarily acute but does not last very long.

Some people are not initially sensitive to bee venom but may gradually become allergic. My wife had this experience. After keeping bees for several years she was forced to give it up because of the danger of being stung. I have been stung many times over the years without becoming more sensitive, although the first stings in the spring cause local swelling.

How does any individual determine in advance the class in which he or she belongs ? The highly sensitive person may learn too late. Your family doctor can refer you to a competent allergist who will test you to determine the type of reaction you will have. He can also, through a course of treatments, desensitize your reaction to stings.

An antihistamine will help those who are only slightly sensitive. Ice on the swollen area will also help. Individuals who are moderately sensitive can procure, on prescription, syringes which will administer a measured dose of ephinephrin, an adrenalin-like compound, which counteracts the damaging parts of the venom. In cases of anaphylactic shock brought on by stings, a medical doctor will administer adrenalin by injection.

How to Start with Bees

Normally beekeeping begins in the spring of the year. A prospective beekeeper can purchase bees as established colonies on combs or as natural or artificial swarms.

Established colonies on combs, such as overwintered colonies, are in one or two brood chamber supers with ten or twenty combs together with the brood and bees. Such a colony should be ready to build in strength at a rapid rate and should gather a good honey surplus.

Nucleus colonies normally are purchased in cardboard cartons with three or four combs, at least two of which contain brood, together with bees, honey and pollen stores and, usually, with a young queen. A nucleus colony, when installed in a hive, is able to build up rapidly and should become strong enough to store surplus honey during the summer honey flow.

Natural swarms can be used to start beekeeping, provided the new beekeeper has hives in which to install the swarms, and other equipment which will be needed. Of course, it will also be necessary to have someone to inform him (or her) that someones' bees have swarmed and that the swarm is free for hiving. There are so many "ifs" and "provideds" that very few people use this method. It could mean a very long waiting period before getting started.

Artificial swarms are very common in the beekeeping industry. They are called "package bees". In the past, all of the package bees that were brought to Canada and the northeastern states came from the southeastern states, mainly from Georgia, Florida and Alabama. A quantity of bees sold by weight, usually 2 to 4 lbs. per package, together with a queen in a separate cage, and a can of sugar syrup, were transported northward in a screen-sided cage, by truck, railway, or by aircraft. The beekeeper had to install the bees in a hive, set the queen cage for slow release, and feed the bees heavily to enable the new colony to become established and survive. There is no brood, no new bees to emerge to replace the losses due to normal mortality over the first month. The population will dwindle to 40 percent or less before emerging new bees are able to begin to overcome the deficit and begin population increase. In eastern Canada a package colony cannot be relied upon to produce surplus honey from the summer honey flow, though it may produce well if there is a good flow in August and September.

No matter which method is used to get the colonies started, it is essential that the sources of the bees and the equipment are certified free of diseases. A beekeeper who offers for sale bees and/or equipment should have legal permission to sell. To obtain permission the colonies and equipment should be checked and certified 'disease free' by a qualified government employed inspector.

All bees brought into the Canada are accompanied by certificates stating they are free of disease. In spite of this, some package colonies were found to be diseased in the years prior to the Canadian embargo on package bees from the southern United States.

The best buy is to purchase entire colonies and equipment from a reliable beekeeper. One thing to remember, if you buy an established colony, is that the queen will be at least one year old and possibly several years old. Try to find out from the previous owner the age of the queen (or queens). If the queen is marked, her age is shown by the colour of the paint spot on her thorax (see "Queen Rearing" in Chapter 6). Queen failure can prove to be a serious set-back during the period of colony build-up prior to the honey flow.

New beekeepers usually do not have much confidence in themselves at first, and may wish to start with a smaller unit so that their confidence and ability grow with the population of the colony. In this case, nucleus colonies are more satisfactory than package bees. Not only is there a population increase right fron the start but there may be an additional advantage in that the northern stock may be more winter-hardy than bees from southern climes.

An established overwintered colony may build up to peak strength before the blooming of the plentiful supply of nectar-bearing blossoms that signal the beginning of the honey flow. They may swarm. Make sure they have plenty of room. Handling bees is discussed in a later chapter.

A Visit to the Bee Hives

Bees can and do sting. After all, the beekeeper is not recognized by the bees as a friend but as an intruder. It is advisable to wear protective clothing and a veil so that the bees cannot sting in vital areas such as the eyes. Gloves may be worn to protect the hands although many beekeepers prefer to work with the hands bare. Handling combs is more difficult when gloves are worn.

Some individuals handle bees during the early part of the season without protective clothing or veil, using only a smoker for protection. I do not advise a beginner to try this. With experience, one can determine the mood of the bees by the pitch of the sound they are making at any particular time and, thus, can assess whether or not full protection is advisable. Whenever a high-pitched whine is detected, full precautions are usually necessary. Later in the season, after honey has been stored, the bees are more alert toward intruders. Protective clothing, bee veil and perhaps gloves may be necessary in order to work the bees without being stung.

An occasional sting is inevitable. No beekeeper is able to manipulate the bees throughout the season without receiving some stings but with proper clothing, veil and judicious use of smoke, the number of stings can be kept at a minimum.

Clothing and Personal Hygeine

Bees do not like clothing made of animal products, such as woollens or leather and may be induced to sting if clothing made of these materials is worn. It is better to wear light-coloured cotton clothing. The shirt or jacket should be closed tightly at the wrists and neck. Trouser legs should be tucked inside the socks to prevent bees from crawling up inside. Some bees will drop from combs as they are handled and will crawl upward on anything, the hive or the beekeeper's leg. The veil should be stiff enough so that it does not touch the skin. A hat made of straw or pith is preferable to one made of felt. Bees do not like felt and may be induced to sting. The pheromone marker which is associated with the sting remains in the felt hat for some time. The next visit to the apiary, wearing the same hat, will be met by bees stinging the hat again almost before the beekeeper has a chance to light the smoker. I discovered this the hard way, early in my beekeeping experience.

If you wear gloves, proper bee gloves are recommended. Light cotton gloves afford some protection but the bees can sting through them. Plasticized gloves are very hot to wear during the summer but provide better protection. Bee gloves with screen inserts at the wrists are somewhat cooler.

Personal cleanliness can affect the attitude of the honey bees toward the beekeeper. They do not like the odour of perspiration and this may induce them to sting. Odours of dirty clothing have the same effect. On the other hand, the scent of certain perfumes, perfumed soap or perfumed hair treatments, may also aggravate the the bees so these should be avoided. The smell of alcohol also excites bees and use of alcohol prior to visiting the apiary is not recommended.

During routine examinations of colonies, handle the frames and bees as gently as possible. Once the bees become aroused and begin to sting viciously, that tendency will persist for a long time. Never drop a comb loaded with bees even if you are stung. Dropping it could result in many more stings. Always avoid quick movements near the hives. Bees do not see well at a distance but the guard bees can always detect sudden movement.

Smoke

Wise use of smoke can be of great assistance to the beekeeper. Stone age men used smoke when robbing wild bee nests. It is well known that honey bees react to smoke much like other creatures, even ourselves. Smoke is associated with fire, and the instincts associated with fire are survival and salvage. Smoke causes the guard bees to retreat and to engorge themselves with honey. This in turn causes them to become more docile. When the hive entrance is smoked lightly, the number of guard bees is greatly reduced and normal guard strength is not regained for about two minutes. A beekeeper is less likely to be stung during the two minutes after using smoke than at any other time.

Since only about half of the smoked bees will engorge with honey it is apparent that smoke also produces other effects. These are not well known, but it is likely that smoke inhibits aggression by deterring bees from leaving the combs, by distraction attention from an intruder (the beekeeper) or by masking the scent of the intruder.

The best type of smoker is one that has a shield. An unshielded smoker must be handled very carefully to avoid being burned by contact with the hot metal. I use a shielded smoker that I can hold between my knees so as to have both hands free, but where it is available on short notice. A smoker that is laid on its side may go out: a smoker that is stood on its base will usually continue to burn as long as the fuel supply lasts.

Light the smoker before approaching a hive and be sure that it is burning well and is producing cool smoke. Pieces of burlap, excelsior, dry leaves, baler twine, planer shavings, etc., all will produce ample smoke. I prefer pieces of burlap (now hard to find), or baler twine (which can be found on many farms). If the smoke is hot, place a bunch of green grass on the top of the firepot. This has a cooling effect on the smoke which is forced through it. Strips of corrugated cardboard makes good fuel and is easy to come by. The strips are rolled to a size to fit in the smoker and new strips are added to keep the fire near the bottom of the smoker. Green grass on top is advisable to cool the smokle.

Use smoke sparingly. A puff or two at the entrance is usual before opening the hive. When using smoke in other places, across the tops of the frames or when separating supers while checking for queen cells, use as little smoke as is required to cause the bees to move. The only time that heavy smoking is necessary is when robbing is evident. All colonies are then smoked heavily at their entrances.

Occasionally a colony does not respond to smoke by becoming more docile but instead becomes more agitated and more difficult to handle. If this happens it is better to close that hive and wait until another day. Such a colony can be subdued by the use of nitrous oxide gas. Ammonium nitrate pellets are placed in a smoker and are covered by green grass. The fumes will immobilize the bees. I do not recommend this treatment. It must be used with caution and in moderation, as it is harmful to bees. Karmo and I, in the mid-50s, investigated the effect on bees and found that their life span is shortened. Prolonged use of the pellets in a smoker will soon burn through the cover of the smoker.

Exterior Observations

It is important to observe the bees carefully when visiting the hives. This is the only way a beekeeper can assess the condition of the colonies. Attention to the behaviour of the bees can provide a great deal of information to an observant beekeeper.

Many things can be observed by watching the bees as they leave and enter the hive. An experienced beekeeper can assess his colonies quite accurately without looking inside. Lifting on a corner of a hive will provide an estimate of the stores available to the bees in the spring. Later in the season, an estimate of the quantity of honey stored by the bees can be obtained in the same manner. An inexpensive platform scale, placed and maintained under a typical colony, will provide more accurate information.

Assessment of a single colony is sometimes difficult, but comparison of activity with that of the other colonies in the apiary indicates relative strength.. If the bees of a colony are flying freely, some of the returning bees are carrying pollen, and the guard bees remain at the entrance, the colony is probably working normally and is in good condition. Some young bees will probably be observed making short orientation flights.

During the nectar flow (or Honey Flow, if you prefer), from about the middle of June to late July, activity should be great, with a constant stream of foraging bees entering and leaving the hive. The heavily laden bees are mostly nectar gatherers. The odour of the nectar is rather noticeable at this time, permeating the entire apiary site. The odour of nectar from one species of plant may be different from that of other plants and differences in the odour can be detected as the flow progresses. The odour of goldenrod nectar in late summer and early fall is particularly pungent.

A colony that appears to be rather inactive and is bringing in very little pollen may be queenless. Guard bees are more prone to attack when something is wrong with the colony.

If bees are seen clustering at the entrance or on the front of the hive, the colony does not have room enough room inside. At least one more super should be added, and the hive should be checked for the presence of queen cells. Bees clustering outside nearly always are preparing to swarm.

On most fine days, drones can be seen taking short flights, and many will fly out of sight. The drones are always on the alert for a virgin queen emerging for her mating flight. A colony which appears to have an excessive number of drones should be checked, particularly if the workers appear listless and the number of guard bees is greater than in the other colonies. This may mean the presence of a drone laying queen or even of laying workers in a queenless colony.

At times, dead larvae may be found at the entrance of a hive. If this occurs in the spring, it could mean that some brood was chilled and has been removed by the workers. If the larvae or pupae appear "sucked out" and shriveled, this is a clear indication of starvation. If the hive is opened the bees will be listless, barely moving and there may already be dead bees on the bottom board. Later in the season, this situation could mean poisoned larvae. If this is the case there will probably also be numbers of dead and dying bees. This was all too common when arsenical compounds were used as insecticides. Many of the insecticides used today will kill the field bees before they can return to the hive. The presence of dead larvae could also indicate that a brood disease is present. Worker bees make every effort to remove diseased larvae and the effects of Sacbrood, Chalkbrood, or European Foulbrood may be seen near the entrance. The mummies of Chalkbrood killed larvae are particularly noticeable at the entrance or on the bottom board. The worker bees are able to remove brood killed by American Foulbrood only with difficulty and many dead pupae remain in their cells. Some selected strains of bees are better cell-openers and removers than other strains.

Dead and dying adult bees in the spring are probably affected by Nosema disease. Whenever dead or dying brood or adult bees are found near the entrance, the colony should be checked to determine the cause. Normally dead bees will be carried some distance away from the hive, but when many bees are affected at the same time in a colony, the remaining bees may be unable to carry all of them away.

Robber bees can be detected by observation. These bees do not fly directly into the hive, but instead are furtive, flying along the side of the hive, then trying to dash suddenly into the entrance before the guards can intercept them. This type of behaviour is seen only during periods when very ltttle nectar is available. Fighting at the entrance indicates that guards are trying to repel invaders, sometimes wasps but also other honey bees which are trying to rob honey from the colony.

Occasionally animals such as skunks, racoons and bears will disturb the bees. The ravages caused by bears are unmistakable: hives are knocked over, supers are smashed and combs are broken and partly eaten. The only other creature which can cause damage similar to that of bears is a human vandal. Usually, claw marks are evident when the damage was caused by a bear. Bears may return to an apiary several times once they have tasted honey. These pests are discussed later in Chapter 11.

Apiaries should be enclosed within fences to prevent the hives being knocked over by cattle, which tend to use the hives as rubbing posts. Bees and horses are not compatible so horses should not be allowed near the hives. The bees always win. Several species of insects and spiders attack flying bees, but these do not generally cause severe losses.

Observations Inside the Hive

Smoke the bees very lightly at the entrance of the hive. Remove the cover and place it upside down near the hive. If you remove a super it should be set across the inverted cover, not on the ground. Try to avoid crushing bees between the super and the cover. If there are honey supers on the hives, these must be removed before the brood chamber can be examined. As they are removed one by one and piled on the inverted cover, each one can be assessed for honey storage by the relative weight. It is not necessary to remove frames from these supers and if honey has been stored in them it is better if they are not removed. Disturbing the frames in a partly filled honey super may cause damage to cappings and leaking of "unripe" honey.

If the colony has a double brood chamber (2 supers), check for swarm queen cells by separating the two supers, giving a puff of smoke between them , then tipping up the top super so that the bottoms of the frames can be seen. Swarm cells usually protrude below the frames. If swarm cells are found, it will be necessary to remove the frames one at a time from the super in order to "cut out" or damage the queen cells.

Before examining the brood chamber, puff smoke lightly over the top bars to move the bees down. It is better to loosen and remove an outside frame first. This lessens the danger of injuring the queen as she is seldom on the outside combs. Separate the middle frames and remove them one by one for examination, replacing each frame in its place before removing the next one.

Use the bent end of the L-shaped hive tool to pry first one end of the frame, then the other, away from the adjacent frame. Usually it is possible to grasp the frame by the ends of the top bar and to lift it out. If it is necessary to pry it up with the hive tool, be careful not to break the end of the top bar. A frame lifter can be used if the beekeeper has one. The type of hive tool that has a hook at one end can be used to lever a frame upward, once it has been separated from the adjacent frame or frames. I usually have both types of hive tool at hand, the L-shaped tool for separating supers and separating frames, and the hook type for lifting out the frames, especially the first one.

The frame is held in both hands by the ends of the top bars. With a little practice one soon learns how to rotate a frame so that light penetrates the cells to allow the best possible observation, and also to turn the frame over in order to observe the other side without changing hands (Fig. 5.1). It is important to learn how to do this. Changing hands increases the chance of dropping the frame.

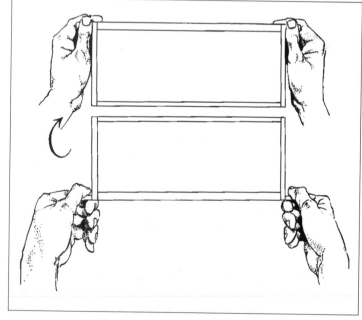

Fig 5.1: Handling a comb, rotating to view the other side of the comb without changing hands.

Fig 5.2: A very good brood comb, showing distribution of brood (oval area at centre) and stores (honey at the top and sides). Pollen (not visible in this picture) is in cells between the brood and the honey. (Photo by E.A. Karmo).

Fig 5.3: Eggs in the cells of a newly drawn comb.

5

It is necessary to remove the upper brood super if the lower one is to be examined. This can be set apart on supports or on top of a queen excluder placed on top of the honey supers. An excluder is necessary to prevent the queen leaving the brood chamber and entering the honey supers. Use smoke sparingly and only when it is necessary to make the bees move from an area that you want to examine. When finished, the supers should be replaced on the hive in the same order as before, unless the beekeeper wishes to alter this for a specific reason.

a) Brood

In examining a comb there are many things to look for. The most obvious of these on a brood comb are open and capped brood, honey stores and pollen (Fig. 5.2). The brood is, or should be, in an elongate-oval area occupying most of the centre of the comb. The brood may be in open cells, in the form of eggs (Fig. 5.3) or young larvae, or may be capped and contain older larvae or pupae. The eggs are small and appear to be glued by one end in upright position as seen in the base of the cell. Newly hatched larvae are white, glistening, and rest in a curled position in their food supply in the base of the cell. The food is Royal Jelly: it has a milky appearance.

If the brood does not appear to be white and glistening, but instead is slightly yellowish or brownish, disease is indicated, possibly European Foulbrood. If perforations or sunken cappings are found, a disease or chilled brood is almost certainly present.

b) Food

Immediately outside (usually above) the brood area and on the sides some cells should be about 2/3 full of pollen. Pollen varies in colour, depending upon the plant species from which it was gathered. In the upper corners is found stored honey, either capped or not. It is quite easy to distinguish between capped brood and capped honey. The capping on honey cells is whiter, glistens, and is run together so that the outlines of the cells are not readily distinguishable; the capping on brood cells is browner, dull and, since brood cells are capped individually, the outline of each cell is easy to see.

The quantity of stores, both honey and pollen, is important. It is essential that ample quantities are available to the bees at all times when they are rearing brood. Honey is required by the adult bees for energy and they require pollen in order for them to produce the Royal Jelly which they feed to young larvae. If the supply of honey is low the colony should be fed sugar syrup. If pollen in the brood chamber is scarce, pollen supplement can be added in the form of patties on top of the combs. The performance of the queen can be judged by checking the quantity and pattern of brood in the cells. It is not necessary to find the queen. If eggs can be seen in the cells, the queen is present and active.

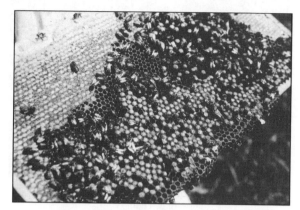

Fig 5.4: Capped drones in worker size cells. The queen has failed and is laying only unfertilized eggs. Note the dome-shaped caps on the cells containing drones.

Fig 5.5: Supercedure queen cells on the face of a comb. The bees are replacing the old queen.

Brood of various stages covering both sides of five or six combs indicates that the queen is reasonably good. The brood pattern is important. Empty cells scattered throughout the brood area may indicate an inefficient queen or a failing queen. Before deciding that the fault lies with the queen, you should check carefully to make sure there is not another cause for the patchy pattern. A shortage of pollen will result in a patchy brood pattern. It could also be due to infection with European Foulbrood, Sacbrood, or Chalkbrood, as the bees tend to remove the diseased larvae from the cells producing a patchy brood pattern. A queen that is failing may also lay drone eggs in worker-sized cells. When this brood is capped, these cells are built higher than the general surface of the comb and have dome-shaped caps (Fig. 5.4) rather than the flat caps of the worker cells.

Sometimes queen cells may be built anywhere on the face of a comb. Such cells are either supercedure or emergency cells (Fig. 5.5). In the first case the queen is still present but is failing and is being replaced by the bees. In the second case the queen is dead or injured or gone, and the bees are producing replacement queens. To do this the bees must find newly hatched larvae or very young larvae that are still on a Royal Jelly diet. The larvae are not moved; queen cells are built around them. If queen cells are found on the face of a comb a beekeeper can select the largest one and damage all of the others. This will ensure that only one queen will emerge. If more than one queen emerges in a very strong colony, a swarm could result. If the colony is not particularly strong I would not destroy the queen cells. Sometimes beekeepers make mistakes and leave a cell in which the developing queen has died and the colony will be queenless, hopelessly so, as the bees can no longer produce a new queen.

Occasionally a colony is found in which the bees have not been able to produce a new queen and the old queen is gone. In the absence of the "queen substance" the ovaries of some of the worker bees develop and they begin to deposit eggs in the cells. These are unfertilized eggs and will produce only drones. The cells with eggs usually have more than one egg, often 12 to 15, and there may be small quantities of pollen in these cells. If pollen is found in a queen cup, it is a sure sign that the colony is queenless and that worker bees are nearly ready to start egg-laying. A colony which has laying workers is in a state of low morale and the bees tend to be very excitable and will sting more readily than bees from a queen-right colony. Such a colony should be given a comb from another colony, without bees, which contains eggs and young brood, so that they can produce a new queen, or a new queen can be introduced shortly after adding the comb of brood. If the new queen is not accepted, it is probably just as well to brush the bees off the combs on the ground in front of other hives. Any young bees will be admitted to these colonies but older bees and the laying workers will not be admitted. They will try to return to their old hive but the beekeeper should have removed it, and these bees will eventually perish.

d) "Swarm" Queen Cells

Swarm cells are queen cells that are produced by a colony which is preparing to swarm. Small "queen cups" are constructed on or near the bottoms of the combs. The queen is manuevered by the workers so that she will deposit an egg in each cup. The cups are extended in length as the larvae increase in size and soon become large, peanut-shaped objects, projecting downward beyond the bottom bars of the frames (Fig. 5.6). A colony may swarm several days before a new queen emerges from one of the cells.

e) Comb Condition

Combs should be checked to assess their degree of perfection. An ideal brood comb has nearly all worker-sized cells or with a few drone cells, usually at the bottom. The cells should be in a straight line across the length of the comb. If they are not, the wax has sagged due to poor support and many of the cells may be distorted and useless for brood-rearing. They could still be used in a honey super if brood-sized supers are also used for honey storage. I prefer to cull such combs. Combs with an excessive number of drone cells should not be used in the brood chamber. Some drone cells are necessary on some brood combs but if many drone cells are available the colony will use them and will produce an excessive number of drones.

Combs which have deep cells then shallow cells alternately, either vertically or horizontally, should be culled. Broken ends of top bars can be repaired temporarily by driving in a large nail to serve as support for the frame. Early in the spring, mould may be present on some combs. These should not be discarded. The bees will clean them and use them as the season progresses.

Frames with broken combs should be culled and replaced. Finally, check to ensure that the frames are spaced properly in the super so that the bee space is correct or nearly so. If

Fig 5.6: Swarm queen cells at the bottom of a comb. The bees are preparing to swarm.

there is too much space the bees will build bridge comb between the frames. This will have to be broken during future manipulations. Don't forget to ensure the bee space between the hive walls and combs 1 and 10. The shoulders of the frames ensure a bee space between frames but only half a bee space between the outside frames and the hive walls if the frame is close to the wall. The beekeeper must set these frames the proper distance from the walls. Combs that are too close are nearly always poorly built or are attached to the wall. ❑

REFERENCES

Vickery, V.R. 1978. Visite du rucher et de la ruche. Publ. Qué. Agr. Cons. Prod. Veget. Québec, (Agdex 616); 11 pp.

APIARY MANAGEMENT

Swarming and the problems associated with swarming are considered to be sufficiently important to warrant an entire chap ter. In this chapter I will deal with other aspects of manage ment. All of these aspects are directly related to colony population and consequently to honey production.

Colony Strength and Honey Yield

For maximum production of honey a colony must have a strong force of forager or field bees. Two colonies whose combined populations equal the population of a strong colony will produce far less honey than the strong colony. The following table illustrates this very clearly.

Colony Population	Honey Production			
	per colony		per 1000 bees	
	lbs.	kg	lbs.	kg
15000	15	6.80	1.00	0.45
30000	40.5	18.37	1.35	0.61
45000	65	29.48	1.45	0.66
60000	91	41.27	1.52	0.70

Adapted from Karmo (1975)

The significant figures are those which show the increase in honey yield per 1000 bees as colony strength increases. The reason is that in colonies with low population a greater proportion of the total number of bees is occupied with brood rearing at the expense of sending foragers to the field. The production per honey bee levels off after the 60000 bee level is reached but the production of the colony increases directly with increase in population. For maximum yield of honey surplus it is necessary to have the colonies at peak strength at the beginning of a honey flow.

The main summer honey flow begins in eastern Canada and northeastern United States about June 10 to 15. It is a few days to a week or more later in eastern Quebec and in most of the Atlantic Provinces but somewhat earlier in New England and New York. This period is the target period for the colonies to reach maximum strength. In other regions and continents the honey flow begins whenever the main nectar plant or group of plants begin blooming.

Spring Buildup

Package bees

The term package bees refers to bees bought by weight in the spring in a "package", formerly from the southern United States, but now in eastern Canada only from New Zealand.

The most common sizes of packages contained 2 or 3 pounds of bees (the United States does not yet use metric measurement). In the past, packages containing 4 or 5 pounds of bees were common but are hardly ever seen now. The packages of bees that came to eastern Canada usually originated in Georgia and Florida and, to a lesser extent, in Alabama. Each package contained a queen but the queen was not necessarily produced by the person (or company) which produced the bees for the packages. It had been quite common to ship packages from Georgia with queens produced in Texas. Nearly all bees destined for western Canada were produced in California.

The package used for many years is a wooden framed box with wire screen sides (Fig. 6.1). The package bee producer placed the package with a large funnel on top on a scale, then shook the bees in by dislodging them from combs until the scale indicated the desired weight of bees. Then he inserted a can of sugar syrup which had small punctures, usually three, in the lower end. A queen in a small cage was added, a slat was nailed or stapled to the top to hold the can and the queen cage in place and the package was ready for shipment. If the package bee producer reared queens for the packages, he placed the queen alone in a two-compartment cage (Fig. 6.2a). She would be fed by bees through the screen of her cage. If the producer did not produce queens but bought them from a queen breeder, the queen would be in a three-compartment cage with six or seven worker bees, her attendants, and one compartment was filled with sugar candy (Fig. 6.2b).

In bygone days, package bees used to be shipped by railway express. The bees should be kept cool but all too often, a well-meaning railway employee would place the packages near steam pipes "to keep them warm". The result was many dead bees on the floor of the package when they reached their destination. I have seen packages with more than three inches of dead bees, but that was many years ago, I am glad to say.

Rail shipments were succeeded by truck shipments. Some Canadian dealers in bee supplies sent their trucks and their employees to the southern states to bring back the bees. These people ensured that there were no delays and that the bees arrived at their destination in good condition. It was possible to have packages shipped by air express or air freight, if it was es-

Fig 6.1:
A "package'" of bees. (photo by E.A. Karmo).

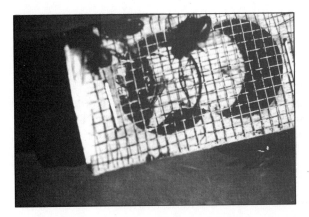 

Fig 6.2: Queen cages. **a)** a 2-cell cage containing a queen; **b)** a 3-cell 'Benton' mailing cage. Note the candy at one end.

sential that the bees arrived at a time when no trucks were operating, but the costs of transportation were much greater.

Package bees from New Zealand, bound for eastern Canada are now shipped in a new type of container, the Arataki Tube. This package is a revolutionary new design which appears to be much better for the bees, takes up less shipping space, and is more convenient for the beekeeper when he installs the bees in a hive (Berry, 1987).

The equipment required to house the bees must be made ready before the date the bees are due. The bees should be installed in their new home as soon as possible. Late on the day they are received is the best time. If they are installed late in the day fewer bees will fly and become lost. The bees have not yet learned the "lay of the land" and those that fly before going into the hive have no recollection of a "home" to return to. Once they have stayed in the hive overnight, and have become aware that there is a queen even she is still in her little cage, they are very unlikely to become lost when they leave the hive.

The bees need to produce wax in order to build cells of the comb. They have difficulty in making wax in cold weather. The only place that will be warm enough for wax making is inside the cluster the bees form in response to cold. The available space will be small because the small number of bees in a package cannot form a large cluster. A beekeeper should not expect the bees to make much progress in building combs until warmer weather arrives.

There must be cells available or the bees will not be able to store nectar and pollen and the queen will not be able to lay eggs to produce new bees. If a beekeeper wishes to install package bees early, say about mid-April, he must have some good completely built combs for the bees. The ideal situation would be to hive the bees on ten drawn combs. Three or four combs and the other frames with wax foundation will allow the colony to get started. If no combs are available and the bees must be installed on frames with only wax foundation, the beekeeper should delay receiving his package bees until the weather is warmer, about mid-May. If you have combs, the bees can be put in the hive very early. I have installed package bees in snowstorms and rainstorms but if the weather is very bad, the bees can be installed inside a shed or barn. They should be moved outside as soon as the weather allows.

I routinely have fed the bees in packages as soon as I received them and again about an hour before I hived them. This feeding made the bees much easier to handle when hiving them. Feeding was relatively easy using a spray bottle full of syrup on the screen-sided packages, but is impossible when the bees are in a tubular package. The bees in the tube, however, will not have the same urgent requirement for food as those in a conventional package would have. They have much better access to food and should not be hungry when received. When the bees were in a screened package some people used a brush to apply syrup to the screen. I

6

have never recommended brushing as the bees are quick to take the syrup and the second brush stroke can damage their delicate mouthparts. A spray bottle, similar to those used in cleaning windows, is much better for applying the syrup. The bees get the syrup and none are injured.

If the weather is very cold it is advisable to keep the equipment inside until shortly before you intend to install the bees. They have a hard enough time being very unceremoniously dumped into a cage, then transported thousands of miles to a place where the temperature is much lower than that to which they had become accustoned. To dump them into an icy cold hive places additional stress upon them - and, bees like people are more prone to disease problems when under heavy stress.

Installation of package bees

The procedures in handling package bees were outlined by Vickery and Levac (1978).

a) Conventional 'Screened' Cages.

When ready to put the bees in the hive, follow these steps:

1. Remove the slats that hold the packages apart.

2. Pry off the square wooden cover on the top of the package. This exposes the queen cage and feeder can (Fig. 6.3).

3. Remove 4 or 5 frames from the super. Leave it open.

4. Take out the queen cage and shake any bees hanging on to it into the hive. Put the cage aside or in your pocket. (Be sure there are no bees left on the outside if you put it in your pocket).

5. Rap the cage smartly against the hive to cause the clustered bees to drop to the floor of the cage.

6. Remove the feeder can. This is not usually easy as the lower rim of the can is very slightly larger than the hole, but the can must be removed.

Fig 6.3:
Queen cage and feeder can removed from a package. (E.A. Karmo photo).

APIARY MANAGEMENT

7. Work quickly now. Turn the package upside down and shake it vigorously over the open space in the hive. Get most of the bees out. It is not necessary to shake out the last 50 or so bees.

8. Replace the frames that you removed but do not push them down. The bees underneath will move and allow the frames to drop into place.

9. Remove the cork from the queen cage. Place another empty queen cage above it so that the openings are lined up. Blow gently on the lower cage. Some of the attendant bees will run up into the top cage. Cover the hole in the lower cage with your thumb or finger (there is no chance of being stung). Shake the other cage to remove the worker bees. Continue until all of the attendant bees are out. If the queen runs up, simply shake the bees out of the other one, then place it on top so the queen will re-enter. Put the cork back in the hole. Make a hole through the candy in the other end of the queen cage. If you use a nail be careful that you don't push it too far. I have known of people who pushed a nail through the queen. A dead queen cannot lay eggs.

10. Place the queen cage flat over the space between two middle frames with the screen side down so that worker bees can feed the queen. If you use tray feeders you may find that the feeder will not seat down with the cage beneath it. If that is the case, place the cage horizontally between two frame top bars and with the screen exposed, not facing a comb. It may be necessary to leave out one comb in order to do this. Push the combs together so there will be a bee space between the outside frames and the hive wall.

11. Feed the bees by adding about 4 litres of medicated sugar syrup. The syrup should be made up 1:1, sugar to hot water, by weight. Make sure the sugar is completely dissolved. The medication required is fumagillin which protects healthy bees from infection by *Nosema apis*, an intestinal parasite. It will not cure bees once they become infected. The type of feeder is much less important than making sure the new colony will have no set-backs. Rather than using a feeder, the syrup can be given in combs. Cells are filled either by brushing syrup over them or by using a home built or commercial comb filler, which sprays the syrup into the cells.

12. Put on the inner cover and cover. Set the nearly empty package on its side in front of the hive with the open top facing the entrance (Fig. 6.4). Any bees left in the package will detect the attractant pheromone being fanned outward from the entrance and will go into the hive.

There is an alternate method of hiving package bees which is popular with some Quebec beekeepers. Instead of shaking the bees, place the queen cage between two combs and shake a few bees over it. After removing five frames, set the package upright in the empty space (Fig. 6.5). The bees should leave the cage and move over to the combs after the beekeeper closes it. The package must be pushed close to the nearest comb. Otherwise they may start building combs inside the package.

After three days remove the package and the queen cage, releasing the queen if she has not been released by the bees. Move the five combs to the centre and replace

Fig 6.4: Bees leaving a package and entering a hive.

Fig 6.5: Installing bees by placing the package inside the hive.

those that were previously removed. I favour shaking the bees over this method but use it if I am forced to install package bees in inclement weather.

b) Tubular Packages

The inventor of the tubular package, Russell Berry of New Zealand, states that bees are easier to install in a hive from this type of package than from the conventional type. Simply remove the gauze cap at the top, remove the "feed sock" with attached queen cage, tip the tube upside down, and sharply strike the floor board (bottom of the tube) and the bees will fall into the hive (Berry, 1987). The queen is installed in the hive and the bees are fed as outlined for the conventional package, above.

Building up a Package Bee Colony

After installing the bees, leave them alone for about three days. Then open the hive and check to see that the queen has been released from her cage. You will need to use a little smoke at the entrance before opening the hive and have the smoker ready when you expose the tops of the brood chamber frames. Remove the queen cage. If the queen has not been released, rip off the screen and release her. Hold the cage very close to the top bars when you let her out so that she will run down between the combs. If she is released too far above the frames she may fly away. Don't keep the hive open any longer than necessary, especially if the weather is cool, as the heat will escape from the hive. Don't make the mistake of looking for the queen on the combs if the bees have released her. Wait until the weather is warmer. If the weather is warm, and the queen has been released, look to see if any eggs have been laid in the combs in the centre of the hive. If you see eggs the queen must be present. If there are no eggs, look for the queen. If the queen is missing, get a replacement from your dealer and install her as soon as possible. Any delay in brood rearing could jeopardize the survival of the colony. It is not necessary to check again until about ten days later (or a week later if that is more convenient). This time check for brood, especially for brood cells that are capped (Fig. 6.6). Note particularly the pattern of the filled brood cells. If it is patchy or haphazard, the queen may be at fault. It could also be due to lack of pollen if the weather has been unfavourable for bee flight. If the colony has pollen reserves in cells, it may be advisable to replace the queen with a new one purchased from a dealer but don't be too hasty in condemning the queen. A patchy pattern could be because of a shortage of pollen. Check the feeder. If it is empty, the colony may need more syrup, again with fumagillin added to control *Nosema* disease.

The colony can now be left for two more weeks or until about a month has gone by since the bees were installed. Check the brood pattern to make sure the queen is performing well. Add a second super on top of the original one. There should be new bees emerging each day and the number of new bees will increase rapidy. The new super provides many empty cells for brood rearing.

Fig 6.6: Comb with bees and capped brood cells as well as open cells.

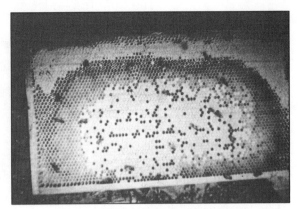

Fig 6.7: Newly drawn comb with capped brood produced by a new queen. Her laying pattern should soon improve.

6

Reverse the brood supers about ten or twelve days later if the last super to be added had drawn combs (Fig. 6.7). This will alter the shape of the brood area and will make available to the queen many cells from which new bees have just emerged. The queen would have nearly completely used the cells in the super which is now on the bottom. If you added the second super with all frames containing comb foundation you will have to wait longer before reversing. The bees will begin work in the new super more quickly if you take two combs of brood from the lower super and place them in the middle of the new one. Otherwise the bees will have to build the cells before the queen can lay eggs in them. Remove the entrance reducers now. The population should be increasing rapidly.

About ten days after reversing the brood supers, tip up the upper super and use a little smoke across the bottom. Look to see if there are any queen cells visible. If there are, it will be necessary to follow the procedures outlined in Chapter 7 on swarming. If not, reverse the brood chamber again. Place a queen excluder on the upper super and add a honey super.

The honey flow should begin in a few days and all the colony will need is plenty of room to store the honey that it makes from the nectar brought from the fields. Remember that this colony cannot be as strong as a wintered colony and it will use a great deal of the honey to produce more bees. It will be strong at the end of the honey flow but the amount of surplus honey for the beekeeper may be quite small.

Nucleus colonies

Starting with nucleus colonies is a relatively new practice in eastern Canada but the future for beekeepers who supply nucleus colonies looks bright. I produced nucleus colonies in Quebec from 1974 to 1977 to prove that they are a reasonable alternative to importing package bees. Now there are some apiarists who are specializing in production of nucleus colonies.

A nucleus colony has several advantages over package bees. The buyer gets an established colony, with a queen, brood and stores of food. There is no initial decline in population but a steady increase. The colony should be stronger than a package colony at honey flow time and thus should be able to provide the beekeeper with some surplus honey. The beekeeper does not have to go through the procedure in installation as with package bees; installation consists of merely transferring the three or four combs to the hive. In areas where there is a good fall honey flow, colonies started either as nuclei or from packages should be strong enough to produce a reasonably good crop.

Nucleus colonies are sold in corrugated cardboard cartons which are specially designed to hold the frames (Fig. 6.8). The nucleus producer makes up the small colonies and supplies a queen. When the nucleus is well established he transfers the combs, bees, queen, brood and stores to the carton, seals the entrance and uses tape to hold the screened top in place. If the purchaser does not have time for immediate installation all that is required is to place the carton on the precise spot where the hive will be and to

Fig 6.8: Cardboard carton for shipping 4-frame nucleus colonies.

cut the tape and pry open the entrance. Cover the screened area in the top to conserve heat and to keep the inside dry. The nucleus should not be left this way too long. Set it aside and set the hive in its place. Then the frames are transferred to the middle of the hive body and frames with combs (preferably) or foundation are added to bring the total to ten.

Nucleus colonies usually are sold about May 15. It may not be necessary to feed them although a small feeding will give them that "extra boost". The producer should have fed them before sale with syrup containing fumagillin against *Nosema* disease.

The nucleus colony will probably need a second brood chamber super within two or three weeks. Then, if desired, reversing can be carried out as outlined for package bees. By the time the honey flow starts (about a month after the colonies are established or sooner) they will need to have queen excluders and honey supers added.

Beginning beekeepers generally lack confidence in their own ability to manage bees and prefer to begin with small colonies and have these increase in population as their experience and self-confidence increase. Nucleus colonies are ideal for beginning beekeepers and are also ideal as replacements for winter loses. In the future it is hoped that the nucleus colonies will be headed by hardy northern bred queens.

Spring Management of Overwintered Colonies

There should be very little difference in the management of wintered colonies, whether they were wintered in a building erected for that purpose or are wintered outside.

When they are set on the summer stands in the apiary they should be fed sugar syrup with medication. Colonies which have been wintered in single brood chambers, may need a second brood super very early. I have often found it necessary to add the second brood chamber super as soon as the bees were unpacked and before the feeders were put on. My target date for unpacking is April 1st. Many beekeepers feel this is too early but I have noted over the years with my own colonies and those of others that more colonies die during the first two weeks of April than at any other time, usually of starvation. I have found too, in several years, that the colonies had been rearing brood and had stopped due to a shortage of pollen before pollen became available from willows and other early blooming trees and shrubs. Pollen should be collected with traps during the summer and stored in a freezer. Then the beekeeper can feed the bees pollen patties in the fall so that they will be able to continue rearing brood. They could be given pollen again in the spring so that there will not be a shortage even if the weather is bad. Colonies that are wintered in buildings in darkened rooms do not begin to rear brood as early as colonies that are wintered outside, and usually have enough stored pollen to rear brood as soon as they are moved outside.

All colonies should be checked thoroughly around the end of April or even earlier if the weather is suitable. Make a careful check for any signs of disease and record the number of combs of brood of all stages. Any colonies with eight or more combs of brood can be marked for using the "double-queen" or "two-queen" system. This is discussed later. The "weaker" colonies can hardly be called weak if they have six or seven combs of brood. These colonies require attention, particularly if some are obviously stronger than others.

Equalization of Colonies

There are several methods of equalizing colony strength in an apiary. The method I prefer is robbing combs of brood from the strongest colonies. I use these with the bees clinging to them to start nucleus colonies by placing two combs of brood, one with eggs and hatching larvae plus the food stores they contain, if they are to be placed in 2-frame nucleus boxes or with the additon of two combs of stores if they are placed in 4-frame boxes. In either case I allow the bees to rear queens. When these queens are mated and laying I can use an entire nucleus to requeen a colony or I can shift the nucs into single brood chamber hives to build up into colonies strong enough to winter. The colonies which lost the brood do not suffer. Almost always some setback is necessary to prevent their peaking in strength too soon, which can result in swarm problems before the honey flow begins.

Combs taken from strong colonies can be given to weaker colonies to increase their populations. In this case the bees should be brushed off the combs before they are transferred. A beekeeper who has both wintered colonies and nucs or package bee colonies can take brood from the stronger colonies to "boost" the others, particulary those started with package bees. Although I have seldom found it necessary to purchase package bees to increase colony numbers, I have had to use them in demonstrations of installation. Several times I found it necessary to give combs of capped brood to the package bee colonies so that they did not die out.

Another way of equalizing colonies is to exchange their places during a day when bee flight is heavy. Set the hive of a strong colony off its stand and move a weak colony to that stand. Then place the strong colony on the stand vacated by the weak one. The field force which had left the strong colony is gained by the weak colony, while its few foragers end up in the strong colony. The strong colony is depleted in strength while the weak one gains. The method is effective but the stronger colony often is too heavy for one person to move.

An easier method is to shake the bees off the combs from a strong colony in front of a hive housing a weaker colony. The young bees run into the hive and the older ones fly back to the original colony. The combs are replaced in the stronger colony.

When using any of these methods of equalizing colonies or delaying colony buildup, a beekeeper must make very sure that there is no disease present in any of the colonies. These procedures will spread disease, if any is present, and could spread the infection throughout the apiary in a very short time.

Multiple Queen Colonies

Moeller (1976) stated that "strong colonies not only produce more honey but they do it more efficiently than less populous colonies". The temporary use of more than one queen in a hive is often called the "double-queen" system. It is a very efficient method of producing exceptionally strong colonies, which invariably produce more surplus honey than colonies handled in any other way. Although there are two queens in the hive, they are kept well separated and each of them laying to capacity produces many more bees than would be possible from one queen.

In order to produce very strong colonies the introduction of the second queen must be done early, before the end of April if possible. The steps are shown in Figure 6.9.

Step 1. Find the old queen and place her in the bottom brood super (**A**). Move the upper brood super (**B**) aside and add a new super (**C**) with ten empty combs. Place a queen excluder next and add a honey super (**1**). Place a double-screen board (described under "Inner Cover" in Chapter 2) next, with the rim slot facing upward and above this set super (**B**). This super should contain mostly capped brood with one comb of younger brood. Install a new queen in a cage in this super. Plug the entrance of the upper colony, the slot in the rim of the double screen board, loosely with green grass. This is to prevent many of the bees leaving at once and going back to the bottom super. Put on the inner cover and cover. The upper colony is ventilated through the double screen and by the time the grass in the entrance wilts and is pushed out by the bees, most of the bees will remain with the new colony. Check for queen release a few days later. The bees above and below the double screen are unable to contact each other directly as they are separated by the double screens. The new, weaker, colony is placed above the old one so that it will have the benefit of heat passing through the screen. The upper colony is thus able to build up more quickly than if it was placed separately on another stand.

Step 2. About mid-May, th lower colony may need more room and it will be necessary to add another honey super (**2**) which is placed beneath the other honey super (**1**).

Step 3. By the end of May the upper colony becomes so populous that it needs more room. A honey super (**3**) is placed above a queen excluder on this colony.

Step 4. When the honey flow has begun, it is time to re-unite the parts of the hive to make a single queen colony. It is best to locate the old queen in the bottom brood chamber in either super **A** or **C**. She will be easier to find if she is marked. Remove her. She has been a good queen so she could be used as a queen mother to produce more queens or if not needed

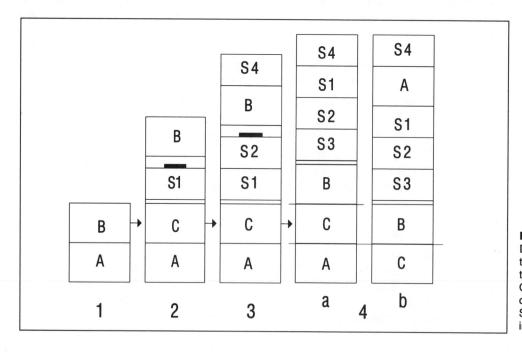

Fig 6.9: Diagram showing the sequence in the Double Queen system of colony buildup. See explanation in text.

she could be killed. Then unite the brood chambers **A** and **B** with newspaper between them. Super **C** could be placed above B, again with newspaper between **C** and **B** The newspaper prevents fighting as the colony odours mix while the paper is being chewed out and removed. If a triple brood chamber is not desired, put a queen excluder above **B**, then honey supers **2**, **3**, and **1**, with deep super **A** on top, then another honey super, **4**. Super **A** should have mostly capped brood. When the bees emerge the super will be used as a honey super. One disadvantage of this system is that the hives may become excessively high and it is difficult to handle heavy honey supers so far off the ground (Fig. 6.10). Several times, double-queened colonies have needed 9 or 10 supers above the queen excluders and all were completely full when they were removed. Other advantages of the system are that swarming is prevented and the colony is requeened by the same operation. The system involves extra labour but I consider it as effort that is well worth while.

Fig 6.10: A double queened colony after reuniting. One brood super, with only capped brood, remains on top.

Queens

Many times I have heard people say that the queen is the most important bee. I don't agree with that. She is, of course, one of the most important. The others are the workers and the drones. Any colony needs all three. The queen is important and the colony fares according to the efficiency of its queen. In the absence of a queen, the workers can produce new queens and this fact enables the beekeeper to provide conditions so that this will happen. This is the basis of all methods of queen rearing.

Rearing queens

The simplest method of rearing queens is to remove the old queen and allow the workers to requeen the colony. The result is a single surviving queen. If such an operation is carried out on a strong hive when nectar in the field is scarce the colony is likely to swarm with the first virgin queen when she emerges. In any case the new queen will not be any better than her mother and there is no control of mating. She may mate with drones of the poorest colonies in the apiary and could prove to be inferior to her mother. If a beekeeper has an isolated apiary with a uniform, superior strain of bees and has uniform colonies, this method could be useful. I know of a beekeeper whose apiary and bees were as described. He practiced this method successfully for more than twenty years, but his case was nearly unique in this region. Other beekeepers have tried this method only to find that their colonies became progressively poorer over the years. Inbreeding of a line will not necessarily produce better colonies: the reverse often is true.

Fig 6.11:
A 4-compartment queen rearing box. Dividers used to make 4 two frame sections, each with an entrance (one on each side of the box) and a screened ventilation hole.

I rear queens on a single queen basis almost every year. I have revamped a few old supers by putting in three lengthwise dividers and a bottom, thus making the super a 4-nucleus hive. Each compartment has a small entrance (Fig. 6. 11) and holds two combs. In the spring when deliberately weakening strong colonies, I put two combs with the bees clinging to them in each compartment, after ensuring that at least one comb in each has eggs or newly hatched larvae. A month later each one has a laying queen, and the queen is the daughter of one of the better queens in the apiary. This method requires no expertise on the part of the beekeeper, other than recognizing a good colony and eggs in the cells.

The queen can be removed and caged or the entire nucleus can be used for requeening a colony. Alternatively the nucleus can be given more space and by fall should become a good colony for wintering.

Queen cells, rather than combs with eggs, can be used to rear queens in the 4-compartment box. In a well managed apiary the beekeeper should not find any "swarm" queen cells. However, if some are found, they can be transferred to the box, being very careful not to damage the tips of the cells. In a short time the little nucleus colony will have a new queen. Using supercedure queen cells to produce new queens is not recommended unless the bee-keeper is sure that the old queen was a superior queen before she began to fail.

There are three common methods of rearing multiple queens. The basic requirements are the same for each of them. It is important to select the very best colony in an apiary as the breeder colony, the colony whose queen will be the mother of the queens that are produced. Choosing an inferior colony or even second best is false economy. New queens are raised to requeen the colonies and also to upgrade the quality of the colonies in food gathering, gentle-ness, winter hardiness, or all of these aspects.

At the same time another colony should be chosen as a good cell-building colony. This colony will be made queenless and the bees will build the queen cells as young larvae are supplied to them.

The queen of the breeder colony lays the eggs. As they hatch they are given to the cell-builder colony which has been queenless and which has no queen cells. If the bees in this colony have started queen cells they must be removed before the comb with larvae from the breeder colony is added. This colony builds the queen cells which are then removed before any queen can emerge. The method by which the eggs and young larvae are handled varies in the three common methods. For detailed information on queen rearing the book by Laidlaw (1979) should be consulted; only brief outlines are presented here.

a) The Miller Method

Dr. C.C. Miller devised a method of queen rearing using cut pieces of wax foundation with points as shown in Figure 6.12. These are fixed in an empty frame and are given to the breeder colony. The bees build the cells and the queen deposits eggs in them. About a week after introduction there will be young larvae in the cells; the youngest larvae and eggs will be near the edges. If the bees have added more comb it may be necessary to cut the combs back to nearly the original shape or to where newly hatched larvae occur. Serious queen breeders will partition the brood area with pieces of queen excluder between frames so that the queen will have only this comb or at the most two or three combs in which to deposit eggs.

The cell builder colony is deprived of its queen by removing her and any combs containing eggs and young larvae together with the bees on them to a nucleus box or an empty hive. This is done several hours before the comb from the breeder colony is to be inserted, but not long enough for the bees to begin making queen cells of any young larvae that may have remained. The bees are brushed off the comb which has the newly hatched larvae and it is placed in the centre of the cell builder colony. This colony then builds queen cells along the cut edges of the comb (Fig. 6.13). Ten days later the comb is removed and the queen cells can be cut off individually, together with plenty of wax at the base. When the cells are removed they will be used as desired to requeen colonies directly or placed in mating hives. Queen mating is discussed later.

b) The Hopkins Method

The procedure in this method is similar to the Miller method but a full sheet of wax foundation is given to the breeder colony. When larvae are beginning to hatch in the centre of the comb it is removed and bees are brushed off. Then on one side, a tool is used to smash down cells in three directions, from end to end and corner to corner following the natural rows of cells (Fig. 6.14). The object is to leave only one cell in a place. Care must be taken to smash the cells deeply enough to destroy the eggs or young larvae in them. I once made the mistake

Fig 6.12: A frame prepared for rearing queens using the Miller method. The wax foundation should not have vertical wires as this one does.

Fig 6.13: Capped queen cells midway on the comb, the lower part built up with drone cells. This trial was not a howling success but did produce 10 queens.

of not ensuring this and the workers rebuilt many of the smashed cells and reared the bees in them, mostly as workers, but also a few as queens.

The comb is then placed flat with the "treated" side down and raised slightly on blocks above the top bars of the brood combs. It is necessary to place an empty super around the frame in order to put on the cover. The empty super will have to be bottom up in order to fit over the frame.

The bees rear queens in cells which are well separated and which are perpendicular to the comb face. They are easy to remove. Normal worker brood may be reared on the other side of the comb in spite of its being placed 90 degrees out of the normal position. Some of these will be destroyed when cutting the queen cells from the comb. It is essential that the cell builder colony is very strong. The method will not work successfully with weak colonies.

c) The Dolittle or "Grafting" Method

Chapleau (1985, 1987) has provided an excellent detailed account of queen rearing on a commercial scale. This method involves transferring very young larvae from the cells where they hatched into specially constructed cell cups. Cell cups are made of beeswax, wood or plastic. An empty frame is made up with a narrow strip of foundation at the top and two cross slats, each bearing on the underside a number of the prepared cell cups (Fig. 6.15). The cell cups are attached by seating them into hot, nearly liquid beeswax.

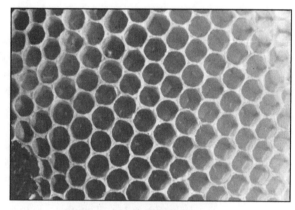

Fig 6.14: Piece of comb showing the cells in rows in three directions, one horizontal and two oblique rows.

The queen breeder colony is checked for combs with hatching or newly hatched larvae. Prior to this a colony, perhaps only a nucleus, must be made queenless and have begun queen cells. These cells are used to supply "royal jelly" which is required for the queen cups so that the transferred larvae will have an adequate supply of food and also to minimize the danger of damaging the larvae during transfer. Some type of tool (Fig. 6.16) must be used to lift the tiny larvae out of the original cells and carry them to the desired queen cups. Good light is necessary and "grafting" is usually done in a clean, well-lighted laboratory. A holding cage for the finished frame-slats is necessary

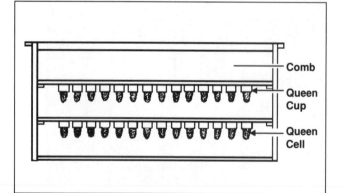

Fig 6.15: Diagram of frame with queen cups and queen cells produced by 'grafting' larvae.

Fig 6.16: Grafting tool used to transfer very young larvae from cells of a comb to queen cups.

if there is a delay in placing the grafted frame into a cell builder colony. Ideally it should be heated to normal brood-nest temperature, about 32 degrees C. (93 degrees F.) with high humidity, 90 percent or near that level. It is important that the larvae be kept in high humidity as dessication will kill them rather quickly. The temperature is not so critical. I have grafted larvae in the apiary and got queens reared in about 40 percent of the cups. Some may have been too old to transform into queens as the light was not particularly good.

The cell-builder colony builds the queen cells and when they are capped the frame is removed (Fig. 6.17). The cups are easily removed from the slats.

Starter and finisher colonies and double grafting are sometimes used by the professional queen producers. Double grafting is the process of replacement of the original larvae in the cups a day later with very young larvae which have been fed lavishly by the nurse bees. This feeding is achieved by placing the grafted frame first into a specially prepared "starter" colony which usually has only three frames, the grafted frame in the middle of two well-filled combs of pollen with a division board feeder of syrup on either side.

The relatively new method of queen rearing with the Jenter cell plug transfer is intriguing. I have not used this method but others who are using it have told me that they are pleased with the results. Kits are available from an apiary operation in British Columbia. Beekeepers who want to try rearing queens using the Jenter method should watch for advertisments in Beekeeping journals.

Queen Mating

Some beekeepers use queen cells directly to requeen their colonies, by placing the cells between the top bars of two adjacent frames and held in place by the wax at the base. If this is done the old queen should first be removed. If the old queen remains, the colony may attempt to swarm, usually unsuccessfully at first because the old queen is too heavy to fly. They may make several attempts. The old queen will leave the hive - on foot - and may or may not get back to the hive. If she is lost, the virgin will soon head the colony; if not, they may swarm with the virgin queen.

Fig 6.17: Excellent production of capped queen cells, Beni Suef, Egypt.

Usually the queen cells are placed in mating nuclei. They are either suspended between the frames or are pushed or pinned (gently through the wax at the base) into a corner of a brood comb. The queens emerge and, after a period varying from a few days to three weeks, fly out on their mating flights, then return and soon begin egg-laying. It is at this stage that commercial queen breeders remove the queen and place them in cages for shipment. A queen mating yard often has thousands of queen-mating nucleus hives (Fig. 6.18). Such yards are usually supplied with "drone" colonies, those which have been selected as superior and then are given sheets of comb foundation of all drone-sized embossed cells. They are kept supplied with worker bees by adding combs of capped worker brood.

Smith and Milne (1981) described a method used years ago by Homer Park by which the number of mated queens produced could be increased. They obtained 93 percent more queens in the same time-frame using this method. A caged newly-emerged virgin queen is placed in a mating nucleus along with a week old virgin queen that is not caged. This queen is free to mate. When mated she is removed, the second queen is liberated, and another newly-emerged queen in a cage is added. Within a week the liberated queen is mated and ready to lay. It is possible, using this method, to produce a mated queen each week from each nucleus.

In the average apiary, where queens may be reared in small numbers, there should be enough drones to mate the virgin queens without any special provisions to supply them.

Marking Queens

A marked queen is not only easier to locate, but the colour of her marking will indicate her age. Queen breeders who mark queens use several different colours, one for each year, in sequence so that the age of the queen is immediately apparent. A beekeeper who produces queens only for his own apiary can do the same thing. Several colours are available from dealers in bee supplies. Other "paints" may be used, such as liquid cellulose or finger nail laquer, if they dry very quickly.

The queen is held immmobile under a special holding tool (Fig. 6.19). A spot of paint is placed on the top of the thorax. It is important that he paint be rather thick so as not to run

Fig 6.18:
A queen mating yard in Florida.

APIARY MANAGEMENT

down the sides of the thorax where it could cover the spiracles. The top of the thorax is the only place that should be painted. The paint dries very quickly so the queen can be placed immediately in a holding cage, ready to be introduced to a colony. The colour of the paint is changed in annual rotation, repeated every five years as follows:

Years ending in 0 and 5 - blue
Years ending in 1 and 6 - white
Years ending in 2 and 7 - yellow
Years ending in 3 and 8 - red
Years ending in 4 and 9 - green

Queen Introduction

A colony should be queenless before a new queen is introduced. The method of introducing a queen in a Benton mailing cage was described under installation of package bees. The Benton cage was designed for shipping queens and is not the ideal way to introduce a queen. A new queen is a strange bee to the colony until they become aware that she is a queen. She should ideally be introduced to the colony in such a way that they are able to obtain her pheromone, the queen substance, and spread it throughout the colony populaton before she is released. A new, strange queen will not be molested by a few bees but may well be killed when in contact with many bees.

Some beekeepers introduce queens directly by throwing them into a mass of worker bees after these bees have been given a severe shaking. Sometimes this works and sometimes it doesn't. There is a greater probability that she will be accepted if she is covered with sugar syrup when she is placed with the other bees. Even so, this method is not recommended except with very small colonies such as nuclei. This is sometimes called the "shook swarm" method of queen introduction.

Fig 6.19: Kit for marking queens, paint and 'hold-down'.

a) Manley type cage

The Manley cage is constructed with a central enclosure which is screen covered and has two access tunnels of 5/16" (0.8 cm) diameter. One tunnel has a queen excluder, as a barrier to the queen, but which allows worker bees to enter. The other tunnel is filled with sugar candy and the worker bees must chew out this candy in order to release the queen. The cage may have on the underside a collar of perforated zinc. The queen is released from a holding cage in a closed space such as inside a car. She will go to a window and the cage can be placed over her. Slide a thin card between the cage and the glass to trap the queen. Keep her inside until the card is placed on a comb, then slide out the card and push the cage into the comb with a screwing motion. Be careful not to cut through the midrib of the comb.

The tunnel with the queen excluder allows six or seven worker bees at a time to enter the central enclosure and to investigate the queen, perhaps to feed her and to obtain samples of her pheromone. When worker bees kill a queen they do it by "balling" her in a tight cluster, seldom by stinging. The enclosure is too small to admit enough bees to ball the queen so they investigate and depart. Within a few hours, many workers will have visited the queen, since none of them stay with her very long, and her pheromone is soon spread throughout the colony. Very often the bees will crowd into the cage through the single queen excluder slot until it is completely full of bees. By the time she is able to emerge through the tunnel cleaned out by the bees, she is known to the entire colony and is accepted (Karmo,1975).

Another similar cage has the two channels but is not pushed into the comb. It is constructed of screen and has a removable wooden plug so that the queen can be placed inside (Fig. 6.20). It is hung between two combs. I have used this type of cage and have found it to be very effective. It is made in England but should be available from North American dealers.

b) Screen cage

A home-made push-in screen cage works very well. It is constructed of 1/8" (.03 cm) mesh wire screen and is easy to make at home. The cage should be about 2" x 4" (5.0 x 10.0 cm) with no bottom. Fold all four sides and wrap the surplus around or cut it off. A 5/6" (0.8

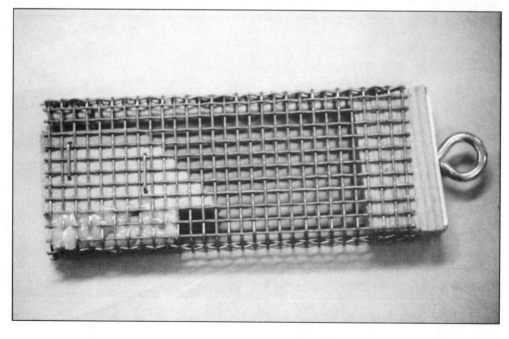

Fig 6.20: Two-channel cage for introducing queens.

cm) hole is cut in one end and the end is filled with sugar candy. The queen is trapped in the way described above and the cage is pushed into a comb of emerging brood in a spot where there will be both capped and open cells under the cage. Bees will emerge inside the cage and the queen will be able to lay eggs in the open cells. By the time the outside bees have chewed through the candy the queen is seen to be producing and she is surrounded by the newly-emerged bees so she likely to be accepted. The only drawbacks are that some pupae are killed by pushing the screen cage into the cells that they occupy, and some of the cells may not be rebuilt satisfactorily by the bees.

c) Queen Candy

Candy for use in queen cages can be made as follows: add 4 to 5 parts of powdered sugar to one part of liquid honey or sugar syrup and knead it to a pliable consistency. It will remain soft for several days in the queen cage, and indefinitely if kept in a tightly closed container.

d) Requeening with Nucleus

A colony can be requeened by adding a queen-right nucleus. If there is abundant nectar available in the field and the bees are busy as in a "honey flow" the brood area of the colony can be separated in the middle by removing outside combs and then inserting the nucleus colony in the gap. If the bees are occupied with a honey flow there will be little or no fighting. If there is no honey flow, it is possible to simulate a flow by feeding with a Boardman feeder in the entrance. In order to be certain that there will be no fighting, the nucleus can be added over a sheet of newspaper placed on top of the brood chamber. By the time the paper is chewed out the nucleus and its queen will be accepted and they can then be moved down into the upper brood super.

Queenless Colonies

When a colony becomes effectively queenless, either by death of the queen, possibly as a result of rough handling, or because the queen has failed, the worker bees very soon attempt to replace her. They are alerted because they no longer receive the queen substance if the queen is missing. Dead queens attract worker bees so the pheronome must continue to cause a response. If a queen is killed by a beekeeper and thrown on the ground in the apiary the body will soon attract numbers of worker bees. A dead queen remaining in the hive would not necessarily alert the workers to queenlessness until the body had been removed from the hive.

A failing queen must lose the ability to produce the pheromone at the time she fails to consistently deposit fertilized eggs in worker sized cells. Apparently this is usually the case; if not, there must be some other means of communication to the workers that the queen is failing. In most cases, the workers are released from the inhibitory effect of the queen substance while there are still eggs and young larvae available so that they can produce a new queen.

Occasionally, one finds a colony that is "hopelessly queenless". In some cases there is a queen present that is still depositing eggs, all of them unfertilized and all deposited in worker sized cells. These drones are reared by the workers and result in worker-sized drones. Eventually the workers die off as there are no replacements. The drones and queen soon die too. Usually, however, the queen is gone and the workers have not been able to produce a new one. Ovaries of some of the worker bees develop, as they are no longer inhibited by the queen pheromone. These workers lay eggs, all of them unfertilized as worker bees cannot mate, up to 15 in a cell in a haphazard fashion. More than one larva may hatch in a cell but only one survives.

It is very difficult to salvage a queenless colony in which there are laying worker bees. Requeening with a queen cell may be successful, especially if the colony is given a comb or two or capped brood. Introducing a nucleus, with a laying queen between the combs of the nucleus may be successful. I have tried both methods and found the nuc method better than the queen cell, but neither worked 100 percent of the time. Jack Arnott told me of an experience of his with ten package colonies that had produced laying workers. He pushed half the combs with the bees over to one side and introduced a queen-right nucleus in the other side. This was completely successful. Rather than risk losing a queen, I usually did not attempt to save such colonies but disposed of them by shaking or brushing all of the bees off the combs and removing the hive. Some of the bees are admitted to other hives but I believe the laying workers are not allowed to enter and soon perish.

Feeding Bees

The usual times of feeding are early spring and in the fall after the honey crop is removed. Feeding at other times can result in adulteration of the honey by addition of honey made by the bees from the sugar syrup. It is illegal to offer such honey for sale. Other than spring and fall, the only feeding a colony should receive (barring catastrophic bad weather so that the colonies are in danger of starving) is when a new queen is being installed, or a cell finisher colony is fed to stimulate the bees to feed the queen larvae. At these times the amount of sugar syrup is small and does not pose a problem.

Types of feeders were discussed in Chapter 2 on equipment. The type of feeder is not important as long as the bees get the food, convert it to honey and store it where it will be easily accessible.

In the spring, a syrup is made of granulated sugar and water, in equal parts by weight. In Imperial measure the calculation was easy, 10 pounds of sugar to 1 gallon of water, as a gallon of water weighs 10 pounds. In Metric measurements, the easiest calculation is 1 1/8 kg per litre,or 4.5 kg per 4 litres of water.

The water should be warm in order to completely dissolve the sugar quickly. Thorough mixing is necessary. When it has cooled, fumagillin can be added to combat *Nosema* disease. Use 1 slightly heaped teaspoonful for each 4 litres of syrup. Add this to a small quantity of water and mix it thoroughly before adding it to the syrup. The colonies should be fed as early as possible. If they have been wintered in a building the feeders should be put on as soon as the bees are moved outside. If they have wintered outside, they should be fed as soon as they are unpacked. My target date for unpacking and feeding is April 1.

For fall feeding, a stronger syrup is required. The bees have some difficulty in evaporating the excess water when the weather is cold so this syrup has less water for the amount of sugar. In order to mix the required amount of sugar (2.5 kg per litre, or 10 kg per 4 litres) into water, the water must be very hot. Avoid boiling the water after adding the sugar or it may crystallize in the feeder. If there is any danger of crystallization, addition of a teaspoon of tartaric acid for each 4 to 5 litres of syrup will prevent it.

Bees under stress, and winter is stressful to bees, are more prone to infection by *Nosema*. Adding fumagillin to the syrup in the same amounts as for spring feeding will prevent healthy bees from becoming infected. The queen can be infected by *Nosema* and may die during the winter. Queen loss during winter often means loss of the colony by springtime.

Pollen is also required by the bees. As the weather becomes colder the workers consume large quantities of pollen and store fats and proteins in their bodies. Pollen is essential for brood rearing so colonies should have plenty of stored pollen in the fall. If not, they should be fed pollen, or if none is available, a pollen substitute. It is easy to use pollen traps on two or three colonies, collecting pollen one or two days in ten. This will provide enough to be made into patties with honey or strong syrup for both fall and spring feeding. If a beekeeper has some pollen, but thinks it is not enough, it can be mixed with a good pollen substitute. Pollen patties should be very thin, approximately 1/4" (.6 cm). Place the patty on waxed paper on the top bars of the upper brood super (Fig. 6.21).

There are many recipes for pollen substitutes and some of these can be purchased ready-mixed. A very good recipe has been developed by Bernard Levac, apiculturist at the Quebec provincial government establishment at Ste. Hyacinthe, Quebec. The ingredients are as follows:

30 parts wheat flour
35 parts casein
30 parts brewers' yeast
5 parts egg yolk powder
Mix 50 - 50 with high fructose syrup.

Although I have not made a practice of feeding pollen in the fall, I believe the colonies would have been stronger if pollen had been supplied. Several times, it was found in the spring that colonies had ceased brood rearing and had no pollen. When they were fed pollen they gained in strength very quickly.

Uniting Colonies

Colonies develop distinctive odours. The guard bees of any colony usually allow only members of their own colony to enter. If two colonies are united together a severe battle may ensue, resulting in loss of bees from each colony.

An obvious question is "Why do we want to unite two colonies anyway ?" The obvious answer is to to ensure the survival of the united unit when there is a probability that one or both of them will not survive on its on own, or that neither of them could produce a crop but the united colony would at least have a much better chance than either of them alone. It may be that a package colony does poorly and is in danger of dying out. It could be united with another package colony and increase the strength of that colony. Perhaps in the fall, some

Fig 6.21: Thin slabs of pollen substitute on waxed paper above the brood combs.

colonies are weak and may not survive the winter unless they are united. If the double-queen system of colony building is practiced, the parts of the colony are re-united at the commencement of the honey flow.

There is a simple method of preventing fighting when uniting two colonies. Place a sheet of newspaper across the top of the brood chamber of the weaker colony. The paper can have several slits cut in it. Then place the brood supers of the stronger colony on top (Fig. 6.22). As the bees from above and below concentrate on chewing out and removing the paper, the colony odours mix and there is litte if any fighting. If each colony has a queen the poorer one could be removed. If not, the two queens will fight and one will die.

Moving Bees

Many beekeepers never move their beehives; others may move some of them twice or more in a season, either for crop pollination or as migratory beekeeping following succession of plant bloom. Wintering bees in a building means moving them to the winter quarters in the fall and moving them out again in the spring. Outside wintering also may involve moving the hives, but usually only a short distance within the apiary. Many hives are moved for crop pollination.

Normally, during the flight season of the bees, the hives must be moved at least 4.5 km (2.5 miles) from the old stands. Otherwise foraging bees travelling in the direction of the old site will find familiar landmarks and as often as not will fly to where the hive used to be - not to where it is!! It is possible to lose much of the field force by moving a short distance. The bees arrive at the old site and form a cluster there on the ground, remaining there until they perish, if there are no hives nearby. If they can see another hive they may eventually enter it.

Even a very short move, no more than twice the width of a hive, can confuse foraging bees returning from the field if the hive is moved while they are out. If it is essential to move a hive to another site within an apiary, move it when the field bees are all in the hive and lean an inner cover, or bottom board, or something as wide as the hive, against the front of the hive. When the bees next emerge to go to the field, they will immediately sense a change and will re-orient themselves before going to the field and will return to the right location. The partial obstruction can be removed after a day or two.

When moving hives some distance they should be moved at a time when they are not flying, otherwise many of the field bees will be lost to the colony. Some people move hives with the entrances open. This usually results in some bees becoming lost and I do not recommend it unless it is done very early in the morning - before the bees have ventured outside the hive. The "lost" bees could easily go into the window of a passing vehicle. Even when no stinging has been involved, there have been a number of accidents caused by the presence of a bee in a vehicle.

If the bees are closed in the hive, some allowance must be made so that they can ventilate. A piece of stiff screen is bent V-shaped and the point of the V is inserted into the entrance. The screen should have enough "spring" to lodge firmly in the entrance. This will suffice for a short move. If the distance is

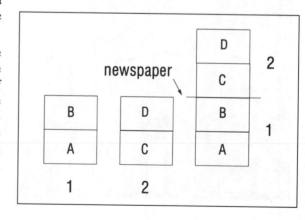

Fig 6.22: Diagram of method of uniting two colonies using newspaper separator.

greater, it is advisable to use a top screen, with the outer cover removed. Double-screened inner covers, such as those described in Chapter 2 will be enough for most colonies. If the colonies are exceptionally populous or if the weather is exceptionally warm, a special moving screen, that is a screen over a 4" (10 cm) vertical rim, may be necessary for clustering. If more than one tier of hives is to be loaded, there must be adequate separation between the tiers so that the lower colonies can ventilate their hives.

It is better to move them at night. The temperature is usually lower and the bees are less active. The hives can be loaded one at a time by hand, but the chore is made much easier if the hives are already on pallets (4 to a pallet) and can be loaded with a fork lift or with an overhead sling mechanism on the truck.

The bees will be quieter if the motor of the truck is running when they are loaded and is kept running until they are unloaded. The vibration caused by the motor tends to keep them quiet. It also seems to stop the nurse bees from feeding the young larvae and over a long move some brood may be lost.

The bees in most colonies use enough propolis so that the combs do not move during the trip. If a colony has had new combs added, these may rock from side to side and some bees, perhaps even the queen, may be crushed. All colonies should be checked reasonably soon after they have been moved to determine if they are still queenright. In any move, it is better to have the colonies placed so that their combs are in the same direction as the long axis of the vehicle. This minimizes the movement of the combs.

Robber Bees

At times of scarcity of nectar in the field, the bees search everywhere for food sources. This also leads them to investigate the possibility of stealing the honey stored by other colonies. Would-be robber bees are noticeable by their behaviour, as they dart back and forth near a front corner of the hive waiting to dart inside if the guards are distracted. Some of the bees are killed by the guards but persistent pressure by the robbers may overcome them. Then the robbers rush in. The cappings of the combs are torn open and the contents of the cells are removed and taken to the home of the robbers. Once robbing starts, all of the remaining colonies can become involved. The hive is stripped of its treasure and the bees are gone; the hive is empty and bare. Once started, other colonies may be attacked and the entire apiary is in an uproar.

Robbing can be initiated by exposing "wet" combs from which the honey has been extracted. Some beekeepers follow a practice of exposing combs so that bees can "dry them", that is, remove any remaining honey. In Quebec, exposing combs is illegal and, in any case, should not be practised.

If a beekeeper is alerted to the fact that the bees are robbing, he can put a stop to it by smoking all of the hive entrances very heavily, enough to stupefy the bees, and then to put entrances reducers in all hives. Usually the beekeeper does not realize that anything is amiss until days later he finds an empty hive with the cells very uneven and with flakes of wax scattered over the bottom board.

It may not be possible to eliminate the robbing instinct but it is possible to help the weaker colonies in an apiary to protect themselves. Make sure the weaker colonies have only small entrances to guard. Nucleus colonies (usually referred to as nucs) can defend themselves in an apiary if their entrances are small, when larger colonies are robbed out.

I have heard a story that robbing can be stopped by removing the covers and inner covers of all colonies in the apiary. This is supposed to keep the bees so busy guarding the open top that they cease robbing. I have not tried this method and I must admit that I probably never will !!

Storage of Supers and Combs

What to do with supers and combs, when they are not in use on the hives, is a problem that is common to all beekeepers. It is illegal in Quebec and should be illegal everywhere to leave combs exposed so that bees can reach them. This is part of legislation designed to prevent spread of diseases of bees. Besides this, there is a problem with Greater Wax Moth, which can ruin combs in a short time. Unused combs should be placed in supers and, as far as possible should be made "bee-tight". If some supers are a bit warped, and don't sit properly in a stack, the crack should be covered with masking tape. I must admit that I learned the "hard way" after losing the combs in an entire stack of supers, that I thought were tight, to the Wax Moth.

I use an inverted single-sided bottom board, with a stand of some sort to keep the bottom board off the ground and also to provide stability, then stack on 8 to 10 supers. On the top I place an inner cover, then a cover, and weight it with bricks or stones. It is useful to have spare supers and combs in the apiary, particularly if the apiary is some distance from the normal place of super storage.

Even in a building, supers of combs, especially combs in which brood has been raised, should be stacked as tightly as possible. In winter they should be in unheated storage, with provision made for control of rodents. Rats or mice can cause a great deal of damage to stored combs if they can find a way inside the supers. ❏

REFERENCES

Berry, R. 1987. Radical New Package for Long Distance Transportation fof Honey Bees. Gleanings Bee Cult. 115 (9) : 542-543.

Chapleau, J.-P. 1985. L'élevage des reines abeilles pour les besoins personnels de l'apiculteur. L'abeille 5 (4) :9-31.

Chapleau, J.-P. 1987. Production commerciale de reines abeilles. Publ. Québec Agr., Cons. Prod. Veget. Québec (Agdex 616), 58 pp.

Karmo, E.A. 1975. Background Data on Beekeeping in Nova Scotia. Circ. Nova Scotia Dept. Agr. Mkting. 106, 4 pp.

Moeller, F.E. 1976. Two-Queen System of Honey Bee Colony Management. Prod. Res. Rep. U.S. Dept. Agr. 161 : 1-11.

Smith, M.V. and C.P. Milne,jr. 1981. Increasing the Efficiency of Queen Mating Nuclei. Amer. Bee J. 121 : 570-571, 574.

Vickery, V.R. and B. Levac. 1978. Les paquets d'abeilles. Publ. Québec Agr., Cons. Prod. Veget. Québec (Agdex 616), 7 pp.

SWARMING AND SWARM PREVENTION

Why Bees Swarm and the Sequence of Events

Swarming of honey bees is a natural phenomenon which ensures their survival. It is colony reproduction. The colony divides its population sending one part with a queen, usually the old queen mother of the colony, to found a new colony at another site. The population that remains behind is left with capped queen cells so that this part will soon be headed by a new young queen. Some subspecies of honey bees swarm more readily than others. For thousands of years, all of the years before 1851, bees were encouraged to swarm by beekeepers or by the robbers of wild colonies. The combs in straw skeps, clay pots or clay tubes, hollow logs, etc., were attached to the hive walls and could not be removed except by damaging the colony. For thousands of years removing the honey meant destruction of the colony so swarming was essential to continue to provide colonies to replace those that were destroyed. The containers (hives) in which the bees were kept were small so that the bees had considerably less space than in a modern hive. Crowding is one of the factors that cause bees to swarm.

As the population of a colony increases during the spring buildup period, the quantity of "queen substance" produced by the queen also increases to a certain extent but the share that is given to each bee gradually becomes less and less. As a result the bee carry out less work in the hive and in the field. This causes more crowding in the hive and the distribution of the queen substance from bee to bee becomes more difficult. The result is that the pheromone fails to prevent construction of queen cells by the worker bees.

As new bees emerge from their cells they tend to remain on the centre combs, probably because this is the warmest part of the hive. Older house bees are displaced to outer combs where they clean cells. The queen examines each cell before she deposits an egg in it. If she finds any honey or pollen or debris, or if the rims of the cells from which bees have newly emerged have not been trimmed, she refuses to use the cells. She can lay eggs only in cells which have been prepared for her by the worker bees. If the hive is crowded and the supply of available cells is less than the egg-laying capacity of the queen, she will lose many eggs while searching for cells. When a queen is laying at her capacity, she cannot hold back, but produces eggs even though she has not found cells in which to deposit them. The "dropped" eggs are not wasted but are eaten by the worker bees; bees do not waste food, especially protein.

When such a situation occurs, the number of queen attendants increases from the usual 7 to 11 to 22 or more and she is fed copiously. The bees perform the DVAV (dorsal-ventral abdominal vibration - the bee vibrates her abdomen up and down) dance on the queen. Soon she is herded to the bottom bars of the frames where "queen cups" have been constructed (Fig. 7.1). She deposits an egg in each of these cells. Queen cups are built to have an initial depth the same or less than a normal worker cell but are built vertically rather than horizontally. As soon as these eggs hatch the treatment given the queen changes drastically. The number of queen attendants is reduced and her food supply decreases significantly as she is fed less often. This results in a significant reduction in the number of eggs produced, although she continues to deposit some eggs each day.

As the number of new larvae requiring food becomes less and less, many nurse bees are displaced as they have nothing to do. Many of these bees will cluster on the front of the hive (Fig. 7.2). If you see bees clustered on the front of a hive in spring you can be assured that the colony is preparing to swarm.

The worker bees inside the hive, the queen attendants and others, "push the queen around" and may even bite at her legs to keep her moving. Each day fewer eggs are laid in the cells. When the queen approaches one of the queen cells she may emit a sound. This is called "piping", due to the resemblance of the sound to that produced by some types of pipes (but not by bagpipes). The worker bees around the queen ensure that she does not damage the queen cells. A queen pipes only when she is near queen cells containing nearly developed queens. If a queen in a cell is nearly ready to emerge she may answer the old queen. As she is confined in the cell the sound is somewhat distorted and is called "quacking". Queen piping is not well understood. Simpson and Greenwood (1974) using artificial "piping" caused colonies to swarm with no provision for a new queen in the hive. Even queenless colonies can be induced to swarm by artificial piping. It is obvious that piping conveys a particular message to the bees of the colony.

Several days before a swarm is due to leave the hive, probably as soon as the queen cells are capped, scout bees begin to search the area for a new home. If they find a suitable cavity, at least 40 litres capacity (about 1.5 cu. ft.), but less than 100 litres (3.75 cu. ft.), they dance on the combs to indicate the distance to and the direction of the proposed home. The wag-tail dance is identical to that performed by forager bees to give information about a new food source. It is not clear how the bees differentiate between dances indicating nest site and food source. It is probable that the dance does not differ but that the dancing bee provides samples in reference to food sources and no sample at all to indicate a suitable nest. A nest-finding dancer will continue dancing for a long period without interruption, even changing the angle

Fig 7.1: Queen cups at the bottom of a comb.

SWARMING AND SWARM PREVENTION

of direction from the vertical to compensate for the continually changing sun position with the passage of time (Lindauer, 1955). Food gathering dancers usually dance for a short time in one place, then move to another, and do not persist in dancing but soon fly out of the hive to forage again.

During this period, the bees clustered on the front of the hive and hanging on the bottoms of the frames become very numerous. It is time of general inactivity with little work being done inside or outside the hive. Few bees are foraging in the field and very little nectar or pollen are brought back to the hive.

Very shortly before the swarm leaves the hive, the bees that are to leave engorge themselves with honey. Combs (1972) found that the quantity of honey in the honey-stomachs of the bees preparing to swarm was four times greater than in bees which were not leaving. The bees gorged themselves on honey gradually for about ten days before they swarmed. Tarenov (1955, cited in Gary, 1975) found that bees with full honey stomachs tend soon to forget the old home. The honey must be sufficient to maintain the bees until they find a new home and until they are organized at the new site. The supply is considered to be enough to last for about six days.

When the time has come to leave the hive, usually between 10 a.m. and 2 p.m. (10:00 to 14:00 hrs), the scout bees which had been searching for a new home begin to perform a special dance on the combs. Lindauer (1955) called this a "whir" dance. The dancing bees run on the combs in a zig-zag fashion, bumping into other bees, waggling their abdomens, and producing a "whirring" noise with their wings. Once this has been started by a few bees, many others join in and produce a great uproar in the hive. Then, with a great roaring of wings the bees tumble helter-skelter out of the hive entrance and take flight.

The abdomen of the queen, due to the enforced exercise regime and reduced diet, has now shrunk somewhat so that she is able to fly. She leaves with the other bees and flies a short distance, then alights on a nearby bush, tree or other structure. A queen that has been laying is usually not able to fly very far.

Fig 7.2: Bees clustered on the front of a hive.

Fig 7.3: Swarm in a pine tree.

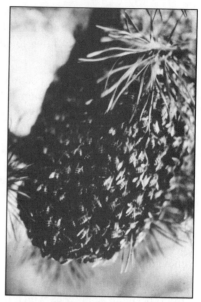

Fig 7.4: Close-up of a swarm to show bees with their heads upward and wings slightly parted to shed rain.

The worker bees and some drones soon form a cluster surrounding the queen (Fig. 7.3). They are guided to her by a volatile fraction of 9-oxo-trans-2-decenoic acid, the queen substance. In the hive the pheromone is usually transferred from bee to bee in food sharing.

The Swarm Cluster

The cluster is composed of a shell of bees, usually only two or three bees thick, with the outer bees oriented with heads upward and wings slightly spread (Fig. 7.4). During periods of rain, the wings act to prevent the cluster becoming wet, usually with a fair degree of success, except in heavy downpours. The outer shell of the cluster is quite dense, providing strength, but the bees clinging to each other in the inner part form many chains of bees connecting the opposite sides to provide stability. Usually there is an aperture somewhere in the shell which allows bees to pass in or out. There may be several such openings. The bees in the shell do not remain on the outside very long. There is a continuous rotation so that about two-thirds of the bees in the shell will change places with bees from inside the cluster at regular short intervals, usually only a few minutes (Gary, 1975).

The interior of the swarm is maintained nearly at a constant temperature of about 35 degrees Celsius, about the same temperature as the brood area in the hive (Heinrich, 1981). The temperature at the outer part of the shell is considerably less, but is maintained above ambient temperature but not above 17 degrees Celsius.

Heinrich (1981) also found that bees in a swarm cluster can compensate for very high ambient temperatures. The shell is opened at intervals so as to provide corridors through the cluster from top to bottom, allowing or forcing hot air out at the top and drawing cooler air in at the bottom.

The age of the bees in a swarm is not proportional to the ages of the bees in the colony. The first requirement of the bees in a new location is for combs with cells. Without cells the queen cannot lay eggs and no honey or pollen can be stored. Most of the bees in the shell are 18 to 20 days old; the bees inside the shell, the majority of bees in the swarm, are young house bees, less than 18 days old. Many of these bees are of wax-producing age, ready to begin producing wax and building combs as soon as they arrive at their new home. They are so in need of producing wax that a coating of wax is left behind on the branch or other object to which the cluster is attached, even though the swarm may have stayed there for only half an hour.

The size of the swarm is determined largely by the total population of the colony. Populous colonies produce large swarms. If the colony is not large, the proportion of the swarm to the total population may well be greater, as small colonies usually send a greater proportion of bees with a swarm.

Scout bees make up about seven percent of the total number of bees in a swarm. They leave the cluster as soon as it is formed and continue to search for a new home. In some cases the scouts appear to have found and agreed upon a new home even before the cluster is formed. Then the cluster breaks again and the bees leave for the new home in 15 to 30 minutes. Some swarms, however, seem to have great difficulty in locating a suitable cavity in which they can live.

The scout bees search the area and if they have found a suitable place return to dance on the surface of the swarm. Several scouts may dance indicating several different places. Those which dance more vigorously will attract other scouts which either have not found a suitable place or have found one which is less suitable. Repeated trips are made until all of the dancing bees are in agreement, having chosen the best site of all of those that were investigated. Then the swarm can break the cluster and go to the new home.

The reason for maintaining the high temperature now becomes apparent. Bees are cold-blooded creatures and, unless they produce heat, will have their body temperature nearly the same as the ambient temperature. Cold bees cannot fly. I have often seen bumble bees, and occasionally honey bees as well, that were unable to return home at the end of the day and remained on flowers all night. In the morning they were at first moribund, unable to fly. They had to vibrate their wings rapidly for a time to increase the temperature of the flight muscles to the point at which they could sustain flight. The bees in the cluster are kept warm so that they can take flight immediately at the critical time.

When the scouts agree, they use the same "get going" signal as when they left the hive. "Whir" dances on the surface of the swarm become numerous, the bees dancing then taking off and ramming the cluster forcing other bees to fly. Some scouts lead, probably producing the scent pheromone as they go to attract the other bees to follow. Other scouts fly to the rear of the swarm and charge through in the direction of the new home, as if to make sure that all of the bees were going in the right direction. The first scouts to reach the new home begin scent fanning immediately to ensure that no bees become lost (Simpson, 1963; Avitabile *et al.*, 1975). Seeley (1982) and Seeley, *et al.*, (1979) experimented with swarms and gave a detailed account of swarm behaviour.

When do the Bees Swarm ?

Burgett and Morse (1974) reported two clearly defined periods in the northeastern United States during which honey bees may swarm. The first period lasts from about mid-May to early July, with by far the greatest number of swarms issuing from mid-May to mid-June. Most of the swarms, about 90 percent, will leave the hives during this period. The other 10 percent, usually less than this, may swarm from early August to early September. In eastern Canada swarms appear to follow this schedule rather closely. After observing and recording dates for a period of years I found that the earliest swarm date was May 17th. When asked when the bees might swarm, I always gave this date and usually was either right on or early by a day or two.

There is an ancient rhyme about swarms that goes like this:

A swarm of bees in May
is worth a load of hay;
A swarm of bees in June

is worth a silver spoon;
But a swarm of bees in July
isn't worth a fly.

It is certain that an early swarm has a better chance of producing a honey crop and a better chance of surviving the coming winter than does a later swarm. Over the past 38 years I have never seen a fall swarm in eastern Canada, though I have heard that they do occur. A fall swarm cannot possibly establish itself as a new colony and build up sufficient population and food stores to enable it to survive the winter in this region. If a fall swarm is captured it should be united with the parent colony if the colony that produced the swarm can be identified. Otherwise the parent colony may also be too weak to survive the winter.

Swarming with a Clipped Queen

The fact that the queen is clipped (two wings on one side are cut off) does not deter swarm preparation. The whole procedure goes on, as already described, to the point where the bees leave the hive. They fly around in circles with a great roaring noise searching for the queen pheromone to lead them to a clustering site. The unfortunate clipped queen leaves the hive with the other bees but she is on foot, unable to fly. After a time, as there is no queen to guide them, the worker bees return to the hive. The queen may be able to walk back too but she may also become lost in the grass. If she returns to the hive, the colony will probably try to swarm again the next day if the weather is suitable. The result is the same.

I had a colony once in which the queen had a deformed wing. I do not know what sort of accident caused this but obviously she had usable wings at the time of her mating flight. The colony prepared to swarm and I did nothing to alter their plans. I had a group of students in the apiary for a few days so I told them this colony would swarm and that I had prepared the demonstration for them. On cue, the bees emerged producing the usual roaring noise. Then I told them that all of the bees would go back to the hive as I had told them not to go very far that day. The students looked at me as though I had stripped my gears. Then, sure enough the bees returned to the hive. The next day the same thing happened, so I used the opportunity to demonstrate why I did not like to have my queens clipped. The students appreciated learning the truth of the matter and the episode did wonders for raising their esteem for their instructor. The second day I removed the old queen and took away most of the combs with queen cells, leaving only one to produce a new mother for the colony. I used the other cells that I had removed to rear new queens for some nucleus colonies that I planned to set up. I hate to destroy queen cells and I seldom do unless the colony that produced them has some undesireable traits.

If the old queen is lost and is unable to return to the hive (she may have become prey to ants or some other predator), the bees wait until the first virgin queen emerges, then away they go. In fact, the swarm may contain several virgin queens. The virgin queen has never produced eggs and her abdomen is small, not a great deal larger than that of a worker bee. She can, and usually does, fly for some distance before she alights and the swarm cluster forms. I know of one swarm, headed by two virgin queens that travelled 8 kilometers from the hive. I tried, without success, to learn the ultimate fate of the swarm, whether it split into two parts with half of the bees going with each one, or whether they formed a single colony, in which case one queen would not survive.

If a queen is not clipped, the swarm will stay for some time near the apiary; if she is clipped, the swarm will be headed by a virgin queen and the chance that the beekeeper will find it and hive it are slim indeed.

Common Methods of Swarm Prevention

Some of the ways used by beekeepers to prevent swarming are called by some authors "Swarm Control". As Jaycox (1989) correctly points out, "Swarming can be prevented, but certainly not controlled." Anyone that has watched a swarm issue from a hive will appreciate the fact that no beekeeper can control those bees at that time, and any attempts that one might make would only make the problem worse. Prevention should be a procedure carried out at a time before the bees make preparations for swarming.

In the spring of the year beekeepers aim at building up their colonies so that they will arrive at peak strength at the time the main "honey flow" begins, usually in June. Colonies started that spring from package bees or from spring-formed nucleus colonies usually do not reach peak strength until near the end of the honey flow, having built up rapidly and used the honey about as fast as they could make it so that little surplus was left. Wintered colonies are at the "opposite end of the spectrum", as they may build up too soon, becoming strong at a time when no major sources of nectar are available. Under these conditions the colony is crowded because so many bees are becoming ready for field work and there is little work for them to do, and the colony may begin to build swarm cells. Once they begin building cells for swarming, the urge to swarm seems to become very strong and is difficult to control.

The beekeeper should practice measures to ensure that premature buildup does not happen. The solution is to delay colony buildup somewhat so that peak strength is reached only when the volume of nectar is so great that the bees are kept busy and do not attempt to swarm.

Temporary weakening can be done in several ways:

a) Robbing Combs of Brood

When a colony has brood in seven or eight combs of a double brood chamber hive, two combs can be removed, these to be replaced by empty combs. This will remove several thousand potential bees, thus slowing the increase in strength. At the same time, the empty combs provide additional cells in which the queen can lay eggs, which also reduces the crowding and provides work for nurse bees. Beekeepers should keep in mind that no brood disease should be present. Shifting combs which have diseased brood only magnifies the disease problem.

The combs of brood can be used to boost the strength of weak colonies, such as those started from nuclei or from package bees. If this is done, the bees should be brushed off the combs into the original hive and the weak colonies are given only combs of brood without adult bees.

Combs with brood can also be used to start nucleus colonies. The combs, with the bees on the combs, are transferred to nucleus hives. The hives I use for this purpose are those described under queen rearing, a super modified with three separators to make four two-frame units, each with its own entrance. Units of this size can be provided with queens by simply tossing a queen in with the other bees. A nucleus colony of this size will nearly always accept the queen. If no queens are available (the usual case) I make sure that the transferred combs have some eggs and young brood. The bees will then rear queens if they have been provided with enough food.

Removing two combs once, about a month before the honey flow is due, usually is enough to delay population buildup so that the colony does not swarm. If a colony is particularly strong (I have seen colonies with 14 combs of brood by the end of April), I would remove more than two combs, usually four or six, and start two or three nucleus colonies. I allow these nucs to rear queens as they are obviously of superior stock. In few cases in the past, I have robbed brood from a colony twice, three weeks apart. This prevented swarming and did not, as far as I could determine, reduce the honey surplus that the colony produced.

7

b) Exchanging places

During the day, while the bees are flying, the hive of a very strong colony is moved off its stand and a weak one is moved to the vacated place. The strong colony's hive is then set where the weak one had been. The strong force of forager bees returns and enters the hive now occupied by the weak colony, while the stronger colony receives only the small force of field bees from the weak colony. The weaker colony is boosted in strength while the stronger colony is temporarily weakened. The main objection to this method is that the stronger colony's hive is too heavy and awkward for one person to move alone.

For this method, or any other manipulation for prevention of swarming, the beekeeper must first ensure that no brood disease exists in the colonies.

c) Reversing Brood Chamber Supers

This procedure is used primarily to build up colonies in the spring but it also helps in reducing the swarming impulse. Reversing, that is, setting the upper brood super on the bottom board and then placing the former lower one on top, provides more empty cells in which the queen can deposit eggs. The method does accelerate population increase, and it may 'backfire' in swarm prevention. If the reversal is done more than three weeks before the onset of the honey flow, the supers should be reversed again ten days later. In any case, the colony should be given more room by adding supers above the brood chamber, if the beekeeper uses queen excluders routinely. If no queen excluder is used, the addition of a third brood super above the other two usually will delay the onset of "swarming fever".

d) The Double Queen System and Swarm Prevention

I have used this method routinely on all very strong colonies. Colonies with eight or more combs of brood are set up as described previously. When the honey flow is under way the two parts are reunited, headed by the younger queen. Although the upper unit sometimes becomes very crowded, I have never had swarms from either the upper or the lower unit. When reuniting the two units has been followed by a week or more of unfavourable weather I have had a few colonies swarm during the honey flow. During the poor weather the bees could not fly out to forage; they were very crowded and so made preparations to swarm.

Colonies that I determine are not strong enough for double queening are systematically weakened by robbing combs of brood to form nucleus colonies.

e) Shaking Bees off Combs

Instead of robbing brood combs or exchanging hive sites, it is easier to shake the bees off combs from a strong colony in front of the hive of a weak colony, then return the combs to the original hive. Young bees will be admitted by the weaker colony and older bees will return to their own hive. If you try this method, be sure that the queen of the strong colony remains in the hive. If she is with the bees that are shaken off, she will try to enter the hive that already has a queen and will be "balled" and killed.

More Drastic Methods of Swarm Prevention

a) "Cutting out" the Queen Cells

Many beekepers appear to think that the only way to prevent swarming is to "cut out" the queen cells every ten days. This is, in fact, a very poor solution to the problem. As already pointed out, a colony does not work well when it is preparing to swarm and brood-rearing is severely curtailed. Fewer new bees emerge day by day and eventually the population decreases because the number of bees that are dying each day exceeds the input of

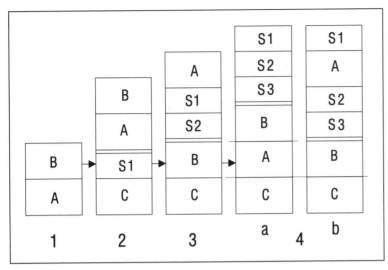

Fig 7.5: Diagram of the sequence in using Demaree system of swarm prevention. See text for details.

new bees. The result is that the colony does not swarm (unless the beekeeper misses a queen cell - which happens all too often) but the strength has declined and the amount of honey produced is less than if a method of swarm prevention had been used. In fact, "cutting out the queen cells" will eventually cause such a drop in population that the urge to swarm is lost (that is, dissemination of the queen substance becomes easier and the amount given to each individual bee is increased). This is not an efficient method of swarm prevention.

b) The Demaree Method of Swarm Prevention

The principle involved in the Demaree method is that worker bees will not desert a queen or young brood. This is at least true of Italian, Caucasian and Carniolan bees. The queen cells that the colony has produced are destroyed and the queen and the young brood are separated. This is a 'last resort' method that is useful once the bees have begun to make preparations for swarming, such as queen cells at the bottoms of the combs.

The queen is located and placed in a brood super on the bottom board with empty combs plus one comb of young (unsealed) brood. A queen excluder is placed above this super, then one or more honey supers. The super (or supers) which made up the original brood chamber are placed above the honey supers. (Fig. 7.5). The queen is now provided with plenty of cells in which to lay eggs. Many bees will stay with her to take care of her and for the larvae which soon will hatch. Many bees will also stay in the upper supers taking care of the brood until the new bees emerge. The upper supers must be checked no more than ten days later. The bees at the top feel isolated from the queen and may make queen cells if the combs contained any eggs or very young larvae. Any queens that emerge cannot leave the hive to become mated. They cannot pass through the queen excluder and eventually die.

After 21 days all of the brood in the upper supers will have emerged. If the supers are left on top they will become honey supers.

I do not like handling honey-filled brood combs if I am uncapping with a knife or a plane. The combs are tough and uncapping is much harder than uncapping combs used only for honey storage. If the large supers are filled with honey they will be heavy, so heavy that many people will have difficulty in removing them from the hive. The human spine will stand quite a lot of abuse, but for one person to lift a super of this size when it is at the top of the stack, filled with honey, is to court spinal problems.

The three week period following the separation of queen and brood will be followed immediately by new bees emerging in the lower super, so there is no interruption in the daily increment of new bees added to the colony. In practice, I have found that the lower unit needs more room before three weeks so, at ten days I remove one of the top supers, from which many bees have emerged, and place it on top of the super which contains the queen. At three weeks I remove the other super from the top and replace it with honey supers. It is not usually necessary to do more than this to control the urge to swarm before the honey flow begins. The bees almost never swarm during the honey flow unless the beekeeper does something that induces swarming, or there is a prolonged period of poor weather when the bees cannot leave the hive.

So the Colony Swarmed - What Then ?

I doubt that very many beekeepers can say that none of their colonies have ever produced a swarm. Almost certainly there will be a season when the apiarist is sick, away from home, or is too busy to initiate measures to prevent swarming and one or more colonies will swarm.

A swarm usually forms a cluster somewhere near the apiary. A newly emerged swarm is docile, very easy to handle, because the bees are engorged with honey. Any animal is better-tempered when satiated with food than when hungry. There is an additional factor in the case of honey bees. When their honey stomachs are full they seem to have difficulty in bending their abdomens downward in order to sting. If the scout bees have difficulty in locating a new home, the bees may remain clustered for days. The longer they stay, the less easy to manage they become, as their store of food becomes depleted. I have a vivid recollection of an incident that occurred early in my beekeeping days. I was asked to hive a swarm for a lady whose husband was away and could not look after it himself. I did not learn until later that the swarm had been hanging in cluster for six days. I do not bother with a veil or smoker, as a rule, when hiving swarms but these bees met me before I got within 50 metres of the swarm. Naturally, after I was left with no doubts as to their temperament, and had about 20 stings to prove it, I retreated hastily to my car, lit the smoker, put on a veil, and then proceeded to teach those bees who was the boss. The swarm was in an awkward place in an apple tree but I hived them just the same. This was my one and only experience with the so-called "German Black" bees. I have hived many swarms since then but none were as hostile as that one. It pays to try to find out how long a swarm has been clustered, if you can. Most of the swarms I have had to deal with were from the apiaries of other beekeepers and their removal was a case of public safety; swarms in schoolyards, service stations (bees are attracted to the smell of gasoline), railway stations, parking lots or similar public places.

Many householders, when a swarm of bees arrives at their premises, call the local fire department. Firemen usually do not know what to do, except that drenching a swarm with a water hose will persuade them to leave and cluster somewhere else. The favourite place to call is the nearest college or university. This is the reason that so many calls have been directed to me. If I can get the nearest beekeeper to look after the swarm, I do, but if the swarm is a potential hazard I move quickly and take it away. One of the most difficult swarms that I captured was well established between the outer and inner windows of a house. Another time, I sat in the back seat of a car holding a branch of an apple tree with a 12 lb. (5.5 kg.) swarm hanging from it, for 56 km (35 miles), and then successfully hived it without losing bees. I do not recommend this.

Hiving a Swarm

The equipment required for hiving a swarm: a standard brood super, bottom board and an inner cover that does not have a hole in it. The outer cover can be added when the swarm has been taken back to the apiary. The super should have at least one old drawn comb; the rest can be new frames with comb foundation. If the bottom board is stapled to the super, the ride home will be somewhat easier. It is a good idea to have a saw in the vehicle, as it may be necessary to cut off a branch of a tree. An axe is really not suitable for this task. I try to avoid damaging trees, especially those on somebody's lawn.

The location of the swarm determines the manner in which the beekeeper must proceed. If it is at low level on branches that can be shaken, place the super, with five of the foundation frames removed, directly under the cluster and dislodge them by shaking the branch sharply. Most of the bees will fall into the hive. Usually some of the bees will soon begin fanning scent pheromone to attract the other bees to enter, especially if the queen has dropped into the hive with the other bees (Fig. 7.6). Some time may elapse before all of the bees enter, and some bees will persist in returning to the branch where the swarm had been attached. This spot is coated with beeswax and attracts bees to return to it. It may be necessary to shake the branch again at intervals, or to brush the bees off the branch with a bee brush. If bees begin to leave the hive and fly away it is time to move the hive out of there and take it to the apiary or whatever site has been selected for it. These bees are foragers, ready to search for supplies of nectar and pollen. Alternatively, the hive can be left until the bees stop flying in the evening and then can be moved to the apiary.

If the swarm cluster is at a high level in a tree, it is necessary to use some sort of a "swarm-catcher". A box on the end of a long pole, with a cover that can be closed by the operator at the other end of the pole is used by many beekeepers. The box is pushed sharply around the swarm which then falls into the box. The cover is then closed, and the box is lowered to the ground and the bees are dumped into the hive. If such a piece of equipment is not available, and a handle long enough is impossible to carry in a car unless it is telescopic, use a ladder. A cardboard carton can be used to trap the bees which are then carried down and are dumped into the hive. Several trips may be necessary. Sometimes the swarm can be scraped off a surface into a box or a hive, but care is necessary to ensure that no bees are damaged. A crushed bee exserts its sting, thus causing the alarm scent to disperse in the air. Although honey bees tend to sting only when they have something to protect, they will act instinctively if they detect the pheromone and may attempt to sting even though their bodies are full of honey and will usually manage to drive their stings into the nearest warm body they can find.

If a swarm is in such an awkward place that attempting to hive it would be dangerous, it is better to leave it there and try using a "bait hive" to capture the bees. No swarm of bees is

Fig 7.6:
A swarm of bees 'marching' into a hive in response to the attractant pheromone.

worth broken bones or worse. I know that in the past some beekeepers have used a shotgun or even a rifle to 'shoot off' a tree limb to drop a very high swarm. I have very seldom found a swarm in a location where this could be done safely and carrying firearms around in a vehicle is not reccomended. I doubt that a policeman would accept the story that the shotgun was only for capturing swarms of honey bees.

Use of Bait Hives

A bait hive is one that is set out for the purpose of catching swarms. The idea is not new: it has been practised for hundreds of years. A hive, consisting of a bottom board, a single brood super with some drawn combs and some foundation, inner cover and cover, is set out near the apiary, but not closer than 150 metres. The scout bees from a swarm do not as a rule investigate potential new homes in the apiary (there are exceptions; I have had one swarm try to enter a hive which was already occupied by a colony with considerable loss of bees). However, the scouts do search mainly at some distance from their parent hive, from 100 metres to more than a kilometre. If they find a bait hive, they usually will decide to occupy it, if it is found to their liking. A bait hive with only wax foundation is not nearly as attractive to the bees as one that contains one or more combs that have been used by bees to rear brood. A dark comb is more attractive than a pale one.

Bait hives should not be set out any time other than during the spring swarming period and they should be checked frequently. Combs and foundation can be ruined by mice. Covering the entrance with wire mesh, 1/2 inch (approx. 13 mm), will prevent entry by mice while allowing access by honey bees. The screen will not prevent entry by the "Greater Wax Moth", *Galleria melonella*, which could ruin the drawn comb. The bees in a swarm are unlikely to be attracted to a hive which is infested by this pest.

Ferracane (1988) described a hive designed for use as a bait hive. The entrance is very small, made by an augur of 1 1/4 inches diameter near the bottom of the super which has a solid bottom. A nail is driven across the entrance hole to prevent entry by mice. Combs are used in this hive, not scraps of honeycomb such as are used by some beekeepers in bait hives.

Taber (1989) noted that a commercially produced mixture of the seven known components of the honey bee attractant pheromone produced by the Nasanov gland has been used to attract honey bee swarms to bait hives. The mixture is available commercially. If the "synthetic pheromone" becomes widely used the number of feral colonies should be greatly reduced and this would remove possible sources of bee diseases. According to Taber (1989) bait hives are being used extensively in Mexico to "help slow the northward march of the Africanized honey bee" and that already have trapped "thousands of swarms in these baited boxes".

What to do with a Swarm

A swarm captured early in the season can be kept as a unit in the apiary. Although it may not produce much surplus honey it should become a very respectable candidate for wintering. Many early swarms do produce some surplus honey but those collected later usually do not, but these too may become populous enough to winter. Swarms are ideal for having combs built from wax foundation, because of the number of bees of wax-producing age. The beekeeper should remember that the swarm queen is at least one year old, possibly older, so that before attempting to winter the colony requeening should be considered. The best time to requeen is during the honey flow.

A swarm may leave a hive shortly before the onset of the honey flow. The beekeeper should attempt to determine which colony lost the swarm, remove all queen cells, and unite the swarm with the parent colony using the newspaper method. Unless this is done, neither the swarm or the parent colony will be able to produce much, if any, surplus honey from the honey flow.

Removing Bees from Buildings

Honey bees will accept cavities in the walls of buildings as nest sites, if they have ready access and the cavities are large enough. I am aware of several buildings in which colonies of honey bees have lived for several years without interference from and without causing any concern to the human inhabitants. Evicting bees is not easy but, using proper procedure, can be accomplished without injury to the inhabitants, bees or humans. The person removing the bees must follow the proper procedure. It is unfortunate that some pest control operators or enthusiastic amateurs think only of destroying the bees. It is, of course, possible to kill the bees but that does not necessarily solve the problem.

If the bees have moved in very recently, the resulting problem is not very serious from the standpoint of the householder. Killing a colony that has a history of long residence is a different matter. If the entrance is sealed after the insecticide is applied, the bees will be dead but the wax combs and the brood and any stored honey will remain. Without the normal air-conditioning supplied by the bees, the temperature in the area is uncontrolled and, in summer, may rise to the point at which the beeswax will melt and the honey will run. It can soak into a wall or ceiling with dire results. All efforts to prevent the honey coming through to the surface are futile. Replacing the affected area of the wall or ceiling may be the only solution. Keep in mind too that the honey is contaminated by the insecticide.

If the entrance to the nest is not sealed, bees from other colonies, as well as wasps, hornets and other insects will be attracted to the honey. They may remove some of the honey, but they will probably be poisoned by the insecticide.

I have never recommended killing the bees that are nesting in houses. They can be removed, and both bees and honey can be salvaged. There are two ways that bees can be removed from a building: I have used both methods.

The first way, which I do not recommend, is to operate from the inside, removing part of a wall if necessary. Don't try this unless you are well protected with clothing, veil and gloves. In many cases, breaking through the wall is out of the question, but a colony that can be reached in an attic can be removed in this way. There is little enjoyment in working dressed for the occasion, flat on your stomach in the attic where you can just reach the area where the sloping roof meets the wall. I said it can be done and I have done it - once !

If you are fortunate enough to have to remove a colony that has its entrance at a low level, the job is easy enough but does take time. If the entrance is high in the wall, removal becomes more difficult. A hive must be set up near the entrance in the wall. A staging of some description is necessary and it must be strong. A cone, made of rolled fine-mesh screen, is tacked to the wall over the entrance with the small end of the cone outward (Fig. 7.7). The hive should contain a small queenright colony (a two-frame nucleus, transferred to a standard super, is ideal). The hive can contain mostly empty combs. The foraging bees from the building come out through the cone but are unable to re-enter the building. After a time they go into the hive. They are welcomed because they are carrying nectar or pollen. As the days pass, the inside colony gets weaker and the outside colony gets stronger. After about five weeks the inside colony is too weak to rear more brood. At six weeks, the cone should be removed.

This allows the bees in the hive to enter the wall and remove the honey which they store in their hive. When no more bees are seen coming and going in the entrance in the building, the entrance can be sealed and the hive can be taken away. The wax in the wall no longer is a problem, once the honey has been removed. No insecticide was used so there is no danger of poisoning honey bees or any other of our valuable pollinating insects. This method of removal is a big plus for everyone: the householder gets rid of the bees without creating a honey-seeping problem, and the beekeeper gains a colony with a good store of honey. This colony will require more room as soon as it is taken away. If it has been set up at low level, it might benefit from having a second brood super a week or two before it is taken to the apiary.

If the hive is on a high staging, it must be handled carefully as it will be much heavier than when it was set up. ❏

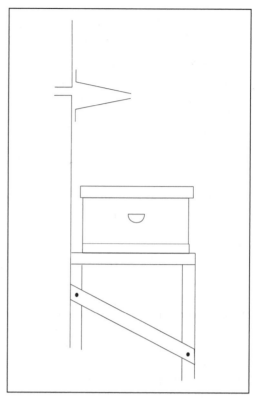

Fig 7.7: Hive and screen-cone on building. Removing a colony of honey bees from the wall of a house.

REFERENCES

Avitabile, A., R.A. Morse and R. Boch. 1975. Swarming Honey Bees Guided by Pheromones. Ann. Ent. Soc. Amer. 68 (6) : 1079-1082.

Burgett, D.M. and R.A. Morse. 1974. The Time of Natural Swarming in Honey Bees. Ann. ent. Soc. Amer. 67 : 719-720.

Combs, G.F., Jr. 1972. The Engorgement of Swarming Honeybees. J. apic. Res. 11 (3) : 121-128.

Ferracane, M. 1988. Bait Hive Basics. Gleanings Bee Cult. 116 (5) : 270-273,275.

Gary N. 1975. Activities and Behavior of Honey Bees. Chapter 7, pp. 185-264 in Dadant and Sons (Eds.) The hive and the Honey Bee. Hamilton Illinois, U.S.A. Dadant and Sons.

Heinrich, B. 1981. The regulation of temperature in the honeybee swarm. Sci. American 244 (6) : 146-148, 150, 153-154, 156, 158-160.

Jaycox, E.R. 1989. "Swarming can be prevented, but certainly not controlled." Gleanings Bee Cult. 117 (5): 284, 286.

Lindauer, M. 1955. Schwarmbienen auf Wohnungssuche. Z. vergl. Physiol. 36 : 263-324.

Seeley, T.D. 1982. How Honeybees Find a Home. Scientific American 247 (4) :158-163, 166, 168.

Seeley, T.D., R.A. Morse and P.K. Visscher. 1979. The Natural History of the Flight of Honey Bee Swarms. Psyche 86 : 103-113.

Simpson, J. 1963. Queen Perception by Honey Bee Swarms. Nature 199 (no. 4888) : 94-95.

Simpson, J. 1972. Recent research on swarming behaviour, including sound production. Bee World 53 (2): 73-78, 86.

Simpson, J. 1973. Influence of Hive-space Restriction on the tendency of Honeybee Colonies to Swarm. J. apic. Res. 12 (3) : 183-186.

Simpson, J. and S.P. Greenwood. 1974. Influence of Artificial Queen-Piping Sound on the tendency of Honeybee, *Apis mellifera*, Colonies to Swarm. Insectes Sociaux, Paris. 21 (3) : 283-288.

Taber, S. 1989. Honey Bee Pheromones. "There's much ado about the smell here". Gleanings Bee Cult. 117: 207, 209.

7

PRODUCTS OF THE BEES

Honey

Most people immediately associate honey bees with honey, but the bees also produce other products that are important to them and to mankind. As honey is the most familiar product, I will deal with it first. How do bees make honey ?

a) Nectar to Honey - the Process

Foraging bees visit flowers, many different floral sources, and collect nectar to be transformed into honey. Many flowers produce nectar, for the sole reason that they require visits by insects for pollination, so that they can produce seed in order to perpetuate their species. This cooperation and interdependence between flowers and bees developed over millions of years. Now neither can exist without the other.

Each bee sucks up as much nectar as it can from one flower after another, until its honey stomach is greatly distended and can hold no more. The marvelous transformation from nectar to honey begins there, in the honey stomach of the foraging bee. The enzyme invertase is added and the conversion from complex to simple sugars is begun.

The foraging bee flies back to the hive and is met at the hive entrance or slightly inside the entrance by a house bee. The two bees place their mouthparts in contact and the field bee regurgitates its load which is then swallowed by the house bee. More invertase is added in the honey stomach of the house bee and the conversion process is continued. The nectar being transformed may be passed to several bees in succession before the chemical change is completed.

The foraging bee, once it has delivered its load of nectar, spends about four minutes cleaning itself and taking enough honey to provide energy for the next trip, then returns to the field.

This is only part of the process. The nectar of most plants is quite dilute, containing considerably more water than the bees will tolerate in the finished product. The excess moisture must be evaporated and driven out of the hive. House bees spread the nectar/honey in a thin layer on the inside of cells, or hang drops in convenient places, to provide greater surface for evaporation (Gary, 1975). The normal ventilation in the hive tends to remove and vent the moisture but, during a heavy honey flow, many more bees assist in ventilation to remove the large amount of excess water. Nectar may contain 60 to 80 percent water and honey must contain less than 20 percent. The acceptable average for moisture in honey is about 17.6 percent.

When the chemical process is complete and the moisture content is reduced to the desired level, the honey is stored in cells of the honeycomb and is sealed in with wax to prevent addition of more moisture (Fig. 8.1). Other lots of honey are being processed and if the cells are not sealed the honey would absorb water as it is very hygroscopic, very water soluble.

The bees do not produce honey for the beekeeper, but they will produce more than they need if the colony is strong, the floral sources are available, and they have plenty of room for honey storage. The surplus honey that a beekeeper harvests is only a fraction of the total produced by the bees. A surplus of 100 kg from a colony may represent total production by the colony of about 400 to 500 kg. The bees use a great deal of honey themselves.

Composition of Honey

It is not possible to provide an analysis which covers the composition of the entire range of honey from different sources. Many factors are involved. Most of the variation is due to the nectars produced by different plants, as the proportions and con stiuents are widely variable. Although a batch of honey is often classified as being produced from a particular nectar source, such as clover, it is hardly credible that all of the honey came from clover nectar. A plant label on honey usually indicates that (as far as the beekeeper can determine) the honey was produced from nectar that was predominantly from that plant source. Some honey, such as that produced from buckwheat nectar, is so strong that considerably less that half of the honey may be of buckwheat origin. The flavour and colour of buckwheat honey easily dominates the honey from other sources.

The following list shows the percentages of the principal components of honey:

PRINCIPAL COMPONENTS OF HONEY

Component	Percentage
Water	17.2
Levulose sugar	38.3
Dextrose sugar	31.3
Sucrose sugar	1.3
Maltose and higher sugars	8.8
Acids (many organic acids)	0.57
Proteins	0.26
Minerals	0.17
Other components	

Adapted from White (1975)

Levulose (fructose) and dextrose (glucose) are simple sugars that do not require digestion by humans but pass readily from the digestive tract into the bloodstream. The total sugar content is about 80 percent. Many acids may be present, including gluconic, citric, malic, succinic, formic, acetic, butyric, lactic, pyroglutamic and amino acids, but all are present in very small amounts, the total of all of them making up little more that 1/2 of 1 percent of the total acids. Many minerals are included, but these too are present in very small quantities, totalling less than 0.2 percent. The following minerals occur in honey: potas sium, sodium, calcium, magnesium, chlorides, sulphates, silica, etc. No mineral is present in sufficient quantity to supply the requirements of the human body.

In addition, there are many very minor components, making up about 2.1 percent of the total. Included are pigments, aromatic substances, alcohols, tannins, vitamins (but in such small quantities as to be insignificant in human diet) and enzymes (also in variable and negligible amounts) (White, 1975). Honey is actually very acidic, but the acid is masked by the sweetness of the included sugars.

Honey and Moisture

As mentioned above, honey is very hygroscopic and will absorb water readily, this depending upon the relative humidity and temperature. The following list (from White, 1975) indicates the levels of water in honey and shows the equivalent relative humidities above and below which honey will absorb or lose water.

Percent water in Honey	Equilibrium Relative Humidity
16.1	52
17.4	58
21.5	66
28.9	76
33.9	81

It is apparent that honey should be stored at low temperature and low relative humidity. Honey at 16.1 percent water would absorb water at relative humidity levels above 52 percent and would tend to lose water if exposed to air drier than 52 percent relative humidity. Honey will absorb moisture faster that it will lose it. The surface layer of honey can absorb water rapidly, the water diffusing slowly to greater depth of honey. When honey is exposed to dry air it tends to lose moisture very slowly due to a dry surface skin which forms on the honey. A refractometer (Fig. 8.2) is used to determine the precise amount of water in a sample of honey.

The moisture content of honey is important to the bees as well as to other consumers of honey. Bees fare very poorly on honey that has fermented. We do not readily accept fermented honey either. Fermentation of honey that is controlled can produce very fine alcoholic beverages but uncontrolled fermentation ruins the honey for any use. Honey will not ferment if the moisture content is maintained a a low level, less than 20 percent. It is obvious then that honey should be kept where humidity is low. More on this later.

Fig 8.1: A comb full of honey from a brood-depth super.

Granulation of Honey

Honey is a supersaturated solution. It contains more dissolved sugars than normally can persist in solution. It will eventually change to a stable saturated state by crystallizing the excess dextrose sugar. This is called granulation. There are a few honeys that do not granulate, heather honey in Europe and manuka honey in New Zealand (White, 1975), but all of the honeys produced in North America should granulate sooner or later, depending somewhat on storage conditions.

Honey with a relatively high ratio of dextrose to levulose tends to granulate rather quickly. Eastern North American fall honey, which is made largely from the nectars of aster, goldenrod and a few minor plants, granulates quickly, sometimes even in the cells of the honeycomb before the honey supers are removed from the hive. On the other hand, the honey produced from a broad spectrum of plants in summer, has much lower ratio of dextrose to levulose and tends to granulate more slowly.

The rapidity of granulation of honey determines the ultimate texture of the product. Honey which granulates quickly has a fine crystalline structure, and so is "smooth", while the crystals of slow granulating honey tend to be coarse, often feeling rough on the tongue.

The ideal temperature for granulation of honey is 14 degrees Celsius (57 degrees F.). If granulated honey is stored at high temperatures, 27 to 30 degrees C (80 to 85 degrees F), it will soften and become partially liquid.

Fermentation of Honey

Honey ferments due to the action of yeasts on the simple sugars producing carbon dioxide and alcohol. The alcohol is usually broken down further into acetic acid and water. The yeasts are of a kind that are tolerant of high sugar concentration. Most yeasts and also bacteria (vegetative stages - not the spore forms) cannot exist in honey because of its high level of acidity. The sugar-tolerant yeasts may come from the flowers visited by the bees or from the soil. Combs from which honey has been removed the previous year also may be sources of yeasts in honey.

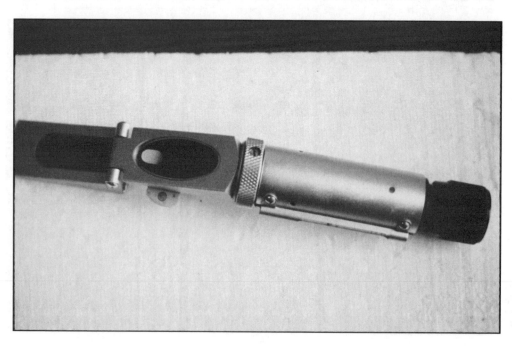

Fig 8.2:
A honey refractometer, used to measure the moisture content of honey. A small amount of liquid honey is placed on the projecting part, which is then folded over the body of the instrument. The moisture content is read directly at the point at which a darker line appears.

The combination of yeasts and water produce conditions in which fermentation can take place. Storage conditions and grannulation also are factors. Honey with a low moisture content, below 18 percent, will not ferment if it is stored properly. If the moisture content is 20 percent or greater, fermentation will ultimately occur. The process of granulation releases free water and thus increases the moisture content, leading to possible fermentation. Storage temperatures of 11 to 15 degrees C (52 to 60 degrees F) promote granulation. If honey with borderline moisture granulates, fermentation inevitably follows. Storing honey at high temperature, 38 to 40 degrees C. (about 100 degrees F.) will prevent fermentation but the quality of the honey is damaged at such high temperature. The ideal temperature for honey storage is 10 degrees C (50 degrees F) or less, as the low temperature inhibits growth of the yeasts.

Honey as a Food

We need carbohydrates to produce the energy we need to do what we have to do (or think we have to do). It is not essential to include carbohydrates in the diet because the body can use proteins and fats to produce all of the energy-giving carbohydrates that we need.

Levulose and dextrose are monosaccharides, simple sugars, that can pass from the digestive tract directly into the blood stream without digestion. Other sugars, such as sucrose (cane or beet sugar) are more complex and must be broken down in the digestive process before they can be utilized by the body. Honey, being high in simple sugars, is a source of quick energy. Most of the dextrose component is passed directly to the blood stream. The levulose fraction acts as a reserve energy supply and is ultimately converted to dextrose before being used by the body to produce a prolonged source of energy.

Honey has been used very widely in feeding infants. My older son had chronic digestive problems on the "recommended formulas", but this disappeared and his progress was excellent when we added honey to his diet. Recently there has been a "scare program" regarding honey in infant feeding, but there is no greater risk of poisoning by botulism from honey than with other foods given to infants.

Much of my early beekeeping has been carried on while working full time and often in areas distant from the apiaries. The only time usually available for the bees was evenings and weekends. Often I was more tired when I started work at the apiary than when I finished, as I nearly always "charged" the bees for my efforts by taking a mouthful or two of their honey.

It has already been mentioned that the minerals and enzymes contained in honey are present in such small quantities that they are negligible factors in human diet.

Honey has very wide use in cooked foods. Use of honey rather than other sugar products gives the product freshness over longer periods and extends shelf-life of these products. Honey can also add flavour, depending to some extent upon the floral sources of the nectar gathered by the bees. Honey can be used in any recipe that lists 'sugar'. An equal amount of honey can be substituted in making bread, rolls or muffins. For other baked products, an equal amount of honey can be used, but the liquid listed in the recipe should be reduced by one-quarter cup for each cup of honey used. Some bakeries make a point of advertising that their products are made with honey.

Honey and Medecine

Honey has been used for many years and in many ways for medicinal purposes. Many cough syrups contain honey and honey can be used in other medications as well.

The use of honey as surgical dressings has been known since the time of the Egyptian Pharaohs, up to 5000 years ago. There are numerous citations of this use of honey in the literature. I can verify that honey is a useful dressing for minor cuts and burns, superior to any other that I have tried. I and my family have used honey on burns and cuts for many years. Our younger son was an active child and always had to see what was going on. One day when was about two and a half years old, he managed to move a chair over to the electric range, climbed up and put his hand on a hot element, recently turned off but still red. His mother immediately applied honey to the burn. The honey dressing was continued until the pain was gone. Honey tends to soothe the pain and, in his case, the healing was complete and today there is no sign of scarring on the palm of his hand.

I once tried to persuade a surgeon in a hospital to use honey to promote healing of the incisions he was to make in my carcase - to no avail. The wounds healed alright, but I am still convinced that honey would have been better.

As a dressing, honey works in two ways. Due to its bactericidal action, any organisms in or around the wound are killed and the honey prevents entrance of airborne disease organisms. It also feeds the tissues directly due to the large proportion of simple monosaccharide sugars. The bactericidal action is due in part to the osmotic pressure that causes disease organisms to rupture and die. Additional action is due to the constant chemical change produced by an enzyme that produces hydrogen peroxide. Hydrogen peroxide does not persist but is changed again to water and oxygen. The temporarily free oxygen kills bacteria.

Beeswax

Beeswax is produced by worker bees by synthesizing sugars. Whitcomb (1946) reported that an average of 5 kg (11 lbs) of honey is required to produce 0.6 kg (1.3 lbs) of wax. Wax is secreted from four pairs of glands on the underside of the abdomen by bees of about 13 to 17 days old. As secreted by the bees the wax is white. The yellowish colour of most beeswax is due to pigments found in pollen.

The chemical composition of beeswax is complex: hydrocarbons, 16 percent; straight-chain monohydric alcohols, 31 percent; acids 31 percent; and 9 percent other substances (Downing *et al.*, 1961). Beeswax melts at 64.38 degrees C (147.9 degrees F); solidifies at 63.50 degrees C (146.3 degrees F). The wax produced by North American bees (*Apis mellifera*) is said to differ chemically and physically from the wax (called Ghedda wax) produced by the Asian bees, *Apis florea* and *A. dorsata* (Witherell, 1975).

Beeswax is used widely in cosmetic products, such as cold creams, lotions, lipsticks and rouges. The candle industry uses great quantities of beeswax, particularly for making candles used in religious ceremonies.

The pharmaceutical industry also uses large quantities of beeswax, in preparation of salves, ointments and pill coatings. Beeswax is used by dentists in the compounds used for making impressions. It is also a component of many furniture polishes. There is also a ready market for beeswax to artists and art supply companies. Wax for grafting fruit trees is made largely from beeswax. Another major use of beeswax is that of the beekeeping industry as large quantities are used to make comb foundation.

North America does not produce enough beeswax to supply our requirements. Large quantities are imported from Latin America and Africa.

Processing Beeswax

Beekeepers obtain wax from the cappings sliced off in preparing full combs of honey for the extractor, wax scraped from frames or other hive parts, and from old combs which are melted down and replaced.

Cappings make the best grade of pale, white wax. Wax scrapings and old combs produce much darker wax. Cappings should be kept separate from the other darker wax. Cappings should not be exposed to bees.

Do not heat beeswax over an open flame but only in a water bath. Cappings or other beeswax can be placed in bags made of several thicknesses of cheesecloth. This is placed in water that is heated but not to boiling. The wax will rise to the top and will harden into a cake, while the impurities remain in the bag. The container in which the wax is allowed to cool should have sloping sides so that the wax cake can be removed easily.

Commercially built wax melters use steam to melt the wax and separate it from the impurities. Use of steam may cause partial saponification of the wax. This is a breakdown process producing acid and alcohol. Commercial establishments use hot water and steam in a press to remove the wax.

Solar wax melters in the apiary are useful for melting old combs and scrapings from hive parts but they do not separate all of the wax from the remaining impurities (slumgum).

Pollen

Bees gather pollen for their own use (Fig. 8.3). A strong colony may gather up to 34 kg (75 lbs) of pollen in a single season. They may use the entire amount for their own purposes. It is their only source of proteins, fats and minerals.

Pollen is rich in protein, but the proportions in pollen from various sources are not uniform. Certain necessary amino acids are missing or present in very small quattities in some pollen, such as that of dandelion. Pollen also contains fats, carbohydrates (sugars, starch and cellulose), many minerals (copper, calcium, magnesium, phosphorus, iron, sodium, potassium, aluminum, manganese and sulphur), and small amounts of vitamins, enzymes and pigments. Variation is great, as noted above, so that pollen from a number of different plant sources is necessary to supply the supply the requirements of the bees. Foraging bees do not discriminate between rich and deficient pollens.

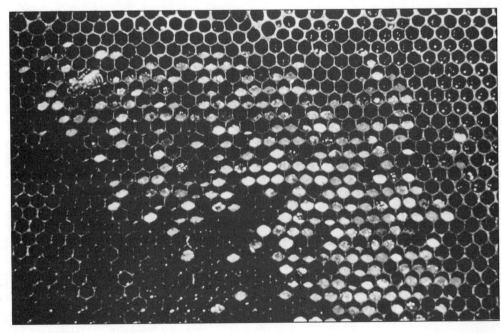

Fig 8.3: Pollen from various sources in a brood comb. This comb was next to the hive wall and has no brood.

Pollen is used in "pollen inserts" for pollination of fruit trees and certain nut crops (see Chapter 10). One of the most useful of the hive inserts is that developed and described by Karmo and Vickery (1954, 1957, 1987b).

Pollen can be collected from the bees as they enter the hives by means of pollen traps. Pollen traps should not be used on all of the colonies in an apiary. Prolonged use can cause pollen deficiencies, and the colonies on which the traps are installed may cause the bees to gather pollen at the expense of the honey crop. The traps should not be used continuously on any hive. In suitable pollen-gathering weather traps should be operational on about three days in ten.

Be very careful not to collect pollen from colonies which are affected by Chalkbrood disease if the pollen is to be fed to bees.

It is often recommended that pollen be fed to the bees early in the spring, particularly where early pollen sources are scarce. I have noted several times that colonies interrupted brood rearing early in spring due to lack of pollen in the hive.

Stored pollen should be kept cool and dry in containers that are sealed to prevent infestation by various beetles, moths or ants. Pollen that is kept frozen will germinate successfully after prolonged storage and frozen pollen retains palatability. Dry pollen at room temperature gradually loses palatability and nutritive value.

Pollen (hand gathered) is used by allergists in a desensitizing process in treatment of persons suffering pollen allergies.

Pollen has recently had wide use as a dietary supplement for human consumption. The value of pollen to humans has yet to be proven to my satisfaction, although I have no evidence that it is harmful. It is a very expensive way to obtain protein, and I believe a proper balanced diet will provide all of the nutritional requirements without the addition of pollen. Pollen is known to have very strong, resistant cell walls and pollen from hundreds of thousands of years ago is found intact at many archaeological sites.

Propolis

The bees gather the resinous material called propolis from flower buds, from coniferous trees, etc., and use it to fill cracks or to reduce the size of entrances. Often it is applied at the ends of the top bars of frames, making them difficult to remove. Metal frame rests are used to prevent breakage of the top bar ends that otherwise could occur due to the strong adhesion of the propolis. Propolis tends to fix hive parts in position, an advantage when hives are moved for pollination or migratory beekeeping. Propolis-gathering bees have been reported as collecting other materials such as asphalt, dry paint and caulking compound.

Propolis is chemically complex, variable in composition and colour. It is quite gummy and sticky at normal hive temperature but when cold is brittle and hard. Cismarik and Martel (1970, 1973) have reported the chemical analysis of propolis. It is composed of about 30 percent waxes, 55 percent resinous substances, 10 percent oils and 5 percent pollen.

The wax used by the bees to build comb contains a small proportion of propolis and, as propolis has been found to have bactericidal properties, may be responsible for the resistance to brood diseases exhibited by some colonies. Akopyan *et al.* (1970) in Russia reported that propolis exerted a degree of control of the organism that causes European Foul Brood, *Streptococcus [=Mellitococcus] pluton*.

Propolis has been used as a component of fine varnish. It is used in the Soviet Union for dressings for cuts, wounds and abcesses of animals (Zaleski *et al.*, 1965).

Royal Jelly

Royal Jelly is the high protein food that is secreted by young bees, usually between 6 and 13 days of age, in their hypopharyngeal glands. They first eat large quantities of pollen and some honey before the glands begin to function.

This is the food that is fed to queens during the larval stage and determines that these larvae will become queens. Young worker and drone larvae are also fed Royal Jelly for the first three days after they hatch from the eggs. It is a highly nutritious food with a very complex composition. Blum (*et al.*, 1959) found 10-hydroxy decenoic acid, in Royal Jelly. This compound is antibiotic and apparently controls any possible bacterial or fungal contamination.

Royal Jelly has been touted as being highly advantageous to human health, but much of the advertising has been misleading and inaccurate. There is no substantiating evidence that the substance is useful either taken internally or as skin creams. Should such evidence be forthcoming, the demand for Royal Jelly will certainly increase.

Any beekeeper can harvest Royal Jelly by following the same procedures as for the Dolittle method of queen rearing (see in Chapter 6). After the queen cups are extended and supplied with considerable Royal Jelly, the cup/cells are removed, the larvae are discarded and the creamy substance is removed with a tiny spoon or by vacuum. A great many cells are required to produce much Royal Jelly. Witherell (1975) stated that an average of 1,000 3-day-old cells would produce one pound (0.45 kg). Bits of debris that inevitably are included should be removed by passing the jelly through a very fine strainer. Refrigeration is required to maintain the quality of the product.

The amount per cell is very small so it can readily be seen that a reasonably large operation is necessary to produce quantities large enough to market. Until a stable market is available, it is hardly worth while to attempt commercial production.

I may add that over the years I have consumed the contents of queen cells (but not the larvae) many times and I have failed to note any beneficial effects.

Honey Bee Venom

Newly emerged bees have very little venom. The amount increases with age until it reaches its maximum at 15 to 18 days of age, at the time a bee can become a guard bee. No additional venom is produced after that time, as none is required. There can be no replenishing of the supply of venom as the sting and attached parts are torn out of the bee when it stings.

Beard (1963) and others have summarized the components of honey bee venom: histamine, dopamine, mellitin, apamin, mast-cell-destroying peptide (MCD), minimine, and the enzymes hyaluridase and phospolipase A. Bees from different areas or from different times in a season do not differ in the composition of their venom. This indicates that the bees synthesize venom: it is not determinbed by nectar or pollen sources or diet.

The venom of honey bees is more toxic than the venom of wasps (see Reaction to bee venom in Chapter 5).

Bee venom is used medically in treatment of rheumatoid arthritis and also for desensitization of individuals that are hypersensitive to bee venom. The latter use is important as hypersensitive people can be killed due to anaphylactic shock produced by a single sting.

Charles Mraz, in many articles in bee journals and in talks to beekeepers, has long been an advocate of bee-venom therapy in treatment of arthritis. I distinctly recall a meeting at which people were lined up to receive a sting at a joint in which arthritis was a problem. I have heard, though I am unable to find a reference at this time, that the bee venom causes the body to produce excess hydrocortizone. If this is the case the venom should be helpful to some people with certain types of arthritis. As I have mentioned before, I have been stung many times and though I have arthritis I am not able to state conclusively that the bee stings have made more difference than momentary relief.

Bee venom is collected at the entrances to hives by insertion of a wooden frame with electric wires that give the bees a mild shock. This stimulates the bees to sting the nylon taffeta cloth beneath the wires. The venom is deposited on a glass plate beneath the cloth. It dries and is scraped off later. The bees that sting usually survive but, of course, have lost their supply of venom. The stinging produces considerable of the alarm pheromone and the colony soon becomes very upset. The device is moved after five minutes to another hive. Collection from about 20 colonies will produce about one gram of dried venom. The liquid fraction can be collected if desired. (Benton and Morse, 1966). ❏

REFERENCES

Akopyan, Z.M., G.A. Shakaryan and S.G. Danielyan. 1970. Sensitivity of microorganisms to propolis in some districts of the Armenian S.S.R. Biol. Zh. Armeniya 23: 217-272.

Beard, R. 1963. Insect toxins and venoms. Ann. Rev. Ent. 8: 1-18.

Benton, A.W. and R.A. Morse. 1966. Collection of the liquid fraction of bee venom. Nature 210: 652-653.

Blum, M.S., A.F. Novak and S. Taber III. 1959. 10-hydroxy-2 decenoic acid, an antibiotic found in royal jelly. Science 130: 452-453.

Cizmarik, J. and I. Matel. 1970. Examination of the chemical composition of propolis. I. Isolation and identification of the 3,4 dihydroxycinnamic acid (caffeic acid) from propolis. Experentia 26: 713.

Cizmaric, J. and I. Matel. 1973. Exasmination of the chemical composition of propolis. 2. Isolation and identification of 4-hydroxy-3-methoxycinnamic acid (ferulic acid) from propolis. J. apic. Res. 12: 63-65.

Downing, D.T., Z.H. Krantz, J.A. Lamberton, K.EW. Murray and A.H. Redcliffe. 1961. Studies in waxes. XVIII. Beeswax: a spectroscopic and gas chromatoghraphic examination. Aust. J. Chem. 14: 253-263.

Gary, N. 1975. Activities and Behavior of Honey Bees. pp. 185-264, in Dadant and Sons (Eds.) The Hive and the Honey Bee. Hamilton Illinois, Dadant and Sons, Inc.

Karmo, E.A. and V.R. Vickery. 1954. The Place of Honey Bees in Orchard Pollination. Mimeo Circ. Nova Scotia Dept. Agr. Mkt. No. 67; 12 pp.

Karmo, E.A. and V.R. Vickery. 1957. Bees to the Rescue. Amer. Fruit Grower, April, pp. 42-45.

Karmo, E.A. and V.R. Vickery. l987b. Inserts for pollen dissemination. Can. Beek. 13: 187-188.

Whitcomb, W.,Jr. 1946. Feeding bees for comb production. Gleanings Bee Cult. 74: 198-202, 247.

Witherell, P.C. 1975. Other Products of the Hive. pp.531-558, in Dadant and Sons (Eds.) The Hive and The Honey Bee. Hamilton, Illinois, Dadant and Sons, Inc.

Zaleski, V., A. Stoike and L. Ilevich. 1965. Propolis in the treatment of animal wounds. Veterinariya 42: 110-111. [in Russian]. Apic. Abstr. 368-369.

HONEY PRODUCTION AND PROCESSING

9

Equipment Required for Honey Production

The bees must have cells in which they can ripen and store honey. This is provided by adding supers of combs above the brood chamber boxes. These supers should contain only nine combs. In the brood chamber the cells are built out only to the depth required for growth and maturation of worker brood. However, if a queen excluder is used, the combs in the honey supers are built with much deeper cells. The bees can store more honey in nine combs with deep cells than in ten combs with cells built to brood depth.

I prefer using queen excluders for several reasons: if queen excluders are not used, brood will be raised in the upper supers and, when they are later used for honey storage, are uneven due to areas of shallower cells; combs in which brood is reared become tough and are more difficult to uncap if uncapping is done manually with knife or plane; and, incidentally, the combs used only for honey are less subject to attack by the Greater Wax Moth than those in which brood has been reared.

There are many beekeepers who do not use queen excluders and who produce good honey crops without them. I would not try to persuade them to change their ways. I have had colonies without excluders many times and I believe as they do that the honey crop produced by these colonies was greater than the yields of the colonies with the excluders. If queen excluders are to be used, they should be installed before the third super is added, not later after the bees have had access to the supers above.

When nine combs are used in honey supers the spacing is important. Slotted frame rests are used to space the frames equidistant from each other and to provide the correct spacing between the outside combs and the hive walls (Fig. 9.1). Commercially produced frame spacers are available at any establishment dealing in bees supplies. I have used all types of spacers and have even made my own out of pieces of heavy aluminum from an old door. They were as satisfactory as the others. If you make your own be sure that the measurements are precise. I also cut some frame spacers to hold only eight frames but, in a limited trial, found at extracting time that supers with eight combs contained no more honey than those with nine combs.

Frames in shallow supers can be of two types, those with end bars with shoulders that require frame spacers for proper spacing, and those with closed end bars, that are self spacing, nine frames to a super (Fig. 9.2).

How many honey supers are required for each colony ? I have been asked this question many times. It is a difficult question to answer because there is so much variation between colonies and also in the depths of the supers used for honey storage. Do the supers contain drawn combs, comb foundation, or a mixture of these ? In general, an average colony in northeastern North America will require 2 or 3 supers of the same depth as the brood supers, or 4 deep shallow supers (6 1/4 inch deep frames), or 5 ordinary shallow supers, *if* they con-

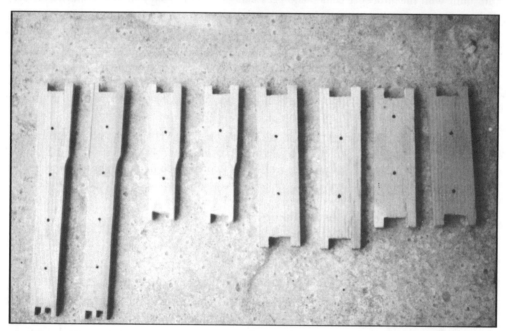

Fig 9.2: Types of frame end bars: left to right; brood size with shoulders, shallow with shoulders, deep shallow closed end bars, and shallow closed end bars.

tain drawn combs. If comb foundation is used, the colonies will require only about 2/3 as much space. Producing combs from the comb foundation will cause a noticeable decrease in the expected honey surplus.

Colonies started in the spring from packages will require much less space and colonies started from spring-produced nucleus colonies will need more than is required for the package colonies. Colonies based upon late summer or fall produced, wintered nuclei will usually require nearly as much space as the average colonies mentioned above. My wintered nucleus colonies have produced well, 35 to 68 kg (77 to 150 lbs) each of surplus honey.

I use the multiple queen system as a method of swarm control and for increased production (but not with wintered nucs). It has been necessary to provide 5 to 11 shallow and deep shallow supers (about half of each) during several seasons; the average has been 6 or 7 (Fig. 9.3). The

Fig 9.3:
Tall hives in an apiary.

colony that required 11 supers was exceptional and produced in excess of 160 kg (350 lb). If the location had been better, that colony might have produced even more surplus honey.

Supering

a) Supering with Drawn Combs.

When a hive is opened for inspection of a colony in spring and the bees are numerous on the top bars in the upper super, it is time to provide more space. Even though there may be no possibility of any surplus honey being stored, the bees need the space so as to reduce congestion in the brood area. I have found, for average colonies, this is necessary on or slightly before May 1st. In the northeastern region swarming can begin by the middle of the month. Adding the honey super may be all that is needed to prevent the onset of swarming.

When the first super has honey stored in the 4 middle combs, and some of it is capped, it is time to add another super. I prefer "bottom supering" if only a few (40 colonies or less) are involved. Lift off the first honey super and place the new one next to the brood chamber and place the original honey super on the top. The bees will continue to work in the first honey super and, as they have to pass through the second, will begin to work in it as well. The same procedure can be followed when adding more honey supers or, when the honey flow starts, additional supers can be added on top of the others. This is "top supering". Figure 9.4 shows diagramatically both top and bottom supering.

b) Supering with Comb Foundation

Comb foundation in closed end bar frames should be sealed into the top groove by hot wax from a wax tube.

If a great deal of comb foundation has to be used in honey supers, it is helpful to have a few drawn combs to entice the bees into the supers, especially in the first honey super to be

Fig 9.4:
Diagram, bottom supering (left), and top supering (right).

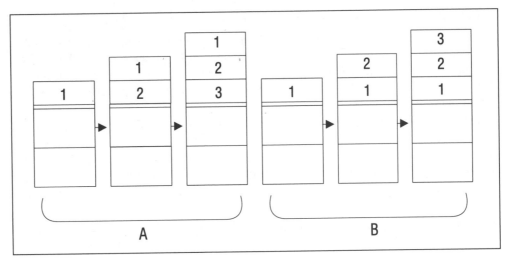

added. These "bait" combs, placed in the middle of the super, will be used readily by the bees and the adjacent frames of foundation will be worked on soon. Bottom supering is the best way to have the bees start working on the sheets of foundation. If bottom supering is carried on consistently, the first super ready for removal will be the one at the top of the stack. If a super with foundation is added at the top the bees tend to ignore it until they are desperate for space, which could be an extended period. There is also a tendency in cases like this to store excess honey in the brood chamber, thus reducing the area available for brood rearing. Additional supers with foundation should be added beneath the other honey supers.

Management for Production of Honey for Extraction

When the honey flow begins, near mid-June on the average in the northeast, it is essential that the bees have plenty of cells in which to ripen and store honey. Their need is not only for empty storage cells; they also need many empty cells in which to spread the dilute nectar in order to evaporate the excess moisture. As a 'rule of thumb', at the beginning of the honey flow, add one more super than you think the bees will need. Whenever many bees are seen on the top bars of the top super (if the beekeeper is top-supering) there is an urgent requirement for addition of another super.

When the honey flow is diminishing in July, do not provide extra space. At this time it is better to provide too little than too much. If there is excess space the same amount of honey may be spread through several supers rather than concentrated in fewer supers. If there are excess supers then more supers must be handled when extracting to obtain the same amount of honey.

A number of years ago, when I kept bees in Nova Scotia, it was impossible for me to visit my apiaries regularly. I had to practice "let-alone" beekeeping. At the beginning of the honey flow, a queen excluder and a honey super were placed above the brood chamber of each hive. Then on top were placed several more supers, each separated from the others by sheets of newspaper. As the bees needed more space they chewed out a layer of newspaper and occupied the super, continuing in this fashion as more space was required. I suppose I could have left out the newspaper but I found that the bees entered only the supers that they needed. Without the paper the honey might have been spread through all of the supers increasing the labour expended. Some colonies had used all of the supers but others had not. In Nova Scotia this method worked very well and the bees produced excellent surplus crops, but I would be afraid to try it in areas where the Greater Wax Moth is a problem.

Requirements for Cut Comb, Sections and Rounds

The first step in each of these 'speciallized' types of production is to prepare the comb in which the bees will store the honey. The foundation used for production of each of these is considerably thinner than that used for brood rearing or for storage of honey for extracting. This is because the wax will form an integral part of the product offered for sale. Obviously there is no wire in this foundation.

Cut comb is, as the name suggests, comb that has been filled with honey and is cut into chunks. These are either allowed to drain to remove the honey from the cut cells and are packaged in foil containers with clear panel lids, or are packed immediately in glass jars that are then filled with liquid honey. The latter is sometimes called chunk honey.

The only preparation of the frames for cut comb honey is installation of the thin foundation. This foundation usually is inserted into a groove in the top bar and is sealed there by hot, liquid beeswax applied with a wax tube (Fig. 9.5). The wax foundation must be handled very carefully. When cold it is brittle and is easily broken. When warm it tends to sag. The

Fig 9.5:
Wax tube.

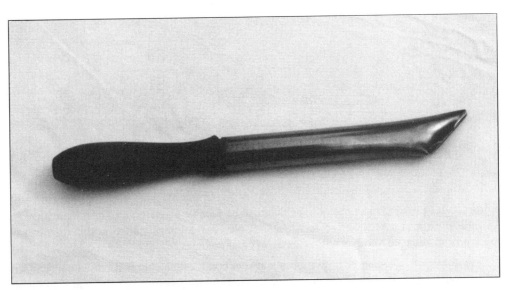

frames should be placed in supers as soon as the wax is put in. As long as they remain vertical, the wax should remain as installed. If the frames are allowed to lay on their sides, the wax will sag and will tend to remain that way.

The procedure in preparing for production of rounds or sections is very different. Sections are made of thin wood which is bent to form squares, 10.2 x 10.2 x 4.8 cm (4 1/2 x 4 1/2 x 1 7/8 inches) in size. A sheet of foundation 10.5 x 43.4 cm (4 1/4 x 17 inches) is inserted in a row of 4 split sections and is sealed by "painting" the tops of the sections with hot paraffin wax. The rows of sections are placed in supers that are built to hold sections, as they are slightly shallower than standard shallow supers. Springs are used to hold the sections in position. The wooden sections in earlier use required that the foundation be cut to fit each wooden section, with some overlap at the top. A hot metal plate was used to seal the wax protruding at the top. The problem with square sections is that the bees do not like working in corners and many of the otherwise perfect sections had little if any honey in the corners.

The use of wooden sections is now being replaced by "rounds", plastic structures that are used four in a row with the thin wax foundation inserted into the row of four. Only the wax in the circular area is available to the bees and as there are no corners, the round sections are usually well filled.

Management for Production of Cut Comb, Sections and Rounds

In general the management of the bees for production of sections, rounds or cut comb is quite similar, though there is more latitude in producing cut comb. Cut comb can often be produced merely by placing a super of the thin foundation beneath the supers previously added for extracting honey, if the colony is strong and the honey flow is such that the bees are making daily gains. If the colony is weak, or the honey flow is poor or interrupted, the combs are likely to be useless for cut comb honey.

For serious attempts to produce cut comb honey, and always for sections and rounds, the bees should be crowded by reducing them to a single brood box and one super containing thin foundation. The upper brood super with brood, queen and bees usually is left on the bottom board. Most of the bees from the other super are shaken off in front of the hive. The combs from this super can be used to boost other colonies or, if there are enough bees still on these

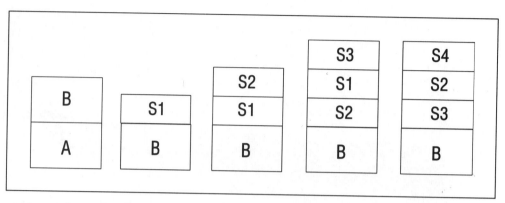

combs, can be used to form nuclei. The nucs can be each be given a queen or if there are eggs in the combs, can be allowed to rear queens. Nucleus colonies started at this time can be built up and wintered to offset winter losses of other colonies.

A queen excluder can be used if producing cut comb chunks but is not used under supers of sections or rounds. These colonies must be checked frequently to ensure that they do not swarm. The honey super should be lifted and turned end for end occasionally as the bees tend to work sooner and better in the back part of the super, rather than near the entrance. The colonies have so many bees that, due to lack of work in the hive, many bees are forced to become foragers at rather young age. A very strong field force is necessary to produce good, marketable sections or rounds. The field force is large and the storage space is limited so the cells are built and honey is stored and capped at a rapid rate. When this super is about half full a second super is added on top. Do not add new supers too soon. When the first super is nearly full and the second one about half full, the second super is placed beneath the first and a third super is added on top. The same procedure is followed when more supers are added, always with the new one first placed on the top (Fig. 9.6). If the bees are given too much room they do not fill the sections or rounds as deeply as is necessary to make an attractive marketable product. It is better to keep them crowded. When a super is full, it is better to take it off as repeated passage of bees over the capped combs may cause some discolouration of the cappings.

When a super of sections is removed, those that are well filled, meaning that the corners are not left empty, the sections are prepared for marketing. The wax is cut to separate the sections and the wooden rim is cleaned by light sanding or scraping to remove propolis, wax or discoloured areas. Then each section is packaged in a "window" carton, is wrapped in cellophane or is placed in a polyethylene bag.

The plastic round sections are easy to remove and are easy to prepare for marketing. Excess wax is trimmed off, a clear plastic cover is placed on each side and these are held in place by a strip of wide tape that goes completely around the container. Round sections are almost all perfectly filled to the rim.

Removing Honey Supers from the Hives

There are several methods for removing supers of honey from the hives. The method chosen by any beekeeper depends to some extent on the number of colonies involved and the amount of honey produced.

In ancient times, burning sulphur was used to kill the bees to allow the honeycombs to be cut out (Chapter 1). In recent years many beekeepers have routinely killed their bees with hydrocyanic acid gas and then removed the honey supers. This is a very bad procedure as any

honey in open cells could be contaminated with cyanide. If colonies are not to be wintered, the honey should be removed by one method or another before the bees are killed. I hate killing bees and recommend very strongly that the bees should be fed and wintered.

The methods used in removing bees from honey supers are: brushing the bees; bee repellent boards; bee escapes; and use of a bee blower.

a) Brushing the bees

If only a few colonies are involved, a super of honey can be lifted off, the combs removed one at a time, and the bees brushed off either on the open hive or in front of the entrance. If this is done on a warm day the bees will fly back and alight on the comb nearly as fast as they are brushed off. It is necessary to have an empty super nearby with a good cover. I use an inner cover for this chore so that the comb can be put in the empty super and covered before it is once again loaded with bees. Some colonies become very agitated when the bees are brushed but others remain quite calm. If brushing is done very early on a cool morning (I mean very shortly after daybreak) there is a minimum of bee activity and the procedure takes very little time.

Be sure you have a proper bee brush, one designed for use with bees (Fig. 9.7). When I bought my first bee hives in 1950, a bee brush came with them. It is still in good condition and will be useful for many more years.

I once forgot my bee brush at one apiary while preparing to remove some honey supers at another apiary. If this happens to you, go back and get the brush. A brush is a brush is a brush is not so when dealing with bees. I looked for a substitute and all I could find was a small branch from a spruce tree. I have never had bees become so hostile as quickly as these bees did, not only from the hive I had open but others as well. I had to quit and go for the bee brush. I thought they would be quiet again when I returned, but they were still agitated and finally I had to give up to return at a later date. I do not use gloves and I had received more than 50 stings in my bare hands. A few days later I had no trouble at all brushing these bees with the proper brush.

I have made a practice of wintering colonies in two supers, in single supers and in 4-frame nucs. The nucs were not a problem, nor were those to be wintered in two supers. The colonies destined to be wintered in one super had two brood supers during the summer season, and so had to be reduced to one super in the fall. I have not used a repellent board for this but it should work. I have not had success with bee escape boards because usually there was some brood in both supers and I had to move frames from one super to the other and to brush the bees off the combs I wished to take away. When I have done this early in the morning I have not had much difficulty in keeping the bees quiet.

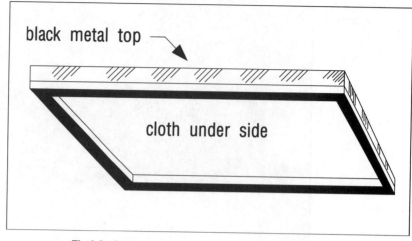

Fig 9.8: Bee repellent board (sometimes called acid board).

b) Bee Repellent Boards

For many years these boards were called "acid boards" because the repellent used with them was carbolic acid. The problem with carbolic acid was that honey in open cells became tainted and tasted of the acid. Its use was discontinued some years ago. The repellents used today are benzaldehyde and butyric anhydride.

Repellent boards look like covers and are used as temporary covers. On the underside is cloth to which the repellent (liquid) is added. The metal top is black to absorb heat from the sun (Fig. 9.8). The cover and inner cover are removed and replaced by the repellent board. Heat causes the repellent to vaporize and, as it forms a heavier-than-air gas, it moves downward and drives the bees downward ahead of it. On fine sunny days this works very well but is much less efficient when the sun is not visible.

Do not leave repellent boards on too long, especially on hot days, or the bees may be driven farther than intended. I have seen (in somebody else's apiary, not mine) the entire population of the a hive driven out the entrance. I say not mine because I don't use it. I can't stand the smell of the stuff. Bee repellent boards have an advantage in that only one trip to the apiary is necessary to remove the supers of honey.

c) Bee Escapes

Bee escapes are of two types. Porter bee escapes, invented by E.C. Porter in 1891, are small metal (now also of plastic) devices (Fig. 9.9) that have a single hole at the top and a pair of flexible copper springs. The escapes, one or two, fit into holes cut through a board similar to an inner cover. Many commercial inner covers have precut holes for use with Porter bee escapes. The board is placed beneath the honey supers to be taken off. A worker bee pushes through the springs and finds itself in the super beneath the board.

The principle on which this bee escape is based is that bees working in the honey supers tend to feel isolated from the brood area and the queen, and so rotate on a regular basis between the honey storage area and the brood chamber. Visiting the brood area presumably is to obtain their share of the queen pheromone. The bees in a honey super pass through the bee escape to the brood area but are unable to return to the honey super. Their passage is blocked by the small copper springs in the bee escape.

During cool nights in the fall, the bees may completely evacuate one or two honey supers overnight. If there are more supers, or during warm weather, a longer period usually is necessary.

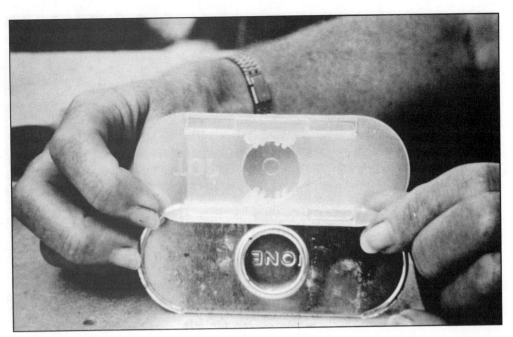

Fig 9.9: Porter bee escapes, one metal, one plastic.

If there is any brood above the bee escape board or, if a queen somehow is above, the bees will not leave the upper supers. They will not desert a queen or young brood. Emerging drones in an upper super can block Porter bee escapes, as the drones are too large to pass through the copper springs and become stuck there.

Another type of bee escape board has been developed and is in wide use in Quebec and now is becoming more popular outside that province. The Quebec bee escape board is a permanent escape board, not a modified inner cover. The principle upon which it works is the same as for the Porter bee escapes - the bees rotate downward to the brood area at frequent intervals. A hole at the top allows the bees to pass through the board to a screen-covered triangular area beneath (Fig. 9.10). There are exits at the points of the triangle that allow the bees to pass out to the super below, but the internal double slat system makes the return trip impossible. Should a bee manage to enter at a tip of the triangle, it does not enter the second exit but proceeds along one side of the triangle and exits again to the super below (Fig. 9.11). I have used Quebec bee escapes for many years and have found them to be foolproof. Well, I guess a fool could put them on upside down but barring that they work extremely well. When not in use they should be stacked in a dry place, not left outside exposed to the weather.

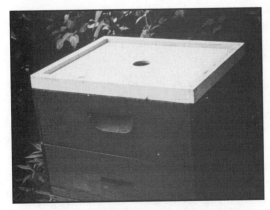

Fig 9.10: Quebec bee escape board, in place on a hive. Supers to be cleared of bees are placed on top.

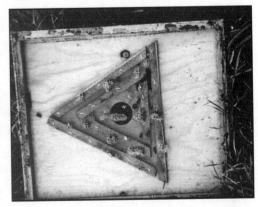

Fig 9.11: Quebec bee escape board, underside.

Bee escape boards have one distinct drawback. Two trips to the apiary are necessary and the honey supers must be lifted twice, the first time to install the escape boards and again when the honey is removed. If an apiary is small to medium in size, from one to 40 colonies, this method is practical, is easy to use, and produces bee-free honey supers.

The same problem can exist with the Quebec boards as with Porter bees escapes; the bees will not move down if there is brood or a queen above the board. Consistent use of queen excluders eliminates this problem.

d) Bee blowers

A bee-blower is a back pack with a gasoline engine that drives air at considerable velocity through a flexible hose and nozzle (Fig. 9.12). A super is lifted off and placed on end on the supers below and the air blast directed between the top bars of the frames blows the bees out and they drop in front of the hive. Sometimes it is necessary to force the frames apart using a hive tool to pry the bottom bars to dislodge all of the bees.

Use of a bee blower requires two persons as the one with the blower on his back will find it difficult to lift the supers and especially to force the frames apart.

The bee blower is efficient but is not fast. Once the bees are driven out of a super it must be covered to prevent re-entry by the bees. Honey bees do not become agitated by being blown out of a super. The cost of a bee blower is comparatively high and is practical only for beekeepers who have more than 50 colonies.

The Honey House - handling honey

In any place where honey is handled, extracted, strained and packed, certain conditions must be observed. These are cleanliness, moisture control and temperature.

a) Cleanliness

In any area where honey is extracted cleanliness is essential. All of the units used in the process: tub, cappings melter or cappings spinner, that catch the cappings when uncapping; the extractor; sump, pump and hoses for transferring the honey (if used), the strainer; pails, tanks and containers in which the honey will be packaged, must be scrupulously clean. In any honey extracting operation, the entire system should be, as much as possible, a closed system to prevent contamination of the honey by airborne dust and absorption of water. Some honey and wax will inevitably get on the floor, especially in the smaller operations, perhaps carried on in the kitchen. This should not be tracked out of the room. It may be necessary to change footwear when leaving or entering the room, as very few materials will track from one place to another as much as honey and beeswax. Some wives are very helpful in the honey extracting operation, but can be "turned off" very quickly if the mess is tracked throughout the house. Extracting can be messy unless it is done very carefully. Domestic strife should never be associated with a fine product like honey.

Honey will absorb odours from almost any source, so it is important that aromatic or odorous materials (tobacco, for example) should be avoided.

b) The Moisture Problem

In a previous chapter, the moisture problem was discussed at some length. Moisture is particularly important in an area where honey is extracted. Excess use of water sould be avoided during the operation so that the moisture content of the honey will not be increased, although use of water to clean the floor occasionally is unavoidable. Dehumidifiers are useful in removing moisture from the air and should be an integral part of the operation in all but the smallest kitchen operation. Most dehumidifiers have a tank to hold the condensed moisture. If at all possible, a hose should be connected to the outlet port to conduct the water immediately to a floor drain, rather than to leave it in the tank where evaporation can occur.

Following periods of wet weather, the moisture content of the honey may be higher than is desirable. This may be a serious problem if the honey is extracted from combs that have honey in many uncapped cells. The moisture problem can be alleviated before extracting by piling the honey supers in a staggered pile to allow warm air (35 degrees C. = 95 degrees F) to pass upward through the stack. A stand, open on one side, can be used as a base for piled supers and warm air from an electric heater can be forced upward through the stack. The air flow is directed into the open side of the stand (Fig. 9.13). Some beekeepers use a vacuum cleaner with the hose attachment reversed to blow warm air through the supers.

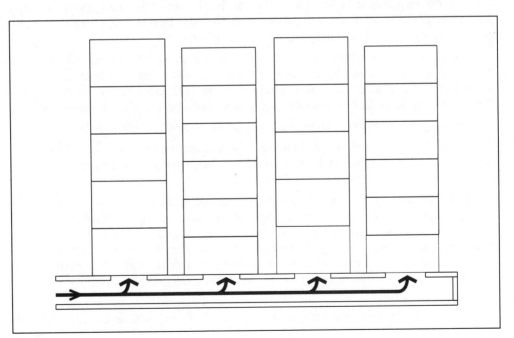

Fig 9.13: Diagram to show methods of warming honey in stacked supers.

If the moisture content, as measured by a refractometer, is still too high following extraction and straining, some moisture can be removed by placing the honey in a warm room in large open trays to increase the surface area for evaporation. A dehumidifier is placed in the room to remove moisture from the air. Rooms such as this are better built into the honey house rather than improvised but an improvised setup is better than none.

c) Temperature in a Honey House

Honey is quite fluid and flows readily at high temperature. As the temperature is reduced, the honey becomes more viscous and flows very slowly. At 15 degrees C (59 degrees F) honey will tend to remain in the cells of the honeycomb, so that extraction is incomplete and the combs appear very wet. It will pass through a strainer very slowly and tends to 'pile up' on the strainer, making the entire operation very slow. If the honey is warm when it is extracted, and if it is to be heated before straining (as in a heated sump tank) the temperature in the honey house should be kept only slightly above the 'so-called' comfort range, that is, about 21 to 24 degrees C (70 to 75 degrees F). If there is no way to warm the honey enough to make it flow readily, the heat in the honey house should be in the 30 to 35 degrees C (86 to 95 degrees F) range, even though it may make the operators rather uncomfortable.

Layout of an Ideal Honey House

A small honey extracting facility is usually in the home or in a building on the same property as the residence. This is not an ideal arrangement. It is nearly impossible to avoid bringing some bees to the extracting room. This could result in allergy problems of a family member due to an occasional sting. Occasional stings tend to produce problems not, as might be expected, the repeated stings endured by the persons that regularly work with the bees in their hives.

Townsend (1976a) advised having the honey house and the residence at separate locations. There is an advantage in this when a beekeeper retires and wishes to dispose of the honey house but retain the residence.

Many honey houses are adaptions of existing buildings. These are "makeshift" operations and can be adequate for small operations as the amount of manual labour is not great. As the quantity of honey produced increases the labour also increases and, sooner or later, a proper building designed as a honey house will be required.

One advantage that is built into a designed honey house, but which is usually difficult or impossible to include in an adapted building is a loading and unloading bay or pit. This is a dug out area so that the bed of a truck will be at the same level as the floor of the building. With such a bay the amount of manual handling of loaded supers is reduced considerably.

There are seven areas to consider in a honey house design (Townsend, 1976a):

1) Space for incoming supers. This can be a warming room where warm air is forced through the stacks of supers or leading directly to such a room. The area should be large enough to house all of the supers unloaded in a day.

2) The extracting area should be a separate room designed for the purpose. The equipment, uncapper, extractor, strainer, etc., should be arranged in a logical sequence. The sump tank should be recessed into the floor with the top only slightly above floor level. Outlets from the uncapping area, cappings spinner or melter, the extractor and the comb-holder will feed by gravity into the sump. The honey pump at the sump tank outlet should pump the honey to a strainer that is elevated so that the strained honey from the strainer outlet will drain directly into holding tanks.

3) There should be a storage area for empty supers. This should be located between the

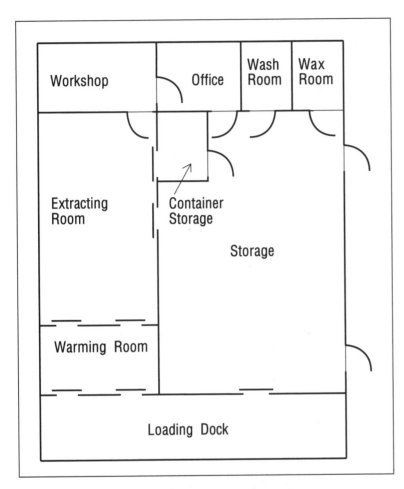

Workshop · Office · Wash Room · Wax Room

Extracting Room

Container Storage

Storage

Warming Room

Loading Dock

Fig 9.14: Floor plan of proposed honey house.

extracting room and the loading bay or can be part of the loading bay provided there is an arrangement to prevent blocking access to the extracting room. Supers with empty combs could be stored over winter in this area but separate super storage in an adjacent unheated building or buildings is desireable.

4) This room is a honey container storage area for empty and full containers. It should not be in a traffic line but should be reasonably close to the loading bay.

5) Wax should be processed in a separate room, one that is equipped with fire extinguishers. Most fires in honey handling facilities start where beeswax is rendered. The room should be located as far as possible from the extracting and container storage rooms.

6) There should be room to serve as a workshop and for storage of spare parts, paint, etc.

7) A room should be reserved as a rest area, including a rest room but which can also be used as an office.

If a sales center is to be included, another room is required.

Figure 9.14 shows a possible layout for a honey house. This plan does not include a room for heating and for a steam boiler if one is required for uncapping apparatus. Heating can be provided by electric baseboard heaters or by steam or hot water radiators. The storage room and the loading bay do not need to be heated so the walls of adjacent rooms should be insulated.

Townsend (1976a) shows several honey house layouts and Kienholz (1983) has several designs as well as recommended layouts for extracting rooms.

Honey House Equipment and Handling the Honey

The equipment required for handling extracted liquid honey depends upon the size of the apiary and the amount of honey produced. A small operation need not involve much equipment or expense but a large operation will require a considerable outlay of capital. Figure 9.15 indicates the equipment required for operations ranging from one to 800 or more colonies of bees. All equipment for handling honey should be constructed of metal that is galvanized, or of polyethylene. This is a minimum requirement. In any operation that is to be continued or expanded, all of the equipment, extractor, strainer, tanks or any other piece of equipment, such as a cappings spinner, should be constructed of stainless steel. Townsend (1976b) gave details of the equipment required in handling honey.

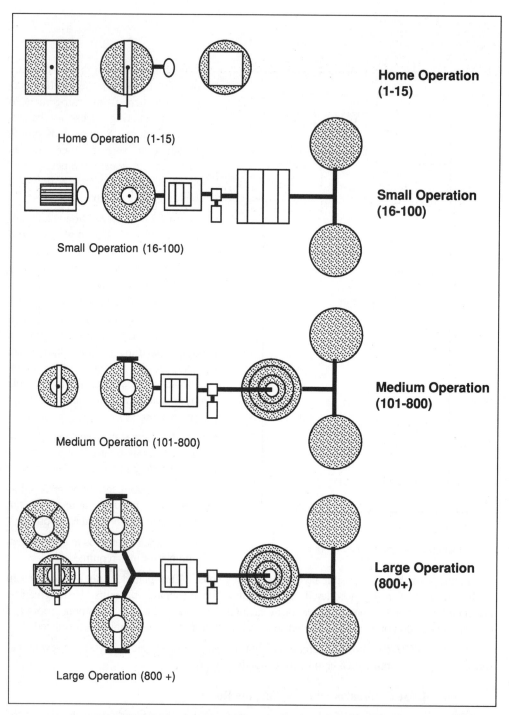

Home Operation (1-15)

Small Operation (16-100)

Medium Operation (101-800)

Large Operation (800 +)

Home Operation (1-15)

Small Operation (16-100)

Medium Operation (101-800)

Large Operation (800+)

Fig 9.15: Diagram, equipment required for various sizes of operations, left to right for each size:

(1 - 15) tub and board with spike for uncapping, manual 2 - frame non-reversible basket type extractor, and tank of some sort with 88 mesh nylon strainer cloth;

(16 - 100) cappings melter for uncapping, motor driven extractor, either 4 - frame reversible basket type or radial, small sump (heated),. honey pump, flat screen strainer, and two tanks for clarifying and packing;

(101 - 800) automatic uncapper over cappings spinner, carousel for combs, 20 or 30 frame radial extractor, sump, honey pump, O.A.C. strainer and 2 tanks (at least);

(800 +) automatic uncapper over cappings spinner and conveyor belt, 2 radial extractors 30 to 50 frame size, large sump, honey pump, O.A.C. strainer, several tanks.

HONEY PRODUCTION AND PROCESSING

Fig 9.16: Electric uncapping knife for manual uncapping of honeycombs.

a) Small operation - 15 or less colonies

A separate honey house is not necessary for a small operation of one to 20 producing colonies, but is desirable if there are more than 15 colonies. Fifteen colonies can produce 3/4 tonnes or more, and this is straining the facility of a kitchen extracting room. For a small operation the only items that must be purchased are an uncapping knife or plane, a small extractor, and fine nylon straining cloth, all of which can be obtained from any dealer in bee supplies. For uncapping all that is required is a tub to catch the cappings, with a board and spike laid across it. The comb to be uncapped is held by one hand with the opposite end bar on the tip of the spike so that it can be rotated easily. A knife is used to slice off the cappings of the cells. Most knives now in use are electrically heated (Fig. 9.16) with a thermostat in the blade or are heated by steam. Two sharp knives, preferably with serrated blades, can be heated in hot water and used alternately. The blade must be wiped dry before use. The blade of the knife is kept flat on the top and bottom bars and the capping is cut with a sawing motion. Some people prefer to start at the top and cut downward but I have found it easier to cut from the bottom up. Be careful that the hand at the top of the frame does not extend beyond the bar as knives can slip and can cause serious injury. If the blade is heated, the result will be a cut and burn combined.

A plane cuts across the comb rather than from end to end. Several passes are required. Some people swear by the use of a plane and will use nothing else, while others have difficulty by cutting too deeply even through the midrib of the comb.

A honey extractor is a centrifuge, with the combs to be extracted situated in a reel which is spun rapidly to cause the honey to fly out of the cells by centrifugal force. The honey is thrown against the inside wall of the container that houses the reel and runs down to the bottom where it can be drained through a honey gate.

Low priced extractors are of the two or four basket type and can be spun manually or by an electric motor. Some extractors have fixed baskets to hold the combs. When the reel is spun the honey is thrown out of the cells facing the extractor wall. A comb has to be lifted out and reversed to extract the honey from the other side. Other extractors (Fig. 9.17) have reversible baskets, so that when the honey has been extracted from one side the baskets can be swung around to place the non-extracted side of a comb next to the extractor wall. Basket-type extractors are very easy on combs and comb breakage is infrequent. The honey gate is a sliding device that can govern or stop the flow of honey into a pail, other container, or into a hose coupling that takes the honey directly to a sump tank. The honey, at this stage, undoubt-

Fig 9.17:
Four frame reversible basket type extractor. Shell is made of polypropylene.

edly contains some wax and may have parts of dead bees and other matter that must be removed. Straining through fine nylon or fine metal strainer will remove most of these quite readily, if the honey is warm. Cold honey passes through a strainer very slowly, so slowly that seems as though it will never be completely strained. The honey is passed from the strainer to a tank that is provided with a honey gate.

Once the honey is clean, it should be allowed to settle for a day or two in a warm place to clarify, that is so air bubbles, that could become froth on the top of packed honey, can rise to the top. The honey can then be drained through the honey gate at the bottom into the containers in which it will be stored for home use, given to relatives or sold.

b) Medium operation - 16 to 100 colonies

A beekeeper with more than 15 colonies, and perhaps up to 100 colonies, requires more equipment and a special place (a honey room - not the kitchen) in which to extract and pack the honey. The initial cost may exceed $2,000 to $4,000. The tub and board are not feasible for handling the volume of honey produced by this number of colonies and some other method of handling the cappings is necessary.

Uncapping can be done manually with a knife or plane, heated electrically or with steam, for a reasonable number of colonies (personal estimates on a reasonable number varies, I would say 30 to 40), but with a greater number of producing colonies a mechanical uncapper is a big help. I speak from experience, having uncapped combs by hand with an electric knife from 60 and 75 colonies (in different seasons).

A cappings melter has double walls, and between them is water heated by an immersion heater. The cappings that are cut off drop to the cappings melter that heats the wax and honey so that they separate and run off into a large container, the honey on the bottom and the wax on the top.

The extractor should be able to extract more quickly than a man can uncap an extractor load of combs by hand. This means greater extractor capacity and usually a different type, a radial extractor. Radial extractors are available that hold 10 to 50 or more combs per load (Fig. 9.18). Combs are placed in this type of extractor around a central shaft, with all top bars facing the extractor wall (Fig. 9.19). When the reel revolves the honey is thrown out of the

HONEY PRODUCTION AND PROCESSING

Fig 9.19: The inside of a radial extractor showing the slots in the outer ring to hold frame top bars.

Fig 9.18: A 20 frame radial extractor, stainless steel.

cells on both sides of the comb to the extractor wall. The cells of the honeycomb are sloped slightly upward and the honey could not be cleaned completely out of the cells if the bottom bars faced the extractor wall. A 10 frame extractor can be driven by hand, but even one of this size, and certainly all larger extractors, should be power-driven.

Using pails to transfer the honey from the extractor to the strainer is a labour intensive effort and requires careful watching to ensure that the pail does not overflow. A heated sump tank (Fig. 9.20) is very useful and saves a great deal of manual labour. A sump tank should be at a lower level than the outflow level of the extractor, ideally it should have its top at or only slightly above the level of the floor, so that the honey will flow by gravity from the extractor to the sump. A sump tank is an elongate, double walled tank, heated from below and on the

Fig 9.20:
Honey sump. Ideally the sump should be set into the floor to allow gravity drainage from the extractor, the cappings, the conveyor, and merry-go-round frame holder if one is used.

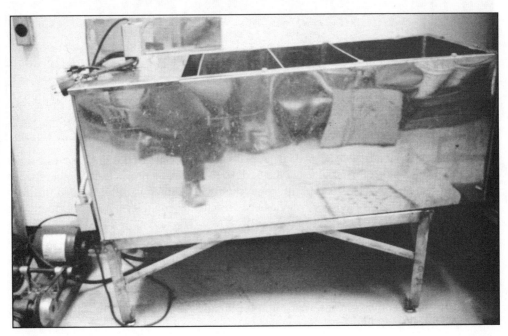

Fig 9.21:
O.A.C. strainer.
The tank is
behind some of
the cylindrical
screens that
have been
removed.

Fig 9.22:
Automatic
uncapper,
electrically driven
with steam
heated vibrating
blades.

sides by a water bath heated to sbout 38 degrees C (100 degrees F). The honey passes a series of baffles, over the top of one and under the next, so that most wax particles and other foreign matter are removed from the honey. In conjunction with a sump is a float switch that activates a motor driven gear pump. When the honey reaches a certain level it is pumped upward into a strainer tank.

Several types of strainers are available, but all operate on the same principle. The warm honey passes through successively finer screens, each of which removes particles larger than its mesh openings. By the time the honey passes through the finest screen and is gravity fed to holding tank, all of the wax and other particles are removed. An O.A.C. strainer (Fig. 9.21) has a series of cylindrical screens, coarsest in the middle and finest on the outside; the honey is pumped (or poured) into the centre cylinder.

Once the honey is in a holding tank, it should be allowed to set and clarify. Some operations use a heated clarifying tank to speed up the process. Finally the honey can be packed directly from the holding tank. Several such tanks will be required for an operation of this size.

c) Medium to Large Operations - 100 to 1000 colonies

The equipment required to process the honey crop from more than 100 colonies requires more capital, probably $8,000 to $16,000, depending upon the size of the operation.

An automatic uncapper is essential. I prefer the type that uses steam-heated knives to uncap combs (Fig. 9.22) rather than a flail type. Extractors are paired, so that one can be unloaded and reloaded while the other is extracting, a period of about 20 minutes. A cappings spinner is used to spin the honey out of the cappings (Fig. 9.23). It is located directly beneath the uncapper so that the cappings fall directly into it (Fig. 9.24), and should have a hose coupling at the outlet to drain the honey directly to the sump tank. A large sump tank is essential, and the gear pump that pumps the honey from the sump to a strainer must have a capacity equal to or greater than the outflow from the extractors. The sump must heat the honey as it passes through to about 38 degrees C (100 degrees F), in order for the large volume of honey to pass quickly through the strainer. The strainer can be of the O.A.C. type, a large strainer with serial in line screens, or the type that uses gravity to filter the honey through diatomaceous earth. If the strainer in use cannot handle the volume, two side by side strainers can be used with a 'flow switch' that directs the honey to one or the other as required. Clarification requires several tanks. These should set on dollys so that they can be moved about as necessary. Packing becomes automatic, using a similar type of apparatus as is used in preparation of bottled goods.

9

Fig 9.23: Cappings spinner.

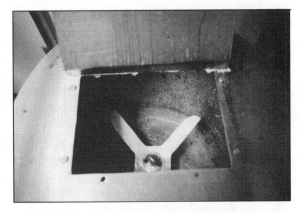

Fig 9.24: Interior of cappings spinner to show revolving blades.

Pasteurization of Honey

The so-called pasteurization of honey involves very rapid heating to high temperature, then very quick cooling. The process destroys yeasts and causes breakdown of any crystalline honey. This increases shelf-life of the product; the honey will not granulate as the "founder crystals" that initiate granulation are destroyed; neither will it ferment because the sugar-tolerant yeasts are eliminated.

Great care must be the rule when heating honey as overheating or prolonged heating will cause discolouration and also will alter the taste. Established large scale honey packers are equipped to pasteurize honey and the process should be left to them. Small scale operations cannot manage the rapid (almost instantaneous) heating and cooling. Attempts to do this usually fail to achieve the desired result and lower the grade of the product.

Packaging Honey for Market

Packing cut comb, sections and rounds was discussed earlier. These products are destined for the "gourmet" trade, for those who want to honey as it is packed by the bees in the original container, the honeycomb. It is usual that a premium price is charged for honey in the comb. This is necessary, as the comb is sold with the honey and the cost of production of the honeycomb each year has to be considered. Every effort should be made to ensure that the product is attractive to the purchaser and will not cause any disappointment when the comb is removed from the package. The practice of packing cut comb or sections that are very fine on the side visible to the buyer, but that are poor to very poor on the other side, does not lead to repeat sales. Fortunately most beekeepers are not guilty of such practices.

Honey Grades and Labelling

Canada No. 1 or U.S. Grade A is top quality honey. Moisture content (less than 18 %), good flavour, and freedom from foreign matter (that is, clean and with good clarity) are the important factors. The average beekeeper (if there is one - most of us are above average, I'm sure) should endeavour to meet these characteristics in all of the honey packed and offered for sale to individuals, to retail or wholesale outlets, as bulk honey for industrial use (such as in baked goods), or to honey packers. Lower grades can be sold for industrial use but should not be sold to retail stores or to individuals. One poor lot of honey guarantees no repeat sales.

Honey is usually sold as a colour grade within the above requirements. The established colour grades are from transparent to dark - completely opaque, and prices for honey often are based upon colour. Pale (Water White) honey usually brings the highest price. There are intermediate grades, such as White (or Light), Amber (or Golden) and Dark, and these grades may be subdivided. Most of the honey produced in northeastern North America is White or Golden (Amber). Some beekeepers differentiate between Golden and Amber, the former paler and the latter darker.

The general public has been "brainwashed" to some extent and persuaded that pale honey is superior to golden honey. This is not necessarily true. Much depends upon individual preference. Some people prefer pale honey, though it may be verging upon tasteless, while others prefer the more tasteful golden honey. There are those too who will pay a premium price for the very dark and quite strong-tasting buckwheat honey, while others will refuse a second taste. If you have annual individual customers, the preference of each can soon be discovered.

All honey offered for sale must be labelled at least with the grade and the net weight. It is an advantage to include the name and address of the beekeeper, much as commecial packers do, in order to solicit repeat sales. Attractive labelling helps to sell a product and a product as fine as honey should always carry an attractive label.

It is not necessary at this time to list on the label the place (or country) of origin of the honey. A great deal of honey is imported into both Canada and the United States in bulk for packaging. There is no way a consumer can determine that this honey is produced in Canada or the United States, or in a foreign country. It must, however, meet the grading standards of the country concerned. There is a definite tendency by consumers to purchase 'home grown' produce so there is an advantage if the label states definitely that the honey is locally produced.

Liquid Honey

Liquid honey is, or should be, sold in glass containers or in clear plastic containers so that the product is clearly visible, not in plastic tubs. Liquid honey in these tubs in a grocery bag is very likely to leak out and make a sticky mess of the contents of the bag, which is bound to discourage future purchases of honey. Liquid honey should be clear and free from impurities. Honey is sold by weight so the net weight of honey should be precise.

Granulated Honey

Granulated honey is best packed in opaque plastic containers (Fig. 9.25). The containers are filled with honey that is liquid or is beginning to granulate. It is stored a a temperature of about 14 degrees C (57 degrees F), the temperature at which granulation proceeds quickly. Some honey, particularly that produced in the summer, tends to granulate slowly and with relatively coarse crystals. This honey can be made to granulate with a fine texture by seeding with 10 to 15 % honey with very fine grain, saved from the previous year. This must be mixed in thoroughly before the honey is packed. Granulated honey should be stored at 12 to 14 degrees C (55 to 57 degrees F). If it is stored at high temperature it will soften and begin to liquify. Subsequent storage in a cold room will not make it regranulate.

Fig 9.25: A plastic honey container, 1 kg size.

Creamed Honey

Creamed honey, also called churned honey, has been whipped in order to produce a fine, creamy consistency. Granulating or granulated honey, usually that has been 'seeded' with fine texture honey, is whipped or beaten to incorporate tiny air bubbles. Storage at cool temperature, as given above, is necessary.

Honey for Industrial Uses

Honey that is sold in bulk, primarily to the bakery trade, is not necessarily of top quality in so far as colour is concerned, but it should be clean and have no more than 19 % moisture. This honey is excellent in enhancing flavours and prolonging shelf life of baked goods.

Honey and Fruit Blends

Occasionally we find jars of blends of honey with strawberry or other fruits. Some people object to adding such things to honey and feel it should only be sold as honey without "adulteration". I have no strong feelings on the subject. If there is a surplus of honey and the product is not moving well, I would have no objection to preparing a blend if there is an indication that the blend will sell more quickly than honey alone. I must confess that I frequently mix honey and strawberry jam on my toast for breakfast. I have not tried marketing honey blended with fruits. ❑

REFERENCES

Kienholz, J. 1983. Honey House and Equipment Layouts. Alberta Agr. Publ.; 30 pp.

Townsend, G.F. 1976a. The Commercial Honey House. Amer. Bee J. 116: 310-312.

Townsend, G.F. 1976b. Honey House Equipment. Amer Bee J. 116: 365 368.

HONEY BEES
AND POLLINATION

The Modern History of Crop Pollination

Prior to World War II, the use of honey bees in crop pollination consisted largely of placing colonies of unknown strength near the crop. Often the colonies were 'package' bees and were so weak that they were of little use. As often as not the bees were kept permanently near the crop. It is well known that honey bees exhibit 'fidelity' to a single plant species: any bee works only a single species until it no longer supplies the requirements of the bee (i.e., pollen and/or nectar), or the bee dies. Therefore if there is a plant species which blooms earlier than the crop and remains in bloom during the flowering of the crop, most foraging bees will continue to work the competing flowers. The aroma of the flowers of a plant differs from the aroma of others and serves as quick identification to the bees, ensuring that they continue to work the same plant species (Robacker *et al.*, 1988). Scout bees will find the crop flowers and will entice young bees graduating from house work to visit them. More and more new recruits will eventually work the crop, but even some of the young bees will work the competing flowers. An example is pollination of apple while dandelion is still blooming. Dandelion is a major competitor of apple for insect visits (Karmo and Vickery, 1954; Free, 1968).

Many flowers have a short period, only a few days, during which fertilization must occur. If the pollen is not transferred to the blossom early in this period, the blossom may fail to be fertilized because of lack of time for growth of the pollen tube through the pistil of the flower to the ovaries.

Another point which affects pollination is that the first few blossoms on the crop plant are not sufficient to attract many bees; the majority of the foraging force, including new recruits, work the competing flowers. Many crops which require pollination were not provided with honeybee pollinators in the past, as populations of solitary bees, bumble bees and other pollinating insects were relied upon to perform the essential service. In general, this reliance was successful until the advent of the organic insecticides near the end of World War II.

DDT was first used on a large scale in 1944 on the human population in Naples, Italy, to control lice and thus ward off a threatened epidemic of typhus. I had first hand knowledge of this treatment as I happened to be in Naples at the time.

Pesticide Problems

DDT and other chlorinated hydrocarbons were harmful to honey bees and other pollinating insects. DDT did not affect them greatly but other insecticides, such as the organophosphorus compound, parathion, caused great reduction of pollinator populations. Early in the 1950's I dusted the inside of one of my bee hives, which contained a good colony of Italian bees, with 10 percent DDT dust. I expected the colony to die, and many bees were killed, possibly as much by the action of the inert carrier of the insecticide as from the toxic effect of the insecticide. The colony recovered and six weeks later showed no ill effects. It built up to strength and wintered successfully, although it produced little surplus honey that year. By contrast, parathion, as well as all of the other organophosphorus compounds, produced very drastic results. These compounds took effect on the insects so quickly that affected foragers usually died in the field. This reduced strength of honey bee colonies. The loss of the field force caused the colonies to send out younger bees as foragers. If these too, and their successors, were poisoned, the colony would be in danger of extinction. Fortunately the residues of most organophosphorus compounds have a short period of insecticidal action.

The effect of the pesticides on wild pollinating insects was much more severe. Early season poisoning of bumble bees affected the queens, perhaps before any workers were produced but, if later, still caused the demise of the bumble bee colony. The numerous species of solitary bees were hit hardest of all as the insecticide caused the death of the reproductive females before any provision for the next generation could be made.

The end result produced a concerted effort to control the use of insecticides. This produced the first modern-day Integrated Pest Management program, directed by Dr. Allison D. Pickett in the apple orchards of Nova Scotia. It also made necessary the use of a pollinator force which could be moved from place to place as required. Honey bee colonies had to be substituted for the native pollinating insects which had been decimated.

One of the early modern papers on the use of honey bees in pollination was that of Karmo and Vickery (1954). This was issued as a mimeographed circular, intended mainly for fruit growers in Nova Scotia, but which soon became widely known. Requests for copies were received from all over the world, including many of the Communist countries. In South Africa, the content was expanded and published by Lotter (1960). The circular recommended certain procedures to ensure good pollination, all of these the result of experimentation and observation and knowledge of the habits and reactions of honey bees. Today these procedures are routinely used in pollination of crops with honey bees almost everywhere that honey bees are used for pollination.

Timing Hive Introduction to the Crop

The aim in crop pollination is to have a fairly uniform distribution of foragers throughout the crop area so that a maximum number of blossoms will be visited by the pollinators. It was recommended that bees be introduced into the crop area only when the crop had produced enough blooms to become the primary source of nectar and pollen, and thus would become nearly the only plant visited by the bees. Bees which are moved in too early will disperse widely on any floral source, if the crop flowers do not supply their requirement for nectar and particularly for pollen.

Rate of Spreading of Honey Bees in a New Location

An extensive study was made of the factors affecting the rate of spreading of honeybees in a new location. In crops with profuse bloom, the rate of spreading is slow, usually no more than 50 metres from the hive during the first day. Where blossoms are scarce, the bees expand their range much more quickly in search of better or more numerous blossoms. This may extend up to 1.5 km the first day.

Colonies must be moved out of their usual flight range when they are moved to crops for pollination. Also, they must be moved at a time when they are not flying, that is, at night, very early in the morning or when rain prevents bee flights. In the first instance, bees not moved beyond their usual range will find landmarks which they recognize, and often will fly back to where the hive used to be. In the second instance, moving a hive when its bees are actively foraging results in loss of much of the field force. These foraging bees are the force upon which adequate pollination depends and care must be taken to ensure that their ranks are not depleted.

Colony Strength for Efficient Pollination

Karmo and Vickery (1985) recommended that only strong colonies be used in crop pollination. In general, colonies started from "package" bees were unsatisfactory as such colonies could not build up quickly enough to provide sufficient field bees to provide adequate pollination for early blooming fruit trees such as apple. The following table illustrates this point very clearly:

Av. Colony size	No. bees leaving/min
1.4 kg pkg colony	15
2.3 kg pkg colony	48.5
1.9 kg wintered colony	64.5
3.2 kg wintered colony	128.3

(From Karmo and Vickery, 1985)

The greater field force of the wintered colonies is due quite an extent to low brood-rearing to foraging bee ratios in these colonies. Stronger colonies tend to work at lower temperatures and to work longer than weak colonies, this strongly indicating that only strong colonies should be used for crop pollination. A field bee may make seven trips a day when visiting apple bloom if the weather is good. Counts have shown that a bee has to visit 84 or more apple blossoms for a full load of nectar and can obtain a load of pollen from the same number of blossoms. By actual count a moderately strong colony worked a total of 51,420 bee trips in an orchard in one day.

Density of Hives

For the best coverage hives should be distributed evenly throughout the crop rather than leaving them all in a single location. The bees from any colony will generally forage close to the hive during the first day in the new site. The foragers from several colonies will hardly exceed the range of a single colony if bloom is plentiful.

A rule of thumb for numbers of colonies in a given area is approximately 4 per hectare (2 per acre), although problem crops may require greater density.

Colony Rotation

Karmo and Vickery (1954, 1987) and Karmo (1961) advised rotating colonies to improve pollination. This was because the bees in a new location continue to extend their range day by day. This may result in the bees visiting a neighbouring orchard (to the dismay of the orchardist who has rented the bees) or to the flowers of other plants, reducing the number of pollinators working the desired crop. In the spring, 1000 or more honey bees each day begin foraging for the first time. These bees are influenced by dancing scout bees to visit certain flowers in certain places. As the days pass, more new foragers are instructed to visit flowers well beyond the crop area, and probably flowers of other species of plants at that. This is especially true in the case of crops in which the blossoms are not of prime attractiveness to the bees.

Wild blueberry is one such crop: it provides only small quantities of pollen and this is highly acidic. Many bees will desert the blueberry fields and search for a more plentiful, less acidic source of pollen (Karmo and Vickery, 1985). Bumblebees have no problem in obtaining pollen from blueberry blossoms. They land on blossoms, their weight causing the blossom to droop. The flight muscles are then vibrated rapidly without wing movement producing an audible buzzing sound. This action shakes the blossom causing the pollen to drop out onto the underside of the bee. Honeybees have not been able to do this and are able to obtain only very small quantities of pollen.

Scarcity of pollen in the hive will cause honeybees to visit plants that they normally do not visit, such as sheep sorrel. They can also be found gathering pollen early in the morning before the time when normal activity would begin.

In such cases the colonies can be removed to another field at least 2.5 kilometres (1.5 miles) distant from the first one after two or three days. The bees from the second field are moved to the first field (Fig. 10.1). If the area is large the bees can be moved no more than 350 metres but the moved-in colonies must be placed on the stands vacated by the other colonies. Any bees, from either group of hives, which return to the old home site, now occupied by another colony, will be allowed to enter as they are loaded with food that the colony can use. Both sets of pollinators must again learn the local landmarks, and thus find the crop flowers first. They work these flowers close to the hive the first day, then begin to extend their range as before.

Rotating colonies entails labour and expense. Where competition of crop bloom with bloom of another plant species is a problem, rotation of colonies becomes an efficient procedure. If competition is negligible, the cost of colony rotation may not be profitable or necessary (Karmo and Vickery, 1985).

Pollen Transfer in the Hive

Many fruit crops, such as most apple cultivars, require pollen from another variety in order for fertilization and subsequent fruit formation to occur. Most apple orchards are laid out with this in mind, that is, provision is made for pollination by setting every third tree in every third row of a suitable variety for cross-pollination. Varieties vary in degree of effectiveness. For example when pollen of Johnathan variety is applied to flowers of Rome Beauty, fertilization is accomplished in about 24 hours. Use of Rome Beauty pollen on Rome Beauty flowers requires about 120 hours for the pollen germs to reach the ovaries and by this time the potency of the pollen is destroyed and it disin tegrates (Karmo and Vickery, 1954).

The working area of a single foraging honey bee is only about 5 square metres, when bloom is profuse. In an orchard this may be only a side of a single tree or at most two sides of ad jacent trees. Many bees will never visit the pollinizing variety. How then is the pollen distributed ?

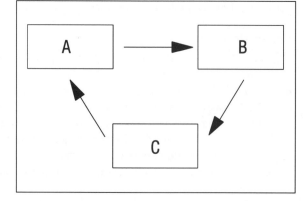

Fig 10.1: Diagram to indicate colony rotation for improved pollination.

A simple test was reported by Karmo and Vickery (1987a) to determine whether or not pollen was transferred from bee to bee within the hive. This test was carried out during the spring of 1953. Two weeks prior to apple bloom a Caucasian colony was confined in a cellar. It was fed sugar syrup but no pollen and was kept confined for three weeks. At that time the reserves of pollen in the hive were nearly completely depleted.

At about 0900 hours on a morning when the weather was suitable for bee flight the Caucasian colony was closed, then removed to an orchard where colonies were actively working apple bloom. Here it was united with an active colony of Italian bees. The united colony was observed closely and continuously until Caucasian bees began to leave the hive. A sample of 20 Caucasian workers was trapped and anaesthetized. In the laboratory the bees were examined for presence of pollen in their hair coats. Every bee carried large numbers of pollen grains.

The pollen was subsequently examined under high magnification and was identified to plant source. Approximately 92 percent of the pollen was from apple, while most of the remainder was from dandelion, indicating that some of the Italian bees had been working dandelion blossoms. This proved beyond a doubt that pollen transfer does occur in the hive and results in cross-pollination even though many pollinators do not have access to compatible pollen in the field.

Another study was made using nucleus colonies with trees enclosed by cages. Colonies taken from the field while foraging were caged with a single variety. Cross-pollination occurred, sufficient to produce a normal crop. Where trees were caged without pollinators, or where bees were caged without compatible pollen, almost no fruit was produced.

Pollen Dispensers

Some fruit varieties are partially self-fruitful although much more and better fruit result when the blossoms receive compatible pollen from another variety. All too frequently, advisory people are presented with the problem of what to do with solid blocks of single fruit varieties. The long term answer is to graft in enough other varieties to serve as sources of compatible pollen. In the short term, before the newly grafted vareties can have an effect, pollen dispensers can be used very effectively.

10

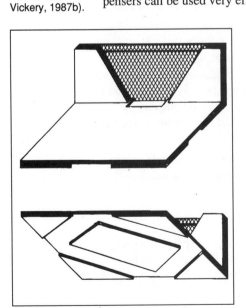

Fig 10.2:
Pollen dispenser, top to show pollen trough and screen, and bottom to show entrance channels (light from outside is blocked). (from Karmo and Vickery, 1987b).

Pollen dispensers are not new. Burrell and King (1932) devised a dispenser and tested it but their results were inconclusive. Other types were developed and tried, notably those of Kremer (1948) and Antles (1953) but these were not particularly effective, were wasteful of pollen or created problems with bee movement. Griggs and Vansell (1949) and Griggs *et al* (1952) tested hive inserts with caged trees of almond and sweet cherry. They determined that hive inserts were not efficient in effecting cross-pollination.

A different type of dispenser or insert was designed by Karmo in Nova Scotia. This type was based upon the premise that bees moved toward light to leave the hive and that an efficient hive insert should provide separate entrance and exit. All bees leaving the hive would contact the pollen provided and carry it to the trees to be pollinated. The first model had the entrance at the right side only and provided a S-shaped entrance passage which effectively excluded the light (Karmo and Vickery, 1954, 1957,

1987b). The entrance at the side caused some congestion of incoming forager bees but in spite of this it worked well. Townsend *et al* (1958) changed the entrance to the centre and used a light excluding diamond-shaped block which allowed two avenues of incoming traffic (Fig. 10.2).

The insert or dispenser caused great excitement among the bees when first installed and appeared to stimulate them to greater activity, foraging for pollen of the same kind. The exiting bees were seen to gather small quantities of pollen from the pollen tray of the dispenser and then return to the hive. Although we did not observe dancing, these bees must have danced, recruiting more bees to go to the field. This aroused the entire colony with the result that large numbers of bees were soon seen nearby searching for similar pollen. The numbers of bees foraging were obviously greater following installation of the pollen dispenser than before it was installed.

By actual counts on apple, the following ratios of apple to other pollen were collected: 49:1; 26:1; 130:1. Other colonies, which were not provided with dispensers or pollen, began work much more slowly. It was estimated that one colony in good weather, with full crop bloom could pollinate several acres of apple orchard in one day, if the pollen in the dispenser was replenished at one to two hour intervals (Karmo *et al.*, 1955).

Another trial was made in an orchard of Red Delicious apples that had a history of non-bearing. No pollinizing varieties were present. Provision of honey bees, two colonies per acre, provided with pollen dispensers and compatible pollen, produced a full commercial crop of fruit. The bloom was light the following year but provision of bees, dispensers and pollen produced a second commercial crop. The following year the block bloomed well. It was provided with bees but no dispensers and no pollen. The result was no crop.

Townsend *et al.* (1958) used the same dispenser with modified entrance, in a block of pears where pollinizing varieties were not adequate. Honey bees had been used previously but no crop increase was shown until pollen was added; then the crop was more than doubled.

Townsend (unpublished report, 1965) used a fluorescent marker mixed with pollen in the dispenser (the N.S.A.C. dispenser, Karmo and Vickery, 1954; or Karmo-Vickery dispenser of Johansen and Degman, 1957). By means of a portable ultra-violet light, he found 100 percent marking of apple blossoms in an orchard after the inserts had been used for as little as two hours.

Pollen can be hand gathered from early-blooming compatible apple varieties, dried, mixed with a carrier, and used in pollen dispensers. Pollen loses viability rather quickly and should be stored in a freezer until used. In the field, germination rate can be maintained by keeping the pollen in an insulated container with dry ice. Pollen is available from dealers and can be purchased from an area where apples bloom earlier than where the cross-pollination is desired. Pollen gathered by the bees and collected in a pollen trap is not satisfactory for use in pollen dispensers. The bees add saliva and nectar to this pollen and its viability is reduced and soon is lost (Karmo and Vickery, 1961).

Martin and McGregor (1973) state that "Pollen dispensers provide the only possible means of pollinating solid blocks of plantings of apples and other crops which require cross-variety pollination".

Small Fruit Crops

Strawberry, raspberry, blackberry and related crops all require insect pollination. Poor or incomplete pollination of these fruits usually results in hard spots on the fruit. Honey bees work the bloom of these crops very well and will, under good weather conditions, ensure that all or nearly all of the fruit will be of marketable quality.

Field Crops

The general requirements for adequate pollination of field crops and legumes are the same as for tree fruits and small fruits. Hives should be spread throughout the crop area for good coverage, unless the crop area lacks competing plants in bloom. In that case the bees will cover the entire area eventually although pollination will be better near the hives. If setting the hives in the crop is undesireable they could be located around the margins of the field in groups so that the coverage will be even.

Alfalfa grown for seed will not usually be pollinated well by honey bees. They dislike being struck by the tripping mechanism and take the nectar without effecting pollination. The Leafcutter Bee, *Magachile rotundata*, is a much better pollinator of this crop and this bee is now reared for the purpose. Honey bees may cause cross-pollination of alfalfa fairly well if the weather is hot and dry because the flowers trip rather easily under these conditions (Martin, 1975).

Problem Crops

Certain crops present problems of inadequate pollination for one reason or another. The case of solid blocks of single varieties has already been discussed.

a) Pears - Colony Conditioning

Pear bloom is rather unattractive to honey bees and they visit pear bloom sparingly for pollen. Pear cannot compete with other plants for pollinator visits if these plants will supply pollen and high quality nectar (Karmo *et al.*, 1955). If strong colonies are newly moved to close proximity of pear trees in full bloom, they will work the blossoms for a short time, then move to other plants. If the pear block contains compatible pear varieties for cross-pollination or the bees are provided with pear pollen in dispensers, a crop usually is produced.

Colony conditioning can induce honey bees to work pear blossoms and produce good pear crops if the other necessary factors are present (Karmo, 1966; Karmo and Vickery, 1987c). Field activity will not begin below a certain threshold which undulates in a diurnal pattern. Foraging will be commenced when the composite index of external factors, such as temperature, light intensity and also nectar concentration reach the threshold. The threshold is gradually revised upward during the daily period of field activity. It will invaribly undergo a delayed but constant downward adjustment when external conditions are deteriorating. Deprivaton of foraging also has a similar lowering effect. The low point in the diurnal cycle is reached in the morning. During the day, flight activity will increase as conditions improve but will decrease rapidly at slight deterioration of foraging conditions. Hence the foraging activity for the day often will cease long before conditions on the downward curve have reached the level which initiated flights in the morning. The threshold of acceptance can be lowered by prolonging the declining phase of the naturally occurring diurnal cycle. Colonies with a low acceptance threshold, if used properly, are receptive to nectar and pollen sources which they might otherwise neglect or work only poorly. Thus it is possible to ensure adequate pollination of crops where poor results due to unattractiveness had been a problem (Karmo, 1966; Karmo and Vickery, 1987c).

Conditioning (or preconditioning) honey bee colonies involves confinement. There are two approaches which differ only in duration: a) confinement in the forenoon and release in the afternoon in a new location; b) confinement for a day and a half, then release about noon in a new location.

By confining the bees the threshold of acceptance is lowered. The bees are anxious to rush out and will work the first blossoms they find. They do not discriminate and will for a short time, accept bloom which they would normally ignore or visit only occasionally. External conditions tend to improve as morning progresses. Thus at the time of release the conditioned bees find foraging conditions to be exceptionally attractive. Returning bees dance on the combs and soon mobilize the entire foraging force to work the crop.

In some trials (Karmo and Vickery, 1987c), colonies have been confined until late afternoon and in every case, whenever the weather was suitable, the bees began foraging immediately. Foraging activity could be initiated late in the afternoon when the bees from unconditioned colonies had practically ceased flying for the day. A preconditioned colony in a new location has a flight range of less than 100 metres during the day of delayed release. In several trials good crops of pears were produced when the bees were able to fly only one to one and a half hours following release.

During confinement the bees become quite agitated and rush out when the entrance block is removed. Confined colonies should never be set in direct sunshine and they must be provided with some means of ventilating the hive. Top screens were found to be adequate especially if water is sprayed on the screen occasionally. Entrances were closed with V-screens pushed in or by wooden slats nailed across the entrance.

b) Lowbush Blueberry

Prior to the work on pollination of lowbush blueberry, *Vaccinium* species, in Nova Scotia by Karmo, Kinsman, Neary, Vickery and others from 1955 to about 1965, pollination of this crop was largely left to native pollinators. Fruit sets of 10 to 20 percent were common. Actual yields were as low as 33 kg (about 72 lbs.) to about 275 kg (about 600 lbs.) per acre.

Early work revealed that blueberry shoots produce an average of 8 flower buds. Each flower bud is capable of producing 4 to 6 berries so each shoot should be capable of producing 32 to 48 berries. The flowers at the bottom of a stem open first followed in succession by flowers from the bottom to the tip of the stem. The flowers on stems of the same clone open simultaneously. Clones are variable in size and can range from a few stems to those covering up to half an acre.

Pollination trials with lowbush blueberry in Nova Scotia were begun in 1954 and were continued for several years. These trials soon proved that fruit sets of 80 - 90 percent were possible and that yields in excess of two tonnes per acre were possible with adequate pollination. Most single clones were found to be self-unfertile, that is, pollen from the flowers of the clone would not pollinate other flowers of the same clone. This applied to the majority of clones. A small proportion are completely sterile and some others are self fruitful to a limited extent.

Most of the blueberry clones in Nova Scotia are of the species *Vaccinium angustifolium*, the "Sweet Lowbush Blueberry", while two to five percent are "Sour-top Blueberry", *Vaccinium myrtilloides* Michx. *Vaccinium angustifolium* is tetraploid and *V. myrtilloides* is diploid. The diploid species is largely self-fruitful but will set more fruit if cross-pollinated. The tetraploid species is largely self sterile but will set fruit when cross-pollinated. Crosses between diploids and tetraploids do not set fruit. When a mixture of pollens of the two species are applied to pistils of flowers of *V. angustifolium* fewer and smaller berries with fewer seeds are produced than when pollen of *V. angustifolium* alone is used. In New Brunswick, where *V. myrtilloides* occurs in greater proportion, up to one-half of the total clones, fruit sets are usually light and total crop is less than in Nova Scotia (Karmo, 1974).

Better fields produce longer stems with more fruit buds and consequently can produce more fruit. In addition the number of blossoms per fruit bud is much greater in more productive fields. Employing up to date methods for controlling weeds and grass in fields should improve the yield in many fields, providing that pollinating insects are provided and have flight weather during the bloom period.

Aalders (1958) was of the opinion that each berry should contain six to ten viable seeds. Less than six seeds usually meant a very small berry or one which dropped prematurely. Each additional seed increases the weight (and size) of the berry by about 10.6 mg (approximately 5 percent of total weight). In addition, each additional seed speeds ripening of the berry to maturity by more than one-half day. It is clear that adequate pollination has a two-fold effect: more berries are brought to maturity and the berries are larger, heavier and ripen more quickly.

The wild bees which assist in pollinating this crop, including bumble bees and solitary bees, normally have a rather short working range, probably 400 metres or less. At the time of blooming of blueberry, however, only young queen bumble bees are around and these tend to roam far and wide before settling down to nest building in June. Solitary bees fluctuate in numbers from year to year. They are confined to areas where suitable nesting sites are available. The modern trend of "clean fields" reduces the available places for nests and thus the only effective pollination they could provide would be at the edges of the fields.

Cage trials in which clones were caged without bees or were supplied with nucleus colonies, so that cross pollination was either possible or not, have proven conclusively that honey bees can play a major role in producing this crop. The resuts of trials are given in the folowing table. The layout is shown in diagram in Figure 10.3, where a central clone is tied to three peripheral clones by cages containing honey bees.

Treatment	% fruit on tagged stems
Insects excluded	0.0
3 Single clones with bees (Av.)	27.2
Clone A, pollen from B,C,D (Av.)	87.6 (83.2 - 90.7)
Av. Clones B,C,D, pollen from A	78.9 (59.3 - 89.3)

Other trials and repetitions of the same type in different years gave consistent results. Additional work, evaluating the effectiveness of honey bees in cage trials for the first, middle and last third of the bloom period proved conclusively that pollinators working only the middle third of bloom consistently produced the highest yields.

Various densities and spacings of colonies have been tried. The general recommendation is to provide two colonies per acre and to space the hives throughout the crop, rather than concentrating them in one area (Karmo, 1978).

Honey bees can be used to pollinate blueberry if other essential factors are met. They will not necessarily produce fruit sets in open fields as high as those obtained where the bees are confined and forced to work blueberry or nothing

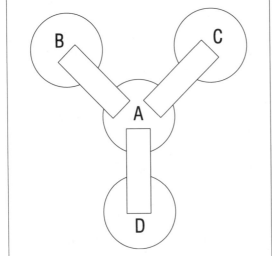

Fig 10.3:
Center clone of lowbush blueberry tied to peripheral clones by cages.

10

at all, but fruit sets averaging greater than 80 percent have been produced in open fields on numerous occasions.

As previously mentioned, the blueberry blossom is not particularly attractive to honey bees. They work it well for nectar but blueberry does not produce an abundance of pollen and it is very acidic, much more so than the pollens of most other plants. If there is a choice, the bees will work other plants for pollen and many bees may range well beyond the crop area, as early as the second day, searching for alternate pollen sources. Some of the difficulty encountered in pollination of blueberry undoubtedly stems from this problem.

A related phenomenon, which has been noted by many who have worked on the problems of blueberry pollination is the tendency of some colonies to show heavy infection of European Foul Brood disease. It must be emphasized that the disease did not come from the crop; it must have been present in these colonies before they were moved to the crop. However, placing the bees in a location where they must rely upon very acid pollen for brood-feeding, causes the disease to become much more destructive to the young brood in the colony. Similar colonies, with the same infection, and at the same time, showed little loss of brood, if they had access to pollen which was not so highly acidic. Under "normal" spring buildup conditions many colonies are able to remove diseased larvae and almost to remove all signs of the disease.

The only easy way to overcome the problems caused by acidic pollen is to ensure that the colonies have a plentiful supply of pollen when they are moved to the blueberry fields. It is suggested that the hives to be moved should be placed close to extensive stands of wild or cultivated raspberry so that the colonies could harvest a surplus of pollen. An alternative would be to feed the colonies with large amounts of pollen, gathered by the bees during the previous year and collected in a pollen trap, in the form of pollen patties immediately before moving them to the blueberry fields. It is doubtful that pollen supplements or substitutes would be sufficient to cause the bees to avoid the acidic pollen of the crop.

In any case if honey bees are to be used for blueberry pollination, they should be moved to the crop shortly before peak bloom, and left long enough to have four or five flight days, and then be moved out again (Karmo, 1974).

c) Bog Cranberry

In general, the same problems are encountered as with wild blueberry. Recommendations for pollination are the same as for that crop (Kevan *et al.*, 1984).

Renting Honey Bees for Pollination

During the past 30 years renting bees for crop pollination has become a big business. Over the years the rental price has increased. Some beekeepers have received as much as $60.00 per colony per crop. The beekeeper should move the hives to the new location(s) or should at least supervise the operation. This is to ensure that the operation is carried out carefully and smoothly, without damage to the hives or their contents. Nurse bees do not feed brood as often during transit and some larvae may not survive. Also, if the frames are not firmly fixed in place by propolis applied by the bees, they may move in transit and there is a probability that some bees, possibly even the queen, will be crushed between them.

Any hives that are moved from a beekeepers's apiary should be clearly marked or branded, to ensure that the hives are returned to the correct owner. This may not seem to be necessary but in large operations bees may be rented from several different sources.

The beekeeper is responsible for providing colonies which are strong enough to have a reasonable force of forager bees. The renter is responsible for the rented material, hives, bees, etc., while they are on his property. It is better for all concerned that each party sign and retain a copy of a written agreement covering the transaction.

If detailed knowledge on plant pollination is desired the reader should consult the collection of papers edited by Real (1983). ❏

REFERENCES

Aalders, L.E. 1958. Report to Blueberry Research Workers Conference, Kentville, Nova Scotia (Unpublished).

Antles, L.C. 1953. New methods in orchard pollination. Amer. Bee. J. 93 (3): 102-103.

Burrill A.B. and G.E. King. 1932. A device to facilitate pollen distribution by bees. Proc. Amer. Soc. Hort. Sci. 28 : 85-86.

Lotter, J. deV. 1960. Recent Developments in the Pollination of Deciduous Fruit Trees. Deciduous Fruit Grower 1960, pp. 182-189; 213-223; 305-311.

Griggs, W.H. and G.H. Vansell. 1949. The use of bee-collected pollen in artificial pollination of deciduous fruits. Proc. Amer. Soc. Hort. Sci. 54 : 118-124.

Griggs, W.H., G.H. Vansell and B. Iwakiri. 1952. The use of beehive pollen dispensers in the pollination of almonds and sweet cherries. Proc. Amer. Soc. Hort. Sci. 60 : 146-150.

Johansen, C. and E. Degman. 1957. Progress report on hive inserts for apple pollination. Proc. Wash. St. Hort. Assoc. 53 : 77.

Karmo, E.A. 1961. Increasing the Pollination Efficiency of the Honeybee through Colony Rotation. Circ. Nova Scotia Dept. Agr. Mkting. 104, 4pp.

Karmo, E.A. 1966. Increasing the Pollination Efficiency of the Honeybee through Colony Preconditioning. Circ. Nova Scotia Dept. Agr. Mkting. 130, 3 pp.

Karmo, E.A. 1974. Blueberry pollination - problems, possibilities. Circ. Nova Scotia Dept. Agr. Mkting. 109 (revised), 15 pp.

Karmo, E.A. 1978. Pollination of the Lowbush Blueberry. Ann. Rept. Nova Scotia Fruit Growers' Assoc. 94 [1977] : 93-96.

Karmo, E.A. and V.R. Vickery. 1954. The place of honey bees in orchard pollination. Circ. Nova Scotia Dept. Agr. Mkting. 67, 12 pp.

Karmo, E.A. and V.R. Vickery. 1957. Bees to the Rescue. Amer. Fruit Grower, April, 1957, pp. 42-45.

Karmo, E.A. and V.R. Vickery, 1961. Report on pollination studies on the apple set by using honey bees in combination with pollen from different sources. Ann. Rep. Nova Scotia Fruit Growers' Assoc. 97 (1960) : 125-128.

Karmo, E.A. and V.R. Vickery. 1985. Colony strength, Colony Relocation and Rotation for Better Pollination. Gleanings in Bee Cult. 113 (7) :382-383.

Karmo, E.A. and V.R. Vickery. 1987a. Pollen Transfer in the Hive. Can. Beek. 13 : 163.

10

Karmo, E.A. and V.R. Vickery. 1987b. Inserts for Pollen Dissemination. Can. Beek. 13 : 187-188.

Karmo, E.A. and V.R. Vickery. 1987c. Pollination of Pears: Colony Conditioning. Can. Beek. 13 : 111.

Karmo, E.A., V.R. Vickery and A.D. Crowe. 1955. Bees and Pollination. Ann. Rpt. Nova Scotia Fruit Growers' Assoc. 91 (1954) : 77-85.

Kevan, P.G., R.M. Gadawski, S.D. Kevan and S.E. Gadawski. 1984. Pollination of Cranberries, *Vaccinium macrocarpon* on Cultivated Marshes in Ontario. Proc. ent. Soc Ontario 114 [1983] : 45-83.

Kremer, J.C. 1948. Germination tests of the viability of apple pollen gathered in pellets. Proc. Amer. Soc. Hort. Sci. 53 : 153-157.

Martin, E.C. 1975. The use of bees for crop pollination. Chapter 20, pp. 579-614 *in* Dadant and Sons (Eds.) *The Hive and the Honey Bee*. Hamilton, Illinois, U.S.A. Dadant and Sons.

Martin, E.C. and S.E. McGregor. 1973. Changing Trends in Insect Pollination of Commercial Crops. Ann. Rev. Ent. 18 : 207-226.

Real, L. (Ed.) 1983. *Pollination Biology*. Orlando & *et al.*, Academic Press Inc.

Robacker, C.C., B.J.D. Meeuse and E.H. Erickson. 1988. Floral Aroma, how far will plants go to attract pollinators ? BioScience 38 (6) : 390-398.

Townsend, G.F., R.T. Riddell and M.V. Smith. 1958. The use of pollen inserts for tree fruit pollination. Can J. Plant Sci. 38 : 39-44.

[Townsend, G.F. and others] 1965. Directions for the use of pollen inserts for fruit pollination. Circ. Apic. Dept. Univ. Guelph, 4 pp.

HONEY BEE DISEASES, ENEMIES, AND BEE POISONING

Honey bees get sick too. Fortunately for us, we may recover from illness. Not so the bees: if any individual bee becomes diseased it nearly always dies sooner than if it had not been diseased. There is no such thing as a cure, but there are preventive measures that a beekeeper can use to protect the bees against disease. It is very important that beekeepers recognize the various diseases and detect them while they are at a very early stage. Many colonies can be saved if disease is detected early, but lack of attention can mean the loss of an entire apiary.

There are also enemies of honey bees. These may be mammals, such as bears and skunks, or parasitic eight-legged creatures called mites. Some bees are caught in spider webs or are captured on flowers by spiders or certain insects. Birds, toads and frogs also will eat bees. Some of these predators are beyond the control of the beekeeper, but there are measures that can be taken against others.

Human activities can cause losses of bees. If hives are located near roads or highways, many bees will be smashed by passing vehicles.

Brood Diseases and Treatment

Although most stages in the lives of honey bees may become diseased, the diseases of the developing brood are the most serious. It is important that the disease is correctly diagnosed. Sunken and perforated cell cappings indicate dead brood, caused by disease or even brood killed by cold. There are a number of publications available on diseases and pests of honey bees. One of the best of these is the recent publication of the Canadian Association of Professional Apiculturists (Dixon *et al.*, 1987). I have been a member of this Association for many years. The discussion of diseases and pests that follows is based in large part on the C.A.P.A. publication (although my original draft was written before the publication appeared). Burke (1981) produced a very useful publication on bee diseases for Ontario beekeepers. A comparative chart of brood diseases is given at the end of this section.The worst brood disease is American Foulbrood, a disease caused by a bacterium.

American Foulbrood (AFB)

The disease organism is a bacterium, *Bacillus larvae*. Infection occurs in the young larvae when they are fed contaminated food, that is, food containing spores of the disease. The spores germinate like seeds in the larval gut and there grow and multiply. The larvae are not killed immediately and the nurse bees do not detect that a larva is diseased. Almost always, the infected larva does not die until the cell has been capped: the larva usually moults to the pupa stage before it dies.

Once the cell is capped, the house bees pay no more attention to it. Even after the time has passed when the adult bees should have emerged from the cells, the bees in most colonies do not examine the cell contents. Eventually, they do uncap the cells and, finding dead pupae,

11

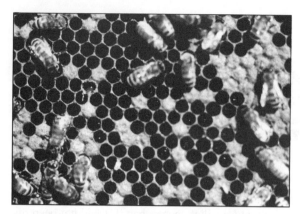

Fig 11.1: Diseased brood. Note cell with sunken cap left of centre. This was a very new and light infection. (photo by D.N. Duffy).

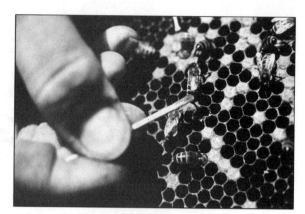

Fig 11.2: Positive ropy test for American Foul Brood (AFB).

attempt to remove them. Honey bees are good housekeepers but they have difficulty in removing dead brood killed by AFB. As the brood dies, it changes colour from the normal pearly-white through various shades of brown to dark mahogany or almost black. It sticks as though it is glued into the cell. Some strains of bees are better than others at uncapping and removing AFB-killed brood.

The attempt to remove diseased brood causes rapid spread of the disease. In each dead pupa or larva the disease organism produces spores, more than 10 million. Some authorities have claimed that the spores produced on a single dead larva or pupa number up to two billion. Whatever the number, when the cell is opened, the bees unwittingly spread them throughout the hive, contaminating food supplies and infecting many more young larvae.

The population of a diseased colony begins to decline and such a weakened colony could be robbed out, spreading the disease to all of the robbing colonies. Adult bees are not directly affected by AFB but they carry AFB spores in their hair coats. Young bees, out on their first orientation flight, may drift to other hives, carrying the disease spores with them. Colonies affected by AFB do not die out quickly, but are quite likely to perish during the winter and can be robbed by other bees early in the spring. I once lost 36 colonies this way when they robbed dead colonies in another nearby apiary that I didn't know about. Other beekeepers in the area had losses too; altogether more than 100 colonies were lost to AFB because of the carelessness of another beekeeper.

It is essential that beekeepers recognize the disease. It will appear as sunken cell caps, sometimes discoloured and sometimes perforated with holes of irregular shape (Fig. 11.1). If the diseased brood has died recently, the "ropy" test will indicate whether the problem is caused by AFB or not. A toothpick inserted into any discoloured pupa (or larva) will pull out a stringy, elastic substance for a few inches before it breaks (Fig. 11.2). Diseased brood usually has a bad odour, somewhat like old-style furniture glue. If a beekeeper wishes to have his diagnosis confirmed, the office of the provincial or state apiarist should be notified. AFB is a reportable disease, that is, the law requires that the proper authorities be notified if any colony is found to have AFB.

In some provinces and states, it is recommended that the colonies be given an antibiotic to prevent further spread of the disease. The antibiotic, oxytetracycline hydrochloride (sold as Terramycin TM 25), can be used when there is no danger of the antibiotic becoming a contaminant in honey which is extracted and sold. The "safe" period in spring is only up to three weeks before the summer honey flow, and as there is some variation between seasons, a four week interval is recommended.

The antibiotic does not kill the spores but inhibits the growth and development of the disaease in the larval gut. Inhibition of bacterial growth allows larvae to proceed normally through the pupa stage and to emerge as adult bees.

Needless to add is that infection detected during the honey-making season cannot be treated. Once the surplus honey is removed treatment can begin in late summer or fall. By this time the disease may have become severe and more widespread. My personal opinion is that infected colonies should be killed immediately and the bees and comb should be burned. Covers, bottom boards and queen excluders can be severely scorched with a blow torch. In spring, colonies can be installed in this equipment with new combs. The problem of spores in the honey supers remains. By the time the honey supers are added it is too late to treat the colonies with an antibiotic.

Ethylene oxide fumigation of equipment, as has been carried out in Quebec, effectively eliminates infection from spores remaining in the equipment (Vickery, 1979).

There are several methods of treating colonies with antibiotics. In some areas it is recommended that the antibiotic be added to sugar syrup, which is then fed to the bees. If a colony has little stored honey this method is effective. I prefer to mix the antibiotic with powdered sugar, for treating against AFB, and place it at the ends of the top bars of the frames in the brood chamber. I use it only on colonies in which I have *not* detected the disease, but which may have spores from drifting bees. The treatment is not applied until any infected colonies are killed and the bees and their combs are burned.

European Foulbrood (EFB)

This disease is called "European' because it was first detected in Europe. Likewise, AFB was first discovered in America, but it is very improbable that either disease originated in the continent for which it is named.

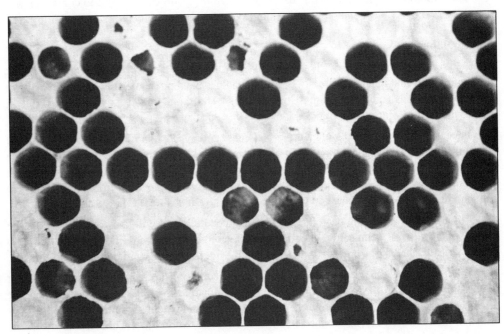

Fig 11.3: European Foul Brood (EFB) in new comb in package colony: there are diseased larvae in both open and capped cells.

EFB occurs world-wide. It is not considered to be as serious as AFB but can cause severe population loss, reduction of honey crop, and death of colonies. The disease can occur at any time but is most noticeable in the spring.

The causal organism is a bacterium, *Mellitococcus pluton*. It produces a spore stage but the spores are not long-lived and persistent over a long span of years, like those of AFB. Several other bacterial organisms may occur in the diseased larvae at the same time but are not considered to be important. *Bacillus alvei* is nearly always present and can be used as a marker during microscopic examination.

EFB attacks very young larvae, ten days old or less, which become infected when fed food containing the bacterium. The disease develops rapidly and the larvae usually die while still coiled in the cells, before the cells are capped. Some of the dead larvae appear twisted in the cells and may also show silvery tracheae through the outer skin. They turn yellowish and then brown, usually with blotchy darker areas. They eventually form rubbery scales in the cells. Sometimes death is delayed so that some cells are capped, giving an appearance similar to that of AFB. If this occurs there are always some dead larvae in open cells (Fig.11.3). The dead larvae are not stuck in the cells and are relatively easy for the worker bees to remove. A beekeeper may not detect the disease at all, if the infection is light, as the bees remove the dead corpses leaving only the empty cells. This can be mistaken as the work of a failing queen that has missed many cells. This was partly responsible for the recommendation to change the queen to cure EFB. Introduction of a young prolific queen may well give the colony a better chance of removing the diseased larvae, or the interval between brood produced by removing the old queen and introducing the new one may provide the time the bees need to complete the job.

This disease, like some others, is a greater problem when the bees are under stress, as they are in the spring, and is less troublesome once the warm weather arrives.

EFB is spread by drifting bees, robbing bees, movement of contaminated equipment by the beekeeper, or even by feeding pollen from an unknown source. If pollen is collected in the apiary, be sure that no disease is present in the hives in which the pollen traps are installed.

The antibiotic, oxytetracycline hydrochloride (Terramycin) can be used to control or prevent infection by EFB. It should be used only as directed by provincial or state authorities.

Chalkbrood

A fungus, *Ascophaera apis*, is the causal agent for this disease. It is a relatively recent problem, found first in Canada in 1972. The spread has been phenomenal, as it is now known throughout Canada and much of the United States. The rapid spread may have been due in part to the former widespread importation of bees in "packages".

Infected larvae usually die after the brood cells are capped. The larvae become hard and mummified and are whitish to grayish and occasionally black (Fig. 11.4). The black areas are due to the fruiting bodies (spores) of the fungus. The mummified larvae are removed readily from the cells but they are heavy so the adult bees have difficulty in removing them from the hive. There are mummies on the bottom board and/or in front of the hive if chalkbrood is present (Fig.11.5).

The bees will detect the dead larvae in the capped cells and will chew small holes in the wax cappings. It has been said thet cappings with one hole indicate AFB; cappings with two holes indicate Chalkbrood. I have not found much evidence to substantiate this claim.

Like EFB, Chalkbrood is worse under stressful conditions, and is most apparent during cool damp periods in the spring. Like most fungi, moisture is necessary for germination of the spores. Increasing ventilation in the hives helps to some extent. I routinely raise the covers on 2 inch thick blocks, above the screened inner covers when I find Chalkbrood.

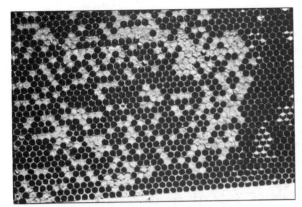

Fig 11.4: Comb with Chalkbrood mummies in cells.

Fig 11.5: Chalkbrood mummies on the bottom board.

Although there have been some reports that it is not a serious disease I have recorded during several seasons that chalkbrood infected colonies did not build up well and produced less surplus honey, in spite of anything I could do to lessen the severity of the disease.

Prevention of the disease requires good management. Do not move combs between diseased and disease-free colonies. Combs which contain many chalkbrood mummies should be removed and replaced with new combs. The spores can remain viable for at least 15 years so any combs that are removed should be destroyed. If brood is removed from the infected colonies, combs of brood from disease-free colonies can be added.

Do not feed pollen from an unknown source as it may be contaminated. Do not collect pollen from any colonies that show even the slightest evidence of chalkbrood. Be sure that the queens in your colonies are young and productive.

11

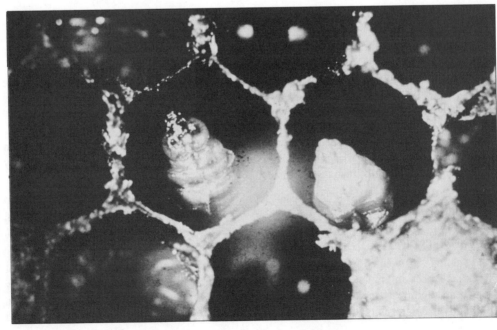

Fig 11.6:
Sacbrood killed larvae. (This picture has appeared in a number of publications - photo by Maurice Smith).

Sacbrood

Sacbrood disease is caused by a virus. Several viruses affecting honey bees are known but to date have not been serious enough to warrant much investigation. Sacbrood losses in North America have probably been underestimated. I have talked to beekeepers in southern Queensland, Australia, who lost entire apiaries to sacbrood. Very young larvae, one or two days old become infected when they ingest the virus with their food. Death usually occurs after the larvae have extended themselves lengthwise in their capped cells. The heads of the larvae are darkened and are slightly raised (Fig. 11.6). The general colour changes from white to dark brown and the body becomes a leathery fluid-filled sac. Eventually, the body will dry and become scale-like and is easily removed from the cell.

There is no treatment for sacbrood. It appears to be a greater problem with some strains of bees, so these should be replaced with less susceptible strains. Sacbrood appears most often in the spring when the bees are under stress so any condition that alleviates stress is helpful. Combs that have sacbrood scales can be culled to remove any source of re-infection.

Comparison of Brood Diseases

Symptom	AFB	EFB	Chalkbrood	Sacbrood
State of brood comb	Capped brood, sunken perforated cappings	Open brood, possibly some cells as in AFB	Capped and open brood cells	Capped brood cells punctured appings
Age of brood	Older larvae or pupae lengthwise in cell	Usually young larvae coiled in cells	Older larvae, lengthwise in cells	Older larvae lengthwise in cell
Colour of dead brood	Dull, white thru brown to nearly black	Dull, white to yellow to dark brown, blotchy	Chalky white, may have black spots	Gray to brown, head darker
Consistency of dead brood	Soft, then sticky to ropy	Watery, granular	Chalky	Watery, granular fluid-filled sac
Odour of dead brood	Putrid	Sour	Yeasty	None
Type of scale	Flat on cell bottom Stuck to cell	Twisted, rubbery, not stuck in cell	Mummified, chalky, brittle, not stuck in cell	Head black, curled to centre, brittle, not stuck in cell

Sunken cell caps, perforated or not, indicate a problem. This may be due to any of the above diseases or to chilled brood. If EFB is present, there will also be infected larvae in open cells as well as those in capped cells (unless the bees have removed them). To determine which disease is present, the cappings of affected cells must be opened. Testing the consistency of of the dead brood with a toothpick or a stiff grass stem, will distinguish between AFB and EFB, a positive stringing out indicates AFB. The other diseases are relatively easy to identify, once the cells have been opened.

If AFB is present, be careful to destroy toothpicks or grass stems that have been used to probe the cells. Burning them in a smoker will destroy the AFB spores. Hive tools, gloves, etc., that are used in examining a colony with AFB should be disinfected (or for hive tools, flamed) as they may carry spores that could infect the other colonies to be examined.

King (1985) pointed out that sanitation in bee hives is very important. Brother Adam of Buckfast Abbey in England does not use drugs to control diseases. He replaces combs every four years, and treats supers, empty frames (the wax is cut out), covers and bottom boards in boiling lye, then repaints the parts exposed to weather. One factor that assists survival of wild colonies is that fact that they do not have a restricting bottom board, and debris falls below their level of activity. Bottom boards should be kept clean. Periodic washing of bottom boards and use of a propane torch, especially to the edges, certainly will help in disease control. The same treatment can be given to supers and covers. The use of slatted bottom boards above the usual bottom board also tends to place debris below the area of general activity and should also help in disease control.

Chilled Brood

Sometimes, especially in spring, cold rather than disease may be responsible for death of brood. Normally the bees maintain a brood nest temperature of about 35 degrees Celsius. During a cold spell or a frosty spring night, the cluster of bees surrounding the brood area has to contract. Some brood on the outside combs or on the periphery of central combs may be left without protection and is chilled and dies. The location of the dead brood is usually a good indicator of the cause. Closer examination, opening the cells and probing the dead larva or pupa, reveals a dark grayish mass that will string out from the cell but which is not sticky.

The pupa stage is relatively cold-hardy compared to the other immature stages, but prolonged exposure to temperatures of 14 degrees Celsius and below, will be fatal.

Strong, populous colonies usually have enough bees to protect the brood. It is the weaker colonies that often suffer cold injury. The use of entrance reducers during early spring helps to reduce heat loss. Good windbreaks and good air drainage also reduce injury from cold. Colonies that are set in places where cold air settles (that is, in frost pockets) are particularly susceptible.

Diseases of Adult Bees and Treatment

Adult bees are carriers of organisms that attack brood. They unknowingly feed larvae with food that is contaminated with spores of bacteria or fungi, or with virus particles. The adult bees are not affected by these diseases but there are other diseases that attack only the adult bees.

Nosema Disease

This disease is caused by a protozoan parasite, *Nosema apis*. This is a single-celled creature that attacks the lining of the gut of the bees. The parasite is very widespread wherever honey bees are kept, but is most damaging in temperate climates especially during cool, wet springs. It is an insidious disease that may not be noticed by the beekeeper until the colonies are severely weakened. Queen bees are susceptible to Nosema, which frequently causes queenless colonies in the spring. Nosema can cause serious reduction of population and in the amount of honey that is stored.

Cantwell and Shimanuki (1969) outlined the effects of *Nosema apis* on colonies of honey bees: shortening of the life span of worker bees and queens; brood production is reduced; often causes supercedure of queens; infected colonies produce less honey; foraging ability of bees in an infected colony is reduced; winter losses are increased.

The damage to the intestinal tract causes some heavily infected bees to defecate inside the hive, although most are able to follow their instinct to fly, leave the hive and defecate in flight. The feces contain the parasite in the spore stage. The spores are resistant and may remain viable for several years. Honey bees are good housekeepers, so they immediately try to clean and remove the fecal material, and themselves become infected.

The spores germinate in the midgut of a bee and extend a filament which enters an epithelial cell of the midgut lining. The parasite multiplies in the cell which finally ruptures, releasing more spores. The spores can either attack more cells of the gut lining or may be passed out in feces, and then can infect more bees. Even the spores which are contained in feces that are dropped outside the hive may cause reinfection if sources of water become contaminated.

Infected bees do not live long. They cannot digest pollen and are unable to produce Royal Jelly to feed to young larvae. The hypopharyngeal glands become atrophied and wings become unhinged. Many infected bees may be seen crawling in front of the hive. Samples of these crawling bees can confirm the presence of *Nosema*. Confirmation is important as other factors, such as poisoning or bee paralysis, can cause similar behaviour. Examination of the digestive tract can be made by pulling a bee apart and examining the gut. A normal midgut is tan-coloured and has a distinct ringed appearance (annulations, similar to the body of an earthworm). In bees that are heavily infected with Nosema, the midgut is whitish, somewhat swollen and is not ringed in appearance (Fig. 11.7). The gut is so small that a good magnifying glass should be used. A more positive analysis can be made if a microscope is available, as the midgut examina tion will be positive for *Nosema* only in the most heavily infected bees. For a microscopic examination a sample of about 30 bees is

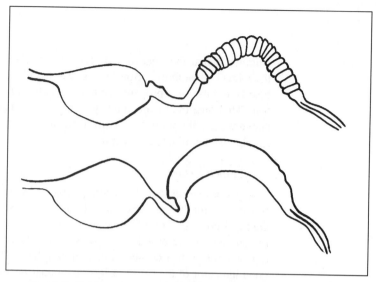

Fig 11.7: Comparison of healthy bee gut (top) with gut from bee with Nosema apis parasite (bottom). The diseased gut is swollen and the rings have disappeared.

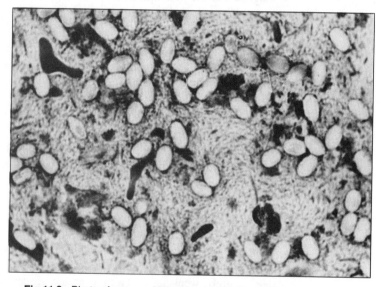

Fig 11.8: Photo of spores of Nosema apis, X 1000. (photo by K.P. Lim).

ground up in a small amount of water, then a drop is examined under high power, at least 400X and 1000X is better (Fig. 11.8), to determine whether or not *Nosema* spores are present.

Treatment for *Nosema* Control

The antibiotic 'fumagillin' is an effective control of the growing stages of the parasite in the midgut of a bee, but it cannot kill the spores. It can be added to sugar syrup and fed to the bees in the spring and again in the fall. Some measured trials have indicated that feeding the antibiotic allowed production of about 30 percent more surplus honey. Heat causes breakdown of the antibiotic so it should not be added to hot syrup.

Spores of the parasite on combs or surfaces of wood are not affected by the antibiotic. It protects bees only by destroying the spores as they germinate in the gut of the bee. Spores on supers, combs, and other hive parts can be destroyed by heating to 49 degrees C. (120 degrees F.) for 24 hours (Cantwell and Shimanuki, 1969).

Bee Paralysis

Paralysis is caused by a virus and produces crawling bees close to the hive. Some bees may be seen apparently fighting near the entrance as healthy bees attempt to remove infected bees from the hive. Infected bees may be darker in colour and may have lost much of their body hair, particularly on the abdomen. Hairless black syndrome is another name used for bee paralysis. I have had very little experience with this disease. I first noticed it in package bees shipped from the southern United States. I have seen it only early in spring and it invariably disappeared with the onset of warmer weather and in that respect I have been more fortunate than many other bee-keepers. It is a serious disease that has caused considerable reduction of honey yields and loss of colonies. As with many other viruses there is no known cure.

Mite Parasites of Honey Bees

Two species of mites are parasitic on honey bees in many parts of the world. Mites are not insects but are eight-legged creatures related to spiders. Most of them are very small, some so small that they cannot be seen except by using a microscope. These mites are *Acarapis woodi* Rennie, the "Tracheal Mite" and the "Varroa Mite" *Varroa Jacobsoni*, and each can be very damaging to honey bees. A third species, *Tropilaelaps clareae*, has also been reported as a parasite of honey bees in some parts of the world.

Tracheal Mite

This mite was unknown on the North American continent until 1986, when it was found to be widespread in the United States, but not in Canada (Dixon *et al.*, 1987). There is little doubt that it will become established in Canada sooner or later. Mite infested colonies were found in southern Quebec, infested from colonies in northern New York. These colonies were destroyed, eliminating the parasite in that area at least temporarily.

The Tracheal Mite attacks adult bees. The mites enter the body of a bee through the large spiracle (breathing pore) on the thorax. This allows entry into the tracheal (breathing) system. The female mite feeds upon haemolymph (blood), then lays several eggs. These soon hatch and both adult and immature mites pierce the wall of the tracheae to obtain blood. The feeding punctures cause mottled appearance and soon turn black.

A heavily infested bee may have 100 or more mites in its tracheal tubes. Mating takes place in the tracheae and mature mated females leave the tracheae through the large spiracle. They crawl along the body hairs and are transferred to other bees as the bees pass close to each other in the hive. From the time a mite enters a bee only 28 days is required until the next generation of mites pass to other bees. Drifting bees spread the mites from one colony to others. Drones and queens are susceptible to attacks by the mites, and drones may be mainly responsible for carrying the mites from colony to colony.

Spread between apiaries occurs with movement of colonies, package bees, nucs or larger colonies. There is some evidence that the mites are spread by swarms of bees from one region to another.

There are two other mite species in the same genus, *Acarapis dorsalis* and *Acarapis externus*, that are present in Canada. Although they are associated with honey bees, they remain externally on the bees and apparently cause no harm (Dixon *et al.*, 1987)

Microscopic examination of the tracheae of bees is the only way to determine the presence of Tracheal Mites. A sample of older field bees is collected and is placed in alcohol. The bees must be dissected to reveal the tracheae or discs are cut from the thorax. These are treated with a warm solution of potassium hydroxide (30+ degrees C. for 8 to 24 hrs). This clears the tracheae so that the dark feeding punctures will become visible under a microscope. If a sample appears to be positive, the tracheae are removed and placed on a microscope slide, with a cover slip, so that examination can be made at much higher power with a compound microscope.

There are several miticides that will kill mites. Apitol and Folbex will kill Tracheal Mites but are not registered for sale for this purpose. Menthol is one feasible chemical control for Tracheal Mite (Clark, 1989). It is useful only when the combination of temperature, dosage and the time of treatment are determined correctly. Results are better at high temperatures (i.e. 37 degrees C.). The duration of treatment can be rather short at high temperature but becomes prolonged at lower temperatures. There is danger of killing bees and brood if the temperature is very high and the amount of menthol vapourized in a short time is great. Beekeepers who intend to treat their colonies with menthol should obtain the latest information on the type of formulation, method of use and the details on temperature and duration of treatment. Considerable care must be taken when any chemical is used to control mites in honey bee colonies.

The mites cannot survive without honey bees. Heavily infested colonies can be killed, then with an interval of about a week, new bees can be established safely in the equipment.

Varroa Mite

Varroa mites are considerably larger than Tracheal Mites and are visible (Fig. 11.9) without magnification on larvae in cells. They are not easy to see on adult bees. Adult mites ride on adult bees and feed upon bee blood. A heavily infested bee has a shortened life span. The mites do not remain long on the bees but enter open brood cells and lay several eggs near a developing larva. The young mites remain in the cell when it is capped and

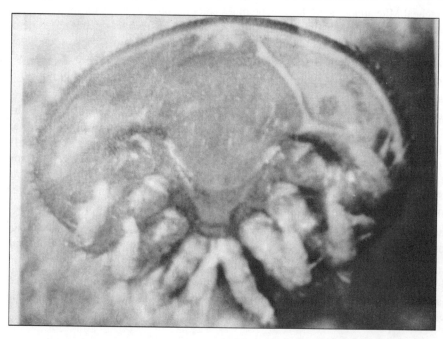

Fig 11.9: Varroa mite, underside. (photo of mite on a publication in Arabic.)

feed upon the larva, often in the area of the wing buds. The mites mature and mate in the cell. The bee is not killed but when it emerges usually has deformed wings and is unable to perform the normal functions of a newly-emerged bee. The mated female mites leave the cell when the bee emerges and either attach themselves to other bees or move directly to cells containing larvae.

Varroa mites can eventually cause death of colonies. They attack drone larvae very readily, appearing to prefer the larger larva, but also attack worker brood. Drifting bees carry the mites to other colonies.

Chemical control with menthol now appears to be feasible but some mites are on bees and some are enclosed in cells, so the timing of the treatment is important. If treatment is applied when brood is present, it must be repeated several times, as any mites in sealed cells will not be affected. If, in any region, there is an interruption in brood rearing, such as in the fall in northern regions, a single treatment could end the problem (if the treatment is 100 percent effective), as all of the mites would be on adult bees and would be vulnerable. Leudi (1989) reported that Methyl Palmitate could replace acaricide chemicals in control of *Varroa* mites. It is used on blotting paper on the floor of the hive. It is a strong attractant for the mites which are then trapped on sticky paper or in a trapping device. Some chemicals, such as Folbex VA, Amitraz, Apistan and Perizin, will kill *Varroa* mites (Murrell, 1989). Use of any method of control in the future should be confined to the chemical recommended and use as recommended by authorities.

There are several ways that a beekeeper can use to determine whether or not *Varroa* mites are present in his colonies. Debris in the hive can be washed to remove mites, then straining the washing liquid to reveal mites. The mites are quite susceptible to tobacco smoke. A beekeeper can cover the floor of the hive with clean white cloth or paper then, with tobacco in the smoker, smoke the bees thoroughly. About half of the mites on the adult bees will drop to the floor. This method should be used with caution. Tobacco smoke is not healthy for bees either.

Tropilaelaps Mite

This mite was originally a parasite of the giant Asian honey bee, *Apis dorsata*. In 1961 it was first found on our honey bee, *Apis mellifera,* in the Philippines, and is now known to infest this bee over much of Asia. Although not much is known about this mite, it apparently feeds on brood but not on adult bees. It is not likely to become serious in any region where brood rearing is interrupted by winter (Dixon *et al.*, 1987).

Checking colonies for this mite is done by washing debris from the hive floor and straining the liquid. The mite is large enough to be observed by the naked eye although a magnifying glass or hand lens would be helpful.

Apiary Registration and Inspection

Registration of apiaries and inspection by qualified personnel is not uniform in the various states and provinces. Some beekeepers resent the appearance of an inspector, an attitude that I think is totally out of line. The inspectors job is to assist beekeepers and to protect the industry. I have had colonies condemned and destroyed because of AFB, not through any fault of mine. If compulsory registration had been in force, the chances are that the apiary we didn't know was there would have been inspected and taken care of before the infection from these few colonies caused heavy losses in the area. I hope to see the day when compulsory registration and inspection is in vogue throughout this continent.

11

Enemies of Honey Bees

a) Bears

Bears can ruin an apiary in a very short time. They love honey and will endure stinging by the bees to get it. Hives are knocked over, supers are smashed (Fig 11.10), and combs are broken and eaten. Frequently only a single hive in an apiary is completely destroyed by a bear, but several others are knocked over, as though the bear is retaliating for stings from the bees of the destroyed hive. Once a bear has found and damaged an apiary, it is likely to make several more visits and cause more damage.

The most satisfactory method of preventing damage by bears is a electric fence that is capable of producing a severe enough shock to convince the bear that the prize is not worth the pain. Some of the fences that are used to keep cattle from wandering do not have enough power to discourage a bear. Suitable fences are available, and if you live in an area where bears are known, a fence is good insurance. The arrangement described by Knepp (1987) is a useful guide. Bears are crafty animals and apparently can smell honey at a considerable distance.

Electric fences often have to be used in places where no electrical power is available and must be operated on battery power. Batteries do become discharged in time and may not be effective when needed. In places like these the use of solar panels to maintain the charge in the batteries appears to be an excellent solution.

Some beekeepers keep hives on flat-bed trailers. The bears do not seem to be able to overcome the problem of climbing onto the trailer. I doubt that I could keep bees that way. The hives must be close together and any trailer can hold only a limited number. Drifting must be a problem and regular hive inspections must be difficult in such a situation. I would rather rely on a good electric fence.

b) Skunks

Skunks like honey too, but they are not able to open a hive to get it. Instead they provoke the

Fig 11.10: Bear damage in an apiary.

bees by scratching on the side or the rear of the hive. The guard bees rush out and are eaten by the skunk. The bees have enough honey in their stomachs to taste sweet to the skunk.

Repeated visits can cause serious reduction of the population in a hive. Usually it is easy to determine the cause of the population decline if a skunk is the culprit. The scratch marks on the hive are quite evident. In the fall, the damage is caused by young skunks, usually males, shortly after thay have left the family den to live on their own. Skunk attacks in the spring are by older males, perhaps those that found the hives the previous fall.

There is one device that will prevent damage by skunks. Take a piece of board (1" x 3" or 1" x 4") and use up all of the old nails you can find. Drive the nails so close together that a skunk is not able to put a foot between the nails. Set the boards, nail points upward, across the back and along the sides of the hive, extending beyond the front for about a foot or more. I got rid of skunks by using such a "skunk board" on a single hive in a 36 hive apiary. Once a skunk has hurt its foot on the nails, it will not come back to the apiary. I do not like hurting wild animals but I don't like them interfering with my bees either.

If you use skunk boards with nails, don't forget where you put them. Grass may grow up around them and hide them. You may not see them and the nails that are supposed to repel skunks end up in your foot. I can recall incidents in my boyhood when I jumped on old boards and drove rusty nails part way or all the way through my foot, with rather bad results.

Another method that I have heard of is to place 'chicken' wire over the front of the hive, bowed well out in the middle. This forces the skunk up on its hind legs and leaves its belly vulnerable to bee stings. I have not tried this method.

c) Birds

Many birds are insect-eaters and they do not seem to differentiate between one kind of insect and another. If they eat an insect with a very bad taste they learn to avoid that kind of insect and any others that look like it. Bees have enough honey in their stomachs to make them a tasty treat. Many bees may be taken by birds as the bees forage among the flowers. There is nothing the beekeeper can do about this, nor should he try. Killing birds is not the answer, and the insect-eaters are protected by law as they eat far more pest species than beneficial ones.

Fortunately the reproductive capacity of an average colony of bees is great enough so that the loss to birds is not noticed.

d) Amphibians and Reptiles

Toads and frogs will feed upon bees if the bees happen to visit flowers near enough so that they can reach the bees with their long tongues. Some snakes eat bees, but cause no great concern. If a smake invades a hive it is usually killed by the bees before it can retreat. I have found preserved snakes entombed in propolis on the floor boards of hives.

e) Insects and Spiders

"Ambush bugs" and "assassin bugs" hide in or on flowers and will kill and suck the body fluids from bees or other insects that visit the flowers. Certain spiders capture bees on flowers in the same manner; praying mantids do too. Web-spinning spiders construct webs which may trap honey bees, and unable to escape, they become meals for the spiders. Many other insects are trapped in webs and it is certain that these spiders destroy more flies than bees.

Of all of the enemies that prey upon honey bees, bears are probably the worst. I say probably because I have seen damage by human vandals that exceeded the worst the bears could do. Vandals, bears and skunks, in that order, are the worst enemies of the apiary. That

11

reminds me to mention that the grass should be kept fairly short near the apiary at all times. I know of a case where a would-be honey thief was badly stung and retaliated by setting a grass fire that wiped out the apiary.

An apiary set close to a road or highway will probably lose more bees to passing vehicles than to all of the enemies mentioned above. We seldom see road signs advertising "Bees Crossing" but there is one on a road near Walla Walla, Washington, U.S.A. (Fig. 11.11).

Storage of Honeycombs

a) Greater Wax Moth - Prevention and Control

This species, *Galleria mellonella* (L.), is a serious pest of stored combs (Scott-Dupree, 1987). It is found nearly everywhere where people keep honey bees but I do not recall that Greater Wax Moth was a pest in Nova Scotia. My first experience was in Quebec when I moved to that province in 1961. The insect is said to be less serious in colder climates (Shimanuki, 1971), not that Nova Scotia is colder than Quebec; usually the reverse is true in winter.

Female moths lay their eggs in small cracks between supers or between the bottom board or cover and a super, or between frames if they are able to get inside. Newly hatched larvae are tiny and are able to crawl through very small cracks. They infest combs by making tunnels in the wax which they line with silky webs (Fig. 11.12). They feed upon wax and especially on old bee cocoons, pollen or debris, contaminating the combs with fecal pellets. Combs in which brood has been reared are favoured by Greater Wax Moth and these combs are almost always damaged more severely than combs in which no brood has been reared.

When larvae become mature they spin very tough cocoons that they cement into cavities chewed into the wood (Fig. 11.13). The cocoons remain in place after the moths have emerged. Moths are silvery-gray in colour. They shun light and, when suddenly exposed to light, often scuttle away on foot like cockroaches.

The Greater Wax Moth is seldom a problem in hives occupied by strong colonies. They may cause minor to major injury if the colonies are very weak.

Fig 11.11:
Bee crossing sign, near Walla Walla, Washington, U.S.A. (photo by Dennis Woodland).

HONEY BEE DISEASES, ENEMIES, AND BEE POISONING

Fig 11.13: Wax moth cocoons.

Fig 11.12: Wax moth damage to a brood comb.

Take care when stacking supers containing combs to ensure that there are no places where adult moths can enter. Gaps can be sealed with masking tape. Do not store equipment in a heated building. Winter cold kills all stages of the wax moth. In summer, placing combs in a freezer overnight will kill the pests, but cold combs will be very brittle and must be handled very carefully.

Exposure to 2 degrees C. for 10 days or 5 degrees C. for 21 days will kill all stages (Dixon *et al.*, 1987). Exposure to - 6 degrees for 12 hours is very effective.

The Lesser Wax Moth, *Achroia grisella* (F.), and the Dried Fruit Moth, *Vitula edmandsae* R., may also cause damage to stored combs, but are less important than the Greater Wax Moth. They can be controlled by the same treatments.

Fumigating with various fumigants will kill these pests but the fumigating gases are quite hazardous to use and are not generally recommended. Heating supers of combs to 40 degrees C. (100 + degrees F) or more will kill the pest in time but remember that wax combs can sag if heated too high too long.

b) Rodents

Mice are the most serious pests of stored combs and occasionally of hives containing bees. Mice feed upon dead bees, pollen and honey. Their nesting habits are such that they may destroy many combs (Fig. 11.14). They will infest stacks of supers in winter, inside or outside of buildings. I have found mouse nests in spring in insulation between inner and outer covers of colonies.

Stored supers and combs should be stacked on closed bottom boards (the single-sided short bottom boards are ideal for this purpose). Rodent baits and traps are recommended if the beekeeper has seen signs of mice in the area.

Colonies that are wintered outside with bottom entrances open should have these entrances reduced to 1.2 cm (1/2 inch) or less to prevent mouse entry. I do not leave lower entrances open on hives near the ground in winter as each of these hives is provided with an upper entrance of 0.8 x 5.1 cm (5/16 x 2 inches).

During the active season a mouse may enter a hive but the bees soon sting it to death.

As previously noted in Chapter 6, bait hives for capturing swarms should have the entrances covered with wire mesh with openings large enough to allow bees to enter but which keep mice out.

Honey Bee Poisoning

Many of the pesticides used to control pest insects are toxic to honey bees. Some kill on contact; some have long residual action. If pesticides are applied while bees are working in the field, many of them may be killed. Even chemicals that do not usually present a hazard may kill bees by direct contact. This is probably mechanical action rather than poisoning by the chemical. Some poisons do not kill quickly but may contaminate nectar and pollen that bees are gathering. If these contaminated substances are stored in the hive they may cause brood and adult poisoning over a prolonged period. Bees gather water from wet foliage. If the foliage is wet due to a pesticide spray, or if previously sprayed foliage is wet by rain or heavy dew, heavy mortality to the bees may be the result.

In addition to honey bee mortality, severe damage may be caused to wild pollinating insects, such as bumble bees and solitary bees, as well as to other beneficial insects.

In general terms, the organophosphorous insecticides cause the greatest mortality, followed by the chlorinated hydrocarbons and carbamates, although there are some compounds in each of these groups which have minimal effects on bees.

Several aspects must be considered when using pesticides in areas where colonies of bees are located or where they are foraging in the field.

1. Location of Hives. If the hives are in a field which is sprayed the injury to the bees will be greater than if they are outside the treated area. If possible beehives should not be placed in areas which will be sprayed or dusted with pesticides, or even nearby these areas.

2. Method of application of pesticides. Applications made by aircraft are usually more damaging than ground applications. Applications made from the air tend to drift and may contaminate areas for which the pesticide is not intended. In almost all cases dust applications cause more mortality to bees than the same chemical applied as a spray. Highly concentrated sprays or ultra-low (ULV) sprays are more damaging than dilute sprays.

3. Time of application. Applications made during the day, while bees are foraging, are usually the most hazardous to the bees. Many insecticides should be applied at night or very

Fig 11.14: Combs damaged by mice that built their nest in a stored super.

early in the morning. Insecticides with short residual action have minimal effects on the bees when they work the area the next day. Also, the crop coverage and control of the pests invariably is improved due to more stable atmospheric conditions during the night.

4. Crops in bloom. The law in Quebec, and in other provinces and states, prohibits application of insecticides on fruit trees during the bloom period. This helps to protect the bees but does not remove the hazard of contamination of blossoms of other plants in the treated area before and after bloom. Dandelion bloom, contaminated by pre-bloom sprays on apple, can be disastrous to honey bees and other pollinating insects. Drifting of pesticide chemicals to areas outside the crop area also can contaminate flowers being visited by the bees. The law does not prohibit spraying of field crops and vegetable crops while bloom is present and honey bee colonies can be severely damaged from these sources.

5. The corn problem. Corn does not require insects to provide cross-pollination. It produces no nectar, but like other wind pollinated plants, produces pollen in great quantity. Honey bees do not usually gather much pollen from corn if other plants are providing plenty of pollen. If pollen from other sources is in short supply, the bees will visit corn in great numbers to collect from this bountiful source. In hot weather they may also collect water from the places where leaves join the stalks and can carry insecticide contaminated water back to the hive.

The European Corn Borer, and other corn pests, often require the use of insecticides for their control. Unfortunately, the pesticide applications must be made when the tassels appear and begin to produce pollen. Foraging bees will be killed if the insecticide is applied when they are working and the pollen becomes contaminated. The recommended chemical, carbofuran, is highly toxic to bees if it is used when bees are active. However, if the granular formulation is used and is applied when the bees are not active, the damage usually is minimal.

Beekeepers are advised to locate bee hives in areas well removed from corn fields if at all possible. If the nearest corn fields are at least 2.5 km away from apiaries, poisoning from this source would be kept to a minimum. In any case beekeepers should ask corn growers and pesticide applicators in the area to advise them of the times when pesticide applications are to made to the crop.

6. Insecticide formulations. The most common formulations are dust (D), wettable powder (WP), emulsifiable concentrate (EC), and granular (G). These vary in effect on bees but the granular form is usually safest. The latest type of formulation, microencapsulated insecticides (M) consist of tiny droplets of insecticide encased in tiny polymer spheres. They are particularly hazardous to bees as the tiny spheres are nearly identical to pollen in size and conformation and they stick to bees in the same way pollen does. Since the chemical is released slowly over a long time, bees can survive and mix the pesticide with pollen as they collect it. The stored pollen is deadly to brood and eventually the colony dies. Microencapsulated parathion is very deadly to bees. Once this type of poisoning occurs, the only way to remove the hazard is to destroy the combs.

7. Herbicides. The herbicides currently recommended for weed control do not present a severe hazard as they are only slightly toxic to bees. However, bees that are on the vegetation at the time of application may be killed. When the spray residue dries on the plants there is very little harmful effect. The herbicides do destroy "bee pasture".

Symptoms of Pesticide Poisoning

1. Great numbers of dead bees at the hive entrances.
2. Bees crawling at or near the hives entrances.

3. Many dead bees are being carried out of the hive.

4. There are dead bees on the floor or on the top bars of the frames in the hive.

5. Bees stop working flowers and the usual hum of activity is lacking (when not produced by weather conditions).

6. Paralyzed or stupified bees are seen on the hives, plants or other objects in the apiary.

7. Foraging bees returning from the field with nectar or pollen are attacked at the hive entrance.

8. Storage of food ceases.

9. Dead or deserted brood, even though stores of honey and pollen in the hive are adequate.

10. Sudden loss of queens.

11. Colonies become weaker when they should be increasing in strength.

12. Several colonies die at the same time.

13. Diseases often are more serious in pesticide-weakened colonies.

None of these symptoms will indicate which insecticide has affected the bees. Not all of the symptoms will occur at one time and some of them could be due to other causes.

The only way to establish proof of bee poisoning is by chemical analysis of affected bees. The analysis is difficult even when the type of insecticide is known. Some pesticides break down very rapidly after application. Any sample for analysis should be collected immediately after exposure. Collect about 500 grams (about 1 pound) of bees, place them in a tightly sealed container and keep them frozen until ready for analysis. If you can get acetonitrile, place about 500 bees in 200 ml (about 12 fl. oz.) of liquid for analysis.

Protective Measures

If pesticide application, that could cause mortality to bees, is to be made near an apiary steps should be taken to minimize the injury.

1. If at all possible, move the bees to a safe location for the duration of the dangerous period. Often this is not possible or is very difficult. Hives are awkward to handle with honey supers in place and may be very heavy. Unless special equipment is available for loading and unloading the hives, many beekeepers would not be able to move them.

2. Confine the bees to the hives during the most dangerous period - during and immediately after the time of application. Use a screen, flat or V-shaped, to close the entrance but still allow for ventilation. If the weather is hot, cover the hives with several thicknesses of burlap and keep this wet during the period of confinement. Cover the hives at night when the bees are all inside. During the day wet the burlap at least once every hour.

If the pesticide application is to be made over the hives, if they are in the field to be treated by aircraft or the application is to be made to a field very near the hives, add a plastic sheet over the burlap to keep out dust, spray or fumes. Remove the plastic soon after the application and burn or bury it.

Confining the bees is harmful and they will probably become very agitated. Be prepared with plenty of smoke when removing the entrance screens.

3. If the application is made when the bees are working, the use of pollen traps can minimize the danger of contaminated pollen being stored in the hive. If contaminated pollen has been collected the combs should be destroyed to get rid of the poison.

Classification of Pesticides

Very toxic pesticides, many with residual action. These compounds are hazardous to bees at any time.

Insecticides

aldicarb
arsenate of lead
azinphos-methyl
carbaryl
carbofuran
chlordane
chlorpyrifos
cypermethrine

decamethrine
diazinon
dimethoate
fenvalerate
lindane
malathion
methamidophos
methadithion

methomyl
mevinphos
naled
parathion
permethrine
phosmet
tetrachlorvinphos

Moderately toxic pesticides

Insecticides

disulfoton
endosulfan
phorate

formethanate
methyl-oxydemeton
DNOC (fungicide)

phosalone
phonophos

Relatively non-toxic to bees

Insecticides and Acaricides

B. thuringiensis
chinomethionate
chlorvinphos
cyhexatin

dicofol
ethion
fenbutatine
nicotine

propargite
pirimicarb
rotenone
trichlorfon

Fungicides

anilazine
benomyl
captafol
carbathine
chloronebe
chlorthalonil
fixed copper
dichlone

dichloran
dinocap
dodine
fenaminosulf
ferbam
folpet
mancozebe
metaloxyle

metirame
sulphur
copper sulphate
thiabendazole
methyl-thiophanate
thiram
zineb

11

REFERENCES

Atkins, E.L., E.A. Greywood, and R.L. MacDonald. 1973. Toxicity of pesticides and other agricultural chemicals to honey bees. Univ. Calif. Div. Agric. Sci. Leaflet 2287.

Atkins, E.L., D. Kellum and K.J. Neuman. 1975. Toxicity of pesticides to honey bees. Univ. Calif. Div. Agric. Sci. Leaflet 2386.

Atkins, E.L., D. Kellum, and K.W. Atkins. 1981. Reducing pesticide hazards to honey bees. Univ. Calif. Div. Agric. Sci. Leaflet 2883

Burke. P.W. 1981. Bee diseases and pests of the apiary. Ontario Ministry Agr. Food no. 429; 25 pp. [reprint, 1981]

Cantwell, G.E. and H. Shimanuki, 1969. Heat Treatment As a Means of Eliminating Nosema and Increasing Production. Am. Bee J. 109: 52-54.

Clark, K. 1989. Menthol as a Control for Tracheal Mites ? Bee sCene (British Columbia) 5 (3):9, 17, 20.

Dixon, D., S.C. Jay, G. Otis and M.W, Winston (Eds.) 1987. Honey Bee Diseases and Pests. Publ. Can. Assoc. Prof. Apiculturists, 17 pp.

King, A. 1985. Why do Wild Honeybee Colonies Survive Without Drugs ? Can Beek. 12: 116.

Knepp, T.H. 1987. Build a Bear Fence. Gleanings Bee Cult. 115: 400-405.

Leudi, M. 1989. New Varroa Lure Could Hold the Key to Nonacaricide Mite Control in Hives ? Amer. Bee J. 129 (10): 637.

Murrell, D. 1989. Chemicals in Beekeeping. Bee sCene (British Columbia) 5 (3) : 11, 15.

Perron, J.-M. et V.R. Vickery. 1988. L'abeille et les pesticides. Govt. Québec. Cons. Prod. Veget. Québec publ.; 16 pages.

Scott-Dupree, C. 1987. Wax Moths: Pests to contend with. Can. Beek. 13 (4): 86-87.

Shimanuki, H. 1971. Brood Diseases of Honey Bees. pp. 86-96, *In* McGregor, S.E., Beekeeping in the United States. Agr. Hndbk, U.S. Dept. Agr., Agr. Res. Serv. No. 335, 137 pp.

Vickery, V.R. 1979. Control of Honeybee Diseases in Quebec. Macdonald J. 40 (4): 4.

THE "AFRICAN BEE" PROBLEM

The African Bee in Africa

Subsaharan honeybees, those found in Africa between the Sahara and Kalahari Deserts have been the honey producers for the peoples of the region for hundreds or even thousands of years. The history of the association of man and bee in this region has not been documented but is very likely to have been of longer standing than anywhere else.

Beekeeping was practised in a very primitive fashion, usually consisting of placing chunks of hollow logs high in the trees by means of vines looped over tree branches (Fig. 12.1). These would be occupied by swarms. Eventually, when honey or perhaps some other product was desired a smoke-producing fire was lit and the log was lowered to the ground. The bees were stupified by smoke. The contents of the log were scooped out and crushed to kill the bees and to break the cappings on the honey combs. Another method of killing the bees was to immerse the entire hive in boiling water. Sometimes the honey was strained out but more often than not, the resulting mixture of ripened and unripe honey, dead bees and parts of bees and brood of all stages, was left for a few days to ferment. At the proper time, the resulting rather potent liquid would be consumed. This procedure was often carried out to provide liquid refreshment at times of celebrations. The treatment by the 'bee-ravagers', and the bird known as the "Honey Guide", eventually produced a subspecies *Apis mellifera*

Fig 12.1:
Log hives in a tree, Faranah, Republic of Guinea, May, 1988. (Photo by Hélène Chiasson).

scutellata, which is very prolific, swarms freely, may abscond, and is quite hostile. This bee is slightly smaller than the bees now used in North America and, although it builds the honey-comb cells slightly smaller than these other bees, it can use the combs built by the others and does so readily.

In Africa, beeswax, the primary product sold by the beekeepers, is exported at an annual rate of several thousand tonnes. Much of the world supply is produced in Tanzania and Angola. The honey, considered only as a by-product, is made into honey beer (Crane, 1975).

The reputation of these bees has become well known in other parts of the world. They have some desirable traits as well as the undesirable ones. Colony buildup is very rapid and the bees are fairly good foragers, working under conditions which would force other races of bees to beat a hasty retreat to the hive. However, their general efficiency is less than that of Italian bees. These factors, coupled with the generally low average production per colony of honey bees in Brazil, brought about the plan to make controlled crosses between the African bees and those kept in Brazil and nearby countries. These were mostly black bees from the Iberian peninsula of Europe, although many beekeepers were changing to Italian bees which, under their conditions, produce nearly twice as much honey as the black bees.

Brief History of the African Bees in the Americas

Seventy-six queen bees were imported from Africa into Brazil in 1956 by Dr. Warwick Kerr, a well known geneticist. He selected twenty-five of these queens to head colonies in various apiary locations around Sao Paulo and proceeded to make crosses with native bees, hoping to improve the nectar-gathering capacity of honey bees in Brazil.

Unfortunately, and in spite of precautions, swarms escaped from these hives and they found plenty of places to live in hollow trees. They built up rapidly and swarmed again and again. Then the alarm was sounded. Animals were found dead, stung to death by these bees. Then came reports of humans being killed by these very hostile bees. The bees, when swarming or absconding, would sting any living thing in the areas where the bees alighted. They seemed to sting without provocation and in tremendous numbers, when compared in similar circumstances with the more familiar Italian bees. The African bees also invaded beehives occupied by other bees. The queen of the colony and many bees were killed and the African queen became the mother of the colony. Virgin queens, whether these were produced by African colonies or by others, were likely to be mated by African drones. In a short time, there were African bees, Brazilian (or Africanized) bees, hybrids between the Africans and other races, and some of the original colonies. The latter were at risk and eventually were nearly exterminated.

At the same time, the bees began to increase their range and another factor, previously unknown, became apparent. Whether swarming or absconding the bees would travel a long distance. The territory occupied by these bees expanded at a rate probably exceeding 300 km per year. They pushed southward into Argentina (I saw wild colonies there in 1976) and Uruguay and westward to the Andes mountains. The greatest push was northward. Eventually they reached Venezuela, where I saw wild colonies in 1981. The forests were not safe for human travel, due to the numbers of feral colonies of these bees, now best known as Africanized, as a certain amount of hybridization has taken place. Hybrids or not, the bees have retained all of the worst traits of the African bees.

Many beekeepers gave up keeping bees and those who continued had to take such precautions when handling them as "double bee suits" and always with veils and gloves. The amount of honey produced in the areas occupied by the Africanized bees dropped to about one-tenth of the former production.

The rapid increase in distribution and the repeated reports of fatalities of wild and domesticated animals, as well as humans, earned the bees the appelation "Killer Bees". Certain people have tried to make a profit by producing scare movies, such as "The Swarm". In general, these movies contained many inaccuracies regarding bee behaviour. The general public may have been fooled but beekeepers were not.

As the bees extended their range it became clear that they were likely to continue their northward movement through Central America and Mexico and finally invade the southern tier of states of the U.S.A. Various barriers and efforts designed to halt the northward movement of the bees all failed. In November, 1984, they were reported in southern Nicaragua. The northern Mexican desert may prove to be a temporary barrier but the latest estimate for entrance into the United States is sometime in 1990.

Not only are Africanized drones superior to Italians and others in catching and mating queens but their genes are genetically dominant in many characteristics. In Brazil a massive program of requeening with imported mated Italian queens has caused dilution so that some of the African traits have been reduced. Some dilution is apparent in other parts of South America where beekeeping was well established. During the northward movement very few areas of intensive beekeeping were encountered by the bees, and very little if any dilution occurred; the bees still exhibited nearly pure "African" traits.

Drone semen of the African bee was brought into the united States more than 20 years ago. It was used to inseminate queens in the southern United States and queens bred from these crosses were released to commercial queen breeders for testing. Most of the colonies headed by these queens or their progeny were destroyed because of their hostile behaviour, but there were free-flying Africanized drones in the area around Baton Rouge, Louisiana, for four years, from 1960 to 1964 (Johansson, 1989).

An alfalfa pollination project used thousands of hybridized colonies (70 % African). No advantage was found and the project was discontinued. Some hybrid queens, however, were used to head colonies tested for pollen collection in California (Johansson, 1989).

It is obvious that the genes of the African bee are widespread in the United States due to migratory beekeeping and sales of package bees. It is probable that some winter failures in northern areas may be due to African contamination. I have had several colonies in recent years that exhibited a higher degree of hostility than is expected from 'normal' Italian bees.

Johansson (1989) listed eleven characteristics of the Africanized bees. They bear repeating here: 1) Failure to cluster; 2) Excessive swarming; 3) Excessive absconding (entire colony deserts the hive); 4) Unrestricted nesting sites (a large cavity for storage of honey for winter in not required); 5) Queen parasitism (small African swarms take over colonies of European bees; 6) Amalgamation (colonies lacking food may enter the nest of another colony); 7) Drone advantage (large populations of drones dominate queen mating); 8) Nervousness ("frenetic" behaviour makes colony manipulations difficult); 9) Robbing (Africanized bees are attracted to other hives when these are opened and excite the colony so much that it becomes unmanageable); 10) Excessively defensive (not agressive when foraging but in nest defense may follow intruders (beekeepers) up to two miles); 11) They fly directly into hive entrances (they do not land outside the hive like European bees do).

In 1984 a ship, carrying a swarm of these bees which also were carrying *Varroa* mites, sailed up the St. Lawrence River and through the seaway. The bees were discovered and destroyed in an American lake port. The identification of the bees was made easy by the fact that they carried *Varroa* mites as these mites were not known to be present at that time in Canada or the United States. Other ships have been found carrying swarms of these bees in ports on the Gulf of Mexico, in Baltimore, Maryland and as far away as Liverpool, England.

A colony which was located in California in July, 1984, apparently did not have *Varroa* mites. There was, however, no doubt as to the identity of the bees (Otis, 1985). The colony was destroyed and in the area around for a distance of 50 miles (80 km) all wild colonies were searched out and destroyed because at least one swarm had escaped from the original colony. This colony had built its combs in an underground cavity. A second wild colony of Africanized bees was found in a tree stump and was destroyed. A hive in a commercial apiary was also determined to have been taken over by Africanized bees (Garelik,1985).

Otis (1985) correctly pointed out that as dilution of the Africanized genes would be rapid, there being a much greater probability that any virgin queen would be mated by bees of European origin, that this single introduction could not have much effect on the industry. When the bees spread into the region the result will be quite different.

Area of Probable Occupation in North America

Based upon the southern limit reached by the bees in Argentina, it was postulated that they could occupy and survive in all of the southernmost American states, Florida, Georgia, part of South Carolina, Alabama, Mississippi, Louisiana and part of Arkansas, Texas, possibly part of Oklahoma, New Mexico, Arizona, southern Utah, southern California and southern Nevada. The northern limit will be approximately at the 34th parallel of latitude (Taylor, 1977). The Africanized bees could survive in parts of the above states although there are higher altitude locations where they could not survive winters. Another trait of the Africanized bees, as they developed and lived for thousands of years in the tropics, is that they do not form clusters in cold weather like the Italian bees and others do. Under adverse conditions they abscond, deserting the old nest and even small amounts of brood carrying as much honey as they can, and migrate for long distances in search of conditions in which they could survive. As they do not form clusters they cannot survive in areas when winter temperatures force other races of bees to cluster.

Significance for Canadian beekeepers

I outlined the probable consequences for beekeepers in Canada in 1985 (Vickery, 1985). It is clear that the Africanized bees could not survive winter in any part of Canada or even in the northern half of the United States. This fact does not solve the problem but accentuates it. The bees will survive in the states which have traditionaly supplied many thousands of potential colonies in the form of "package bees" as well as queen bees to Canadian beekeepers. If we are forced to use Africanized package bees in Canadian apiaries, many beekeepers would quit keeping bees, as has happened in other countries through which these bees have passed. If we rely on package bees in the future we would have to replace all of the colonies each year with packages of hostile Africanized bees.

If the Africanized bees are kept in Canadian apiaries, there is no reason to believe that they would stay in the hives and perish with the onset of cold weather. The colonies would probably abscond and fly almost anywhere. Such an event could produce many fatalities, humans as well as other animals, as the bees attacked indiscriminately over a very wide geographical range. Rather than risk such circumstances, all possible precautions must be taken to keep Canada free of Africanized bees or bees carrying any Africanized genetic material.

It is perhaps probable that some hybridized Africanized - Italian honey bees could cluster and perhaps survive our winters. This possibility cannot be determined until trials are carried out with various crosses and this is not likely to happen until the threat is much closer than it is now.

An additonal complication is that the Africanized bees in Mexico and Central America are known to be carrying parasitic mites, *Varroa jacobsoni*, with them. At the time of writing (October, 1988) this mite is not known to be established in Canada although it has recently been found in the United States. The depredations of the mite are well known (See *Varroa* in Chapter 11). The present embargo on importing bees from any area where the mite becomes established will probably prevent or slow the advance into Canada but is unlikely to keep the mites bees out of this country permanently.

Levin (1983) stated that the value of crops pollinated by honey bees in the United States was almost 19 billion dollars annually. I have given a figure of 1.5 billion dollars as the annual value of pollination in Canada (Vickery, 1985). Wherever the Africanized bees have invaded, the number of beekeepers and number of colonies maintained by each beekeeper have shown drastic reduction. Rinderer (1982) stated that the honey crop in Venezuela decreased by 80 per cent. after the Africanized bees arrived there and that many beekeepers went out of business.

It seems certain that crop pollination can be seriously affected and this fact may be the most important of all in areas where the Africanized bees become dominant. Pesticide applications in many crops has seriously affected native pollinator populations, leaving honey bees as the essential tools in pollination. If Africanized bees, with their lower foraging effeciency, are established in the southern United States, pollination on the entire continent will be at risk. Even if a Canadian emargo prohibits bees from the United States from entering Canada, once the Africanized bees are in the southern states, practices such as shipments of package bees and queens, as well as migratory beekeeping would spread these bees all over the United States in a very short time. Without an embargo the Canadian situation would be hopeless. Some Canadian beekeepers, myself included, have been recommending for a decade that the beekeeping industry in Canada should become self-sufficient in bees as soon as possible. In order to do this it is necessary to winter all of the colonies that are worth wintering. Winter losses can be made up from the surviving colonies each spring.

Rather than production of bees to be sold by weight in packages, some apiarists have begun producing and selling nucleus colonies, formed in the spring. Nucleus colonies have a definite advantage in spring buildup as compared with colonies established from package bees. This trend should continue, with a number of apiarists concentrating on production of nuclei rather than a honey crop. I produced nucleus colonies for sale in the spring in Quebec, from outside-wintered colonies, beginning in 1974, just to prove that it could be done. Making up early spring nuclei did not cause noticeable decrease in the honey crop and it did help to prevent swarming.

The greatest problem with making up nuclei in eastern Canada early in the spring (preferably by May 1st) is that we cannot rear queen bees and have them mated before mid-May as we would not have sufficient numbers of spring-raised drones of mating age. This problem could be overcome by importing queens, so long as we have a source which is not covered by an embargo. The southern United States has supplied early reared queens in the past but this source has now been cut off. We do not want queens with Africanized genes, nor do we want bees carrying mites, either *Varroa* or the Tracheal Mite or both. This leaves New Zealand and possibly Australia as sources of queens, together with British Columbia if their production of early queens is sufficient to meet the demand.

Another way in which Canadian beekeepers can produce more colonies for sale is to make up the nucleus colonies following the main summer "honey flow", winter them and of-

12

fer them for sale in the spring. This was advised by Gruszka (1985). I have wintered 4-frame nucleus colonies successfully in Quebec on top of four and eight-colony winter packs (see Wintering, Chapter 13). The nucleus colonies were made up early in August and each was given one of a batch of queens reared from one of the best colonies in the apiary. They were fed in late September with sugar syrup containing fumagillin. One year, in October, the nucs were used in a greenhouse pollination trial on red clover for two weeks. Shortly after mid-November they were packed for winter. They were unpacked and fed during the first week of April and then once again they were caged on greenhouse benches for pollination. In spite of the losses of bees each time in the greenhouse, the colonies built up well. By mid-May each one had two brood-chamber supers. Without exception they produced good crops of surplus honey up to a maximum of 63.6 kg (140 lbs.).

Similar nucleus colonies were wintered for five successive years and on a larger scale. The only nucleus colonies that were lost overwinter (two of 80) had starved. Four-frame nucs require at least 6.5 kg (14 to 15 lbs.) of stores in order to winter successfully. Nucleus colonies like these can produce more honey than nucleus colonies formed in the spring and the problem of finding mated queens early in the spring is avoided. There is seldom a problem finding a source of queens in the summer. There is little doubt that nucleus colonies can be wintered in modern wintering facilities. They can also be wintered outside if certain procedures and methods are followed.

"A total embargo on (importation of foreign package bees into Canada) might not be so bad after all. Instead of an out-flow of hundreds of thousands of dollars for package bees (average $30 -$40 each), the money will remain in the country and will therefore help to boost our own beekeeping industry" (Vickery, 1985). ❏

REFERENCES

Crane, E.,1975. The World's Beekeeping - Past and Present. Chapter 1, pp. 1-18, *in* Dadant and Sons (Eds.) *The Hive and the Honey Bee*. Hamilton Illinois, U.S.A. Dadant and Sons.

Garelik, C. l985. The Killers. Discover 6 (10): 108-111; 114-115.

Gruszka, J. 1985. Making Nucs for Wintering. Can. Beek. 12 (5): 103.

Johansson, T. 1989. The Africanized Bee. Apic *sic* mellifera scutellata (formerly adansoni). Can. Beek. 14 (8): 186-187.

Levin,M. 1983. Value of Bee Pollination to U.S. Agriculture. Bull. ent. Soc. Amer. (Winter, 1983), pp. 50-51.

Otis, G. 1985. African bees found in California. Can. Beek. 12(5): 111-112.

Rinderer, T.E. 1982. Behavioral genetic analysis of colony-defense by honey bees. Pp. 249-254 *in* P. Jason (Ed.), Social Insects in the Tropics. Université Paris Nord 13 (1).

Taylor, O.R. 1977. The past and possible future spread of Africanized honey bees in the Americas. Bee World 58 (1): 19-30.

Vickery, V.R. 1985. The Current Status of Beekeeping in Canada. Macdonald J. (Ste-Anne-de-Bellevue, Que.) 46 (3): 36-37.

FALL MANAGEMENT AND WINTERING BEES

The Winter Cluster

It is usually considered that a population of 30,000 to 40,000 bees is necessary for winter survival. In temperate climates, honey bees have developed a remarkable method of withstanding cold temperatures. A single bee is able to function at a temperature of 6.1 degrees C (43 F.), but below that it loses the ability to move and soon perishes. Many bees together form a cluster when the lowest temperature among the bees approaches 14 degrees C. As outside temperature decreases the cluster contracts until all of the bees are involved and at 6 - 8 degrees C a shell or insulating layer of bees 2.5 to 7.6 cm thick is formed (Fig. 13.1). Bees crawl into any empty cells within the shell and crowd together in the spaces between the combs (Moeller, 1977). Bees in the shell are not very active but they do rotate positions slowly so that any single bee does not stay long enough on the outer periphery to become chilled and fall from the cluster. Inside the cluster are fewer bees but these bees are much more active. They consume honey and generate heat by vibrating the wing muscles, probably without moving the wings. Bees in the warm interior of the cluster pass honey to those on the outside.

At the beginning of winter the cluster usually forms over the lower part of the honey and pollen stores. They move upward as winter progresses. The cluster is usually in the form of an ellipse but is capable of movement, especially when ambient temperature increases. The

Fig 13.1:
The winter
cluster early in
winter.

13

temperatures in different parts of the cluster are about 6.7 degrees C on the outside of the cluster, 12.8 to 13.3 degrees C in the shell and at least 24.4 degrees C in the centre. During broodless periods (mid-October to late January) maximum temperatures in the heat-generating area fluctuate between 26.4 and 35.5 degrees C. Brood rearing usually starts in outside-wintered colonies early in February as a response to increasing day length. Then the interior of the cluster is maintained at 33.9 to 34.5 degrees C.

The cluster size changes in response to fluctuations in external temperatures. In spite of the sometimes rapid and extensive changes in external temperature the bees continue to generate enough heat to maintain the outer limits of the shell at about 7 degrees C. When the ambient temperature drops below 7 degrees C the bees contract the cluster to reduce the surface area from which heat is radiated and lost. At the same time, bees in the centre of the cluster become more active to generate more heat. If the external temperature rises above 7 degrees C the cluster is expanded. There is always a balance between cluster size, the thickness of the insulating shell and the amount of heat generated in the centre of the cluster. According to Betts (1943) honey bees use their stored food most efficiently at 7 degrees C and actually consume less than expected.

A cluster of bees can withstand long periods of cold weather if they have access to enough honey so that they can continue to generate heat. A colony that was placed in a refrigerated room, at average temperature of -24.2 C for 84 days, maintained a minimum temperature of 27 degrees C in the centre of the cluster for the entire period (Owens, 1971).

Cold starvation can and does kill honey bee colonies (Greve, 1973). The cluster can move vertically or horizontally on the combs but this movement is very slow and takes place mainly, if not entirely, during warmer periods. Prolonged cold weather can prevent movement from comb to comb and cold starvation can occur, even with plenty of honey stored in combs that the bees are unable to reach. A single warm day, with temperature near or above freezing, may be enough to allow the bees to move to honey stores which previously had not been available to them.

Honey which granulates quickly, even in the cells, constitutes another hazard for clustered bees in winter. I have seen many hives in the spring in which the bees had starved to death because they were unable to use the granulated honey.

Colony Requirements for Wintering

Wintering success is dependent upon three essential requirements: a) colonies in the fall must be strong and disease-free with a high proportion of young bees and a productive queen; b) plenty of stored food (honey and pollen) strategically placed so that it will be available to the bees during the winter; c) some sort of protection which provides a barrier to wind but allows for ventilation (Karmo, 1958).

The Colony

It is not always advisable to try to winter every colony. Those that meet the first of the above requirements should be noted during a colony check in August. A weak colony can be united with another colony, particularly another weak colony, if one of them has a young prolific queen. The poorer queen should be removed, then one hive is placed on top of the other, separated by a single sheet of newspaper. It is better to destroy weak colonies with mediocre or poor queens than to try to winter them. It is better and cheaper to take such losses in the fall than to feed them and hope they will survive. A small population can cluster over only a small area of stored honey and is much less able to move than is a large cluster. Cold weather, for several weeks may mean cold starvation for weak colonies. There is also the possibility that, in a weak colony, the queen is not as prolific as she should be and she may fail during the winter resulting in the death of the colony.

It is essential that a colony to be wintered is free of brood diseases. All colonies should be checked for such problems after the removal of the honey crop and before cessation of brood-rearing in the fall. Diseased colonies frequently die early in the spring as they are not able to build up. Bees from other colonies rob the remaining honey stores and the disease is spread to these colonies.

Nosema disease of adult bees is caused by an intestinal parasite. It is very common in North America. The level of disease in a colony builds up during the winter and can cause spring dwindling rather than population increase. Nosema can also affect queens and if the queen of a colony dies during the winter the colony usually dies too because there are no bees to replace those that are lost by normal mortality at that time of year.

Fall feeding

Fall feeding can make the difference between successful wintering and disaster. The sugar syrup is made into winter stores by the bees and is stored in the cells which are vacated by emerging brood. This places the food supply in the winter cluster where it will be available to the bees. Ideally the syrup is made of two parts sugar to one part water by weight. Only syrup made with sucrose should be fed to honey bees. Some preparations, containing higher sugars, should not be used. In general the commercial preparations with high sugar content based upon sucrose are quite satisfactory.

Feeding syrup is the ideal way to provide protection from *Nosema* disease by addition of fumagillin to the syrup. The antibiotic protects bees by killing the protozoan parasite in the gut before it can cause injury. The dosage which will provide effective control is a rounded teaspoonful of fumagillin (Fumadil-B, No Ceema Tm Fix, or other trade name) for each four litres of sugar syrup. If I use commercially prepared syrup I prefer to add the fumagillin myself, even if the commercial syrup can be purchased with "drugs" added.

A total of 18 kg (40 lbs.) of stored honey (part of which is from sugar syrup) was found to be necessary for wintering a colony in a single brood chamber in Nova Scotia (Karmo, 1958). This referred to outside wintering and in a multiple colony pack. This method is quite satisfactory for Nova Scotia, Prince Edward Island and most of New Brunswick. In Quebec, Ontario and northern New Brunswick, as well as in New York and the New England states, colonies are most often wintered outside in double brood chamber hives. Thirty-two kilograms (70 lbs.) is considered to be adequate for these colonies. The total weight of these hives, with bees and stored food, should exceed 50 kg (110 lbs).

Feeding may be done in various ways. Cans or plastic buckets inverted over a hole in an inner cover are used by many beekeepers. The cans (with friction top lids) have numerous small holes in the lids, easily made with the tip of a sharp nail, in order for the bees to take the syrup and without the danger of the syrup leaking. The pails usually have plastic lids with an area of very fine screen through which the bees get the food. I do not like 'Boardman' (entrance) feeders or 'Division board'(frame type) feeders at this time of year. The syrup in the entrance feeder gets cold and in cold weather the bees do not come to the entrance to get it. In addition the capacity of the entrance feeder is small, requiring many refills.

The "Division-board" feeders also lack capacity and require refilling. I use a piece of screen in these feeders for the bees to cling to but even with the screen, many bees are caught and die in the syrup. Many more can be killed when refilling the unit as there always seem to be many bees inside.

13

Fig 13.2: Modified tray feeder, screen cover replacing the original metal and wood cover.

Fig 13.3: Unmodified tray feeder with dead bees.

I use trays mainly because of the ease of feeding and the fact that the syrup in the tray is kept warm by heat from the bees below. Also the capacity can be large enough so that the entire requirement can be given a colony at one time. The commercial tray feeder sold in eastern Canada is the "Miller" type with a central structure enabling the bees to reach the syrup and return with it to the combs below. I have modified this type by removing the wood and metal box over the central bee-way and replacing it with one made of screen (see Fig. 13.2). This prevents bees getting out of the box and becoming stuck and dying in the syrup (Fig. 13.3). The tray feeder that I have developed has the bee-way extending from the front to the middle. This feeder has proved to be very efficient.

In some areas of northeastern North America there is heavy production of honey in the fall, while in other areas this flow does not occur. Feeding the bees makes up the deficit when no fall honey is stored. When much fall honey is made it is nearly always derived from nectar from goldenrod and aster. The aster honey, in particular, is low in levulose sugar and tends to granulate quickly, even in the cells of the combs. The bees are able to use only miniscule quantities of granulated honey in the winter and do not use it to much extent at any time. Even if this fall honey is not granulated, it is not the best winter food for the bees as it can cause dysentery and possible death of the colony (Levac *et al.*,1981). The fall feeding of sugar syrup provides food which will remain liquid throughout the winter. I have frequently found it necessary to remove three or four combs full of honey from the middle of the upper brood super, replacing them with empty combs before feeding, to ensure that the syrup-honey will be where it is most needed. Feeding should be completed by mid-October so that the bees will have time to invert the sugars, eliminate water and store the syrup (Duffy and Vickery, 1982).

In order to rear brood the nurse bees must consume pollen before their hypopharyngeal glands can begin to secrete the protein-rich "royal jelly" or "bee milk" which is fed to the newly hatched larvae. This pollen must be available to the bees in those combs which are inside the winter cluster. Brood rearing in outside-wintered colonies usually begins early in February. Aster provides abundant pollen in the fall and if the weather is suitable so that the bees can gather it, they may be able to fill the equivalent of about three combs. If the weather is bad there may be a shortage of pollen in the hive. In my experience the bees very early in spring cease rearing brood two years out of three due to exhausted supply of pollen. I use pollen traps to gather bee collected pollen periodically during the summer and feed each colony a good-sized pollen pattie in the fall on waxed paper on top of the combs before placing on and filling the tray feeder.

It is necessary to have new bees produced in order to replace the heavy winter mortality. Farrar (1936) concluded that the number of bees in a colony in the spring when new pollen becomes available is nearly proportional to the pollen reserves stored in the combs in the fall.

Ventilation

When honey is consumed by bees in winter, to enable them to produce heat, two metabolic by-products are also produced, carbon dioxide and water. More colonies are lost each year due to moisture problems than to cold temperatures. About one litre of water is produced for each kilogram of honey consumed by the bees. If this moisture does not escape, it can condense on the cold walls, the inner cover, the combs or can even drip onto the cluster of bees. Bees on the outside of the cluster are killed and gradually the population declines. Any ice which may have accumulated on the inner cover can melt during a thaw or even because of heat escaping from the cluster. This will soon kill the entire population.

Some provision must be made to allow the moisture to escape. A preferred method is an upper entrance made by cutting a notch 5 or 6 cm long and 0.8 cm deep in the rim of the inner cover. (That's about 2 inches by 1/4 inch if you still use the old measure). During the summer months the notch is in the top side. In the fall, after feeding, the inner cover is turned over and the notch provides an adequate upper entrance. This allows the moisture, as well as the carbon dioxide, to escape and the bees are able to fly on sunny days. The inner covers (Fig. 13.4) have a large double-screened area in the centre which also improves ventilation. Bland (1977) stressed the importance of providing for removal of the carbon dioxide from the hive as, without upper ventilation, the cluster will be pushed downward in the hive away from the food stores above.

Some beekeepers advocate drilling an auger hole, 2 to 2.5 cm (3/8 to 1 inch) in diameter, through the front of the upper brood super. It is more efficient to remove the moisture and gas as high in the super as possible, which is the reason for the preference for the rim-slot upper entrance. I have on occasion lifted a super in which the beekeeper, that I was assisting, had drilled the hole in the middle of the hand-hold. My middle finger went right through the hole and got six stings before I could put the super down. So much for holes in supers!

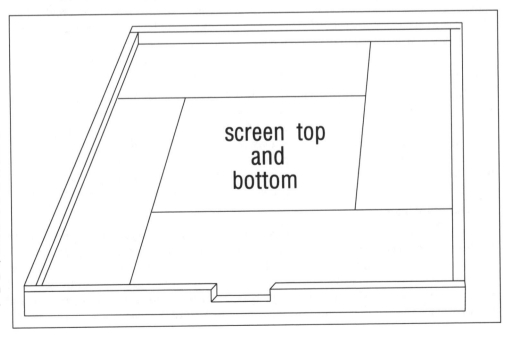

Fig 13.4: Inner cover with rim slot: can be used with rim slot downward as upper entrance in winter, with rim slot upward and non functional in summer, or as bottom board for upper colony in double queen system.

Even in other places, they can provide another exit for hostile guard bees when least expected by the beekeeper.

Wintering the Bees

Wintering in Buildings

Beekeepers that keep many colonies, particularly those who have beekeeping as their main occupation, prefer to have as many factors as possible under personal control. When wintering is considered this usually means a building that offers considerable winter protection.

Many beekeepers carry their hives to buildings and suppose this is adequate for wintering. I have seen some facilities in which the hives were set on an earthen floor. Unless the building is designed or adapted so that the temperature is nearly constant at about 4 degrees C (39 degrees F), and provides adequate ventilation, the only protection provided is from wind and possibly has less temperature fluctuation by about 2 or 3 degrees C. Inside the building the bees do not get the benefit of heating by the sun on bright days, which is often enough to allow cluster movement. It is my personal belief that the bees are better wintered outside unless the building is so designed for the purpose of wintering bees.

Maintaining a constant temperature plus or minus about 1.5 degrees C requires sources of both heat and cold; in other words there must be a furnace and refrigeration. In a well insulated building, an essential requirement to keep the cost at a reasonable level and where ventilation is adequate, a large number of colonies can be stored satisfactorily. The ventilation system should move 2.5 litres of air per second per hive stored (Levac *et al.* 1981). Each colony is producing carbon dioxide and water and the quantities produced by many colonies in a restricted space is considerable. The suggested rate should allow maintenance of relative humidity of 50 to 60 percent. Low relative humidity can cause dessication of young larvae in open cells.

When placing hives in winter storage there should be a space of 15 to 20 cm (6 to 8 inches) between the hives and any wall. The lowest hives should be supported 15 to 20 cm above the floor on solid support that allows free air movement underneath them. A similar space should be allowed between rows of hives. The hives can be stacked three high, provided that allowance is made for ventilation between the cover of a lower hive and the bottom board of the hive above it. The rear of the bottom boards of hives nearest the floor can be raised about 5 cm (2 inches) to allow circulation, if the hive is not placed upon a base as mentioned above. The room is kept in darkness throughout the storage period.

The temperature must be maintained below 6.7 degrees C (approx. 43 degrees F), usually from + 2 to 0 degrees C, in order to keep the bees clustered. This temperature will allow cluster movement. If the temperature rises above 6.7 degrees C the bees may become active and begin crawling out of the hive entrances, over the floor, on the outsides of the hives and and up the walls. Beekeepers who have kept bees in buildings without refrigeration have sometimes been forced to move the hives out of the buildings in March because they could not keep the temperature low enough, and the colonies were hurt by subsequent very cold periods.

Outside Wintering

It is generally agreed that honey bees wintered outside in Canada and in much of the northern United States require some degree of winter protection. There are many examples of colony survival with no protection at all. During many of the past 15 years I have deliberately left some hives without any protection except for the windbreak of small trees. All of these colonies survived if they had enough bees, a young queen, plenty of stores, and had been fed the antibiotic fumagillin to protect the bees against *Nosema* disease. This merely shows what the bees can do. There is, however, no disputing that, on average, colonies that have winter protection are stronger in the spring and develop into better producing colonies.

Many bees will die over the winter period. Any bees that had been foragers in the fall will not survive very long after the the hives are set up for winter. The older bees cannot last until spring and their demise means that the stores last longer. More bees will continue to die throughout the winter. On bright sunny days some bees will leave the hives for cleansing flights, even though the temperature may be well below freezing. They soon become chilled, unable to fly and fall to the snow and perish. These are usually the older bees as they have retained feces for a longer time than the younger bees and the cleansing flight is more urgent. The snow around the apiary may be liberally spotted with dead bees at times. Novice beekeepers may be perturbed at this mortality but it is a normal occurrence. Every winter I receive calls from new beekeepers who have seen "all of those dead bees on the snow". When brood rearing begins, the dead bees soon will be replaced. Brood rearing requires many nurse bees. In strong colonies there will be plenty of bees for this task while weak colonies may fail and perish due to their inability to replace the winter losses.

Insulation

The use of insulation has been somewhat controversial. Early in this century beekeepers packed their hives with as much insulation as possible. Often this was in the form of an outer box with several inches of sawdust packed beteen the hive and the box. We now know that over-protection is not beneficial and can increase moisture problems. Moderate use of insulation has been shown to be useful (Farrar,1944, 1952; Braun and Geiger, 1955; Owens, 1951). The bees make no attempt to heat the entire hive so the insulation has very little effect on the cluster, except when sudden changes in outside temperature occur. When a sudden drop occurs, the insulation allows the cluster to contract gradually and to better organize its position in relation to food stores. Rapid contraction usually leaves some bees stranded and these bees soon perish. Slow contraction allows them to move with the cluster. Insulation will cause a slight decrease in food consumption.

Too much insulation prevents response to warm external temperatures and does not allow the bees to shift position on the food stores or to take cleansing flights. Insulation all around colonies is practiced in western Canada in a four-colony pack (Braun and Geiger, 1955; Bland, 1977; Peer, 1978). I have insulated the tops with good results but only rarely have used insulation of the sides of the hives.

Time of packing

In eastern Canada the optimum time for packing the bee hives for winter is about mid-November. Earlier packing may stimulate the bees to begin brood rearing. If this happens the stored food will be used at a much more rapid rate and the colony may run out of food before spring. Food consumption during the broodless period is very low, only one to three pounds (0.45 to 1.36kg) per month. Karmo (1975) reported that consumption of food is much greater when brood is being reared and may exceed one-half pound (0.22kg) per day or 15 pounds (6.8 kg) per month as brood-rearing is accelerated in early spring.

Single Colony Packs

Black cardboard wintering cases are produced commercially and are generally available. The case consists of a double-fluted cardboard sleeve, stapled on the seam, painted black on the outside and waterproofed with wax at the bottom edge. The top consists of four flaps which are folded over the top of the hive or above insulation placed above the inner cover (I prefer 2 inch (5 cm) thick styrofoam). The sleeve which is constructed to fit a two super standard hive, fits the hive very closely (Fig. 13.5). The outer cover is placed on the top and is

13

Fig 13.5: Hive packed singly in cardboard sleeve, with green wind deflector over upper entrance.

Fig 13.6: Three hives packed singly with slats nailed on at the upper entrances.

weighted with rocks or bricks or is tied down by means of cord from the hive stand on one side, over the top and fastened to the hive stand on the other side. A hole must be cut in the case at the upper entrance and wood cleats (or a wind deflector - see later) should be nailed on to hold the case tight against the hive. If this is not done, bees will come out the entrance and can become trapped between the case and the hive (Fig.13.6). This pack usually gives good results. The main drawback is the very slow rate at which the cluster is able to move to un-tapped food supplies. The cases can be used more than once if they are stored carefully during the summer. A similar case, made of plastic, had been available but is not as good as the cardboard case.

A popular variation of this method is the use of light weight black building paper to wrap around the hive. This wrap produces results about the same as the "sleeve" pack. Slats should be used in strategic places to hold the paper close to the hive and to prevent its being torn and stripped away by wind.

Multiple Colony Packs

When colonies are packed together they have fewer walls exposed to external conditions. The heat produced by one colony will assist in heating others. The winter cluster is usually less compact and is able to move more easily to make use of food stored anywhere in the hive.

Row packing

This is a labour-saving method used by some commercial beekeepers. Many colonies are placed tightly together side by side. Building paper is fastened at one corner by nailing on a wooden slat, then is wrapped around the entire row. It is held tight by wooden slats. Insulation can be placed on top of the hives and the building paper is folded flat over it. A length of building paper is placed on top and folded down over the front and back of the row, making the pack waterproof. An upper entrance must be provided for each colony as the lower entrances usually become blocked by snow. The use of wind deflectors over the entrances is advisable.

Packing in blocks

There are many variations of block packing but all are designed to provide economy of heating. Blocks consists of four colonies or packs of multiples of four colonies. Labour involved in this method is somewhat greater but generally results in excellent spring buildup.

The labour is significantly less than moving the hives to indoor wintering facilities. There are two methods commonly used in Canadian apiaries.

Western Four-colony Pack

This method is commonly used in the prairie provinces (Bland, 1977; Peer, 1978). It is somewhat similar to the method developed by Karmo (1958, 1975) in Nova Scotia. In October the colonies are placed in blocks of four facing east and west. The blocks are wrapped in precut, two-inch fiberglass rolled insulation, with the vapour barrier on the outside. This is held in place with twine or cord. Four inches of insulation is placed on the top above the inner covers and the block is then wrapped with building paper. The paper is folded over at the top and a 44 inch (112 cm) square of 5/16 inch (8 mm) plywood is placed on the top. Baler twine is tied around the sides and over the top to secure the plywood and to bend it into a slightly rounded shape, highest at the middle. Holes are cut through at the upper entrances (these are usually precut) and a piece of plywood with a 4 x 3/4 inch (10 x 2 cm) slot is nailed over each entrance.

This method was used by Duffy and Vickery (1981, 1982) in Quebec but with a different type of cover (Fig. 13.7), the type described later under Multiple colony blocks. The colonies passed the winter very well and all of them were very strong in the spring. There was a problem of ice buildup in the entrances which had to be cleared periodically. The use of wind deflectors over the entrances should solve the problem.

Multiple-colony Blocks

The technique used in Nova Scotia, uses colonies in single brood supers, in multiples of four. Four colonies are placed on a solid base, facing east and west, and tiers of other colonies are added on top, making blocks of eight, twelve, sixteen, twenty or twenty-four colonies. The blocks that I have set up in Quebec have the four bottom colonies of the blocks in double brood chambers (Vickery, 1977) (Fig. 13.8). Earlier trials showed that bottom colonies in single brood chambers either perished or were very poor in spring in southwestern Quebec.

Fig 13.7: The "Don Peer" western winter pack, 4 hives but with insulated cover.

13

The base used to support the blocks is built of a frame of 2 x 4 inch (5 x 10 cm) lumber 40 x 33 1/4 inches (101.6 x 84.5 cm), that is twice the length and twice the width of a super, covered top and bottom by 1/2 inch (1.27 cm) plywood. This is treated with a wood preservative (pentachlorophenol, not creosote). All hives must have "short" bottom boards, that is bottom boards of the same external dimensions as a super. This allows tight wrapping of the entire block, which would be impossible with longer bottom boards.

Although the lower colonies are in double brood chambers, we have found no advantage in having the hives placed in the tiers above the lower one in more than a single brood super. All lower colonies are provided with upper entrances. If colonies in double brood chambers are used for the second tier they could have both upper and lower entrances, although I have wintered colonies in two supers in the second tier with only an upper entrance and with good results. Colonies in single super hives do not need an upper entrance. The number of tiers is limited only by the height of the stack, the efficiency of the barrier protecting the apiary site from wind, and the ability of the beekeeper to put the highest hives in place (see Fig. 13.9).

Wind will influence a high stack more than a lower one. We have used blocks of eight amd twelve hives routinely with excellent results. Hives above the lower tier, on the south side can have entrances facing south. It is a simple matter to equip these hives with bottom boards with the entrance on the side (Fig. 13.10). All hives are packed without the outer covers. The bottom board of an upper hive is placed directly on top of the inner cover of a hive in the next lower tier. Hive entrances should face east, west or south but, if possible, avoiding north. After stacking the hives the entire block is wrapped with black building paper secured by wooden slats. All entrances are opened by cutting through the building paper. The problem of locating the entrances can be solved before wrapping by driving a small nail about 2 cm (1 inch or slightly less) above the middle of each entrance, leaving about 2 cm of the nail protruding. The nail heads can be found easily by passing the hand along the face of the building paper. The paper is held tight at the entrances by adding a wind deflector over each entrance (Fig. 13.11). The telescoping cover is large enough to fit over the wrapped block. It is constructed of 1 x 4 inch (2.5 x 10 cm) lumber, faced top and bottom with 1/4inch (6.3 mm)

Fig 13.8:
Setting up hives in multiples of four, 2 blocks, 24 hives, before wrapping in November.

FALL MANAGEMENT AND WINTERING BEES

plywood and filled with insulation. The telescoping sides are made of thin plywood and the entire cover is covered with building paper held in place by wooden slats.

I have used wind deflectors of two types: one type forms a "porch" outside of the entrance, with two entrances placed at the ends so that wind cannnot blow directly into the entrance. The other is a sloping structure which opens well below the hive entrance. Both types are shown in Figure 13.11.

The multiple colony block provides excellent protection to each colony. All hives have some walls adjacent to those of other colonies. Upper colonies are heated from below. The result is that no colony forms a tight winter cluster but one giant cluster, or "super cluster" (Karmo, 1958), involving the entire block. The upper colonies are able to keep their bottom boards free of dead bees. Many times during winter I have removed a wind deflector from an upper hive and looked in the entrance. In every case there were bees on the bottom boards. The wind deflectors do not allow wind to blow directly into the entrance. This allows the bees to occupy any part of the hive. Wind blowing into the upper entrance of a hive causes the cluster to be located well below the tops of the frames and crowded toward the front wall of the hive. Wind blowing into the lower entrance of an upper hive causes the cluster to be located in the upper front part of the hive. In either case, the wind can prevent access to some of the stored food.

The character of a winter cluster can be determined from temperature measurements (Furgala, 1975). I have used thermistor probes in various locations in wintering hives for a period of years. The probes were connected to an automatic scanning telethermoneter which measured the temperature at the location of each probe for one minute then switching to the next probe. Readings could be made at will. In addition the telethermonmeter was connected to a chart recorder which provided a continuous record of the temperatures at each probe.

There was no significant variation in the temperatures measured in the heat-generating centres of the

Fig 13.9: Twenty-six winter packed hives.

Fig 13.10: Hive with entrance on the side. It had been a south facing hive in a multiple winter block.

Fig 13.11: South sides of two winter blocks.

13

clusters, even when the hives were packed by different methods. Changes in out side temperatures had no detectable effect upon temperatures at cluster centres. Significant differences were noted in tem peratures in the insulating layers in colonies packed by other different methods. Cluster size also varied. Temperature readings in the shell layer showed clearly the expansion and contrac tion of the cluster. The clusters of upper colonies in multiple blocks changed in size much less than in the lowest colonies in the block. Temperatures in the lower clusters fluctuated considerably. Clusters in the upper colonies were much more ex panded and at one time when temperature changed by 12 degrees C in 24 hours, there was no detectable change in cluster size. No differences were found in temperatures recorded just outside the limits of the cluster. This was expected as cluster size is regulated by the bees so that 6.7 degrees C is maintained at the outer edge of the shell.

The results indicate that the best possible method of out side wintering is a multiple-hive block, with a lower tier of 4 colonies in two brood supers, one to three tiers of hives above, with the addition of insulation on all four sides of the lower tier. All entrances, except the lower entrances of the lower hives, should be provided with wind deflectors. Blocks of this type have produced excellent colonies in the spring. Limited use of slatted boards between the lower super and the bottom boards indicate that the lower colonies in hives so equipped may winter better with them. I have also noted that the colonies in hives with the slatted boards build up faster in the spring. Incidentally, the only winter losses in years have been from starvation of two upper colonies (my fault - I didn't feed them enough) and two from queen failure (again my fault - I should have checked more closely).

Food Consumption

Almost always the colonies packed in multiple hive blocks consume less food than colonies packed singly. During one winter this was reversed with the upper block colonies consuming more than the single-pack colonies or the lower block colonies (Duffy and Vickery, 1982). The reason for the reversal was the exceptional strength of the upper colonies that spring. Most of them were so strong that they had to be divided or set up in double-queen system before the end of April. The extra use of stores produced many more bees. In contrast when lower tier colonies are insulated they rear much less brood and use less stored food than the upper colonies or lower colonies which are not provided with side insulation.

Wintering Nucleus Colonies

Nucleus colonies, as discussed in Chapters 5 and 6, can be wintered very well and can provide the entire answer to the dis appearing supply of "package bees". Nucleus colonies will in- variably build up more quickly and will produce more honey than colonies started from "package bees". Inside wintering of nucleus colonies is recommended for prairie beekeepers (Gruszka, 1985). If the nucs are made up early enough (July) they can be wintered success- fully in single brood chambers outside, even in the severe winters experienced in Saskatchewan. Nucs made up in August with two combs of brood can be built up, fed and wintered as four-frame nucs outside on the top of a multiple colony pack (Fig.13.12). Two four-frame nucleus hives are set in the place of one single brood chamber hive. The two hives are slightly narrower than the full sized super and I routinely use a slab of one-inch (2.5 cm) styrofoam to fill in the space on the exposed side or sides. To date this method has worked very well (Vickery and Willis, 1985).

Fig 13.12: Multiple winter block with eight 4-frame nucleus hives on the top, 4 on this side facing east, 4 on opposite side. Note two types of wind deflectors.

Wintering Queens

In addition to wintering queens in nucleus colonies, it would be of considerable value to have a supply of mated queens early in spring without having to rely upon importation. A sys tem of storing mated queens was developed by Harp (1967, 1969). This was designated the HARP method by McCutcheon (1983), who summarised the procedure.

Compartments, made from wooden strips of 1 1/2 x 1 1/2 inches (3.8 x 3.8 cm) are formed on each side of a sheet of comb foundation. At a time when foundation is drawn well, during a honey flow or in a swarm colony, the cells are built by the bees in the compartments. A comb can accomodate up to 48 compartments. Queens are reared in late summer or fall and each is left in a mating nucleus until mated and laying. Then a queen is placed in each compartment, which then is covered by a square of zinc queen excluder held on by thumbtacks.

Only exceptionally strong colonies should be used to house the queens. The original queen of the colony is removed and the colony is fed copiously with honey. In the upper brood super, the caged queen comb is placed in the middle with an empty comb on each side. The the colony is fed heavily with syrup medicated with fumagillin. Combs of brood (with the bees brushed off) are added on either side of the caged queens as long as brood is available in the fall.

McCutcheon (1983) advises adding more brood combs as soon as the colonies begin to rear brood in mid-winter. As spring approaches, the colony is fed heavily with medicated syrup and pollen or pollen supplement. It would be difficult to add combs of brood in mid-winter in eastern Canada and nearly impossible in the prairie provinces or in the mid-western United States, but could be done in British Columbia or in some of the northern states which have mild winters.

McCutcheon (1983) reported 75 percent success in wintering queens and that the queens functioned normally when installed in colonies. The method is worth trying in various parts of Canada, especially in areas where spring nuclei and "package" bees are produced.

First Requirements in Spring

a) Colonies Wintered Inside

It is customary to remove the hives from storage as soon as the weather warms up in April. They do not need to be taken to a permanent apiary site at this time but can be kept at any convenient location while they are being fed. This location ideally should be near sources of early pollen, such as willow, red maple, poplar or alder. In areas which are deficient in pollen producing plants, pollen or pollen substitute, or a mixture of these should be fed in the form of patties on waxed paper on the top bars of the frames. If a temporary location is used, it should be at least one or one and a half kilometers (nearly a mile) distant from the apiary site to which they will be moved.

b) Outside Wintered Colonies

The time of unpacking colonies which are wintered outside is somewhat variable with the region. In Nova Scotia, for example, it is recommended that the hives should be unpacked by

13

May 1st (Karmo, 1975). On the other hand I recommend and practice unpacking a month earlier, near April 1st, in southwestern Quebec. Many colonies will be quite strong at that time (Fig 13.13) and will require food in order to continue rearing brood. The reason for the difference is the delay in warming in the Atlantic provinces, due in part to drift ice, while spring conditions in southwestern Quebec, Ontario, northern New York and New England states are considerably advanced. It is necessary to unpack and set out and feed colonies wintered in blocks earlier than is necessary to deal with single-packed colonies. There is a limit to the amount of stores that can be packed into the ten combs of a single super. I do not want to risk losing colonies by starvation in April but to feed them and get them started toward the buildup for the "honey flow". If I wish to divide colonies or to "double-queen" them, it is obvious that these operations should be done as early as possible.

Colonies which are winter packed in blocks invariably have the brood nest area off-centre when unpacked in the spring. It is usually necessary to remove a comb or two from the opposite side, push the remaining combs over and insert the combs one has removed between the brood and the wall.

Spring Feeding

The bees should be fed as early as possible in the spring with sugar syrup. Home-mixed syrup for spring feeding is usually stated to be 1:1, that is one part granulated sugar (sucrose) to one part water by weight. This is a much thinner syrup than that recommended for fall feeding. It seems to me that the only reason for the thinner syrup is because it is easier to get the required amount of sugar dissolved in the water. The spring syrup can be much more concentrated. The amount to feed is dependent upon the amount of available honey stored in the hive. Granulated honey is not readily available. The interval between feeding and availability of nectar in quantity from flowers also determines whether the bees need to be fed once or twice. I generally give them about four litres (one American gallon) at the first feeding and about one-third to one-half that amount if a second feeding seems to be warranted. It is not usually necessary but pays off if the spring weather is cool and damp. The first lot of syrup is

Fig 13.13:
A strong colony unpacked April 1st, before adding the tray feeder.

FALL MANAGEMENT AND WINTERING BEES

always medicated against Nosema by adding a rounded teaspoonful of fumagillin to each four litres. This is important to ensure that the colonies increase in strength. *Nosema* is always a greater problem during periods of stress, such as fall and winter, and again in the spring when the unpacked colonies have to produce all of the heat they require. As mentioned previously, pollen early in spring is very important. I feed pollen patties to each colony as soon as it is un-packed whether there is pollen available from plants or not. This ensures that brood-rearing will continue uninterrupted. ❏

REFERENCES

Betts, A.D. 1943. Temperature and food consumption of wintering bees. Bee World 24 (8): 60-62.

Bland, E. 1977. Wintering honeybees in Saskatchewan. Gleanings in Bee Culture 105 (11): 485-487; 514.

Braun, E. and J.E. Geiger. 1955. Comparison of methods for wintering honeybees in the Prairie Provinces. Publ. Canada dept. Agr. 689: 3-8.

Duffy, D.N. and V.R. Vickery. 1981. Outdoor wintering of honeybees. Macdonald J. (Ste-Anne-de-Bellevue, Que.) 42 (6): 3-8.

Duffy, D.N. and V.R. Vickery. 1982. Outdoor wintering of honeybees. Can. Beek. 10 (3): 57-61.

Farrar, C.L. 1936. Influence of pollen reserves on the surviving populations of over-wintered colonies. Amer. Bee J. 76 (9): 452-454.

Farrar, C.L. 1944. Productive management of honeybee colonies in the northern states. Circ. U.S. Dept. Agr. 702: 1-28.

Farrar, C.L. 1952. Ecological studies on over-wintered colonies. J. econ. Ent. 456 (3): 445-449.

Ferracane, M. 1987. Wintering. Gleanings Bee Cult. 115 (11) : 642 645

Furgala, B. 1975. Fall management and the wintering of productive colonies. Chapter 16, pp. 471-490 *in* Dadant and Sons (Eds.) *The Hive and the Honeybee*. Hamilton, Illinois, U.S.A. Dadant and Sons.

Greve, C. 1973. Preparing bees for the winter. Gleanings in Bee Culture 101 (12): 379-380.

Gruszka, J. 1985. Making nucs for wintering. Can. Beek. 12 (5): 103.

Harp, E.R. 1967. Storage of Queen Bees. Amer. Bee J. 107 (7): 250 251.

Harp, E.R. 1969. A Method of Holding Large Numbers of Honeybee Queens in Laying Condition. Amer. Bee J. 109 (9): 340-341.

Karmo, E.A. 1958. The wintering of bee colonies in Nova Scotia. Circ. Nova Scotia Dept. Agr. Mkting. no. 82; 9 pp.

Karmo, E.A. 1975. Beekeeping in Nova Scotia. Apiary Management. Pp. 40-41, Winter Packing; pp. 37-39, Fall Management. Publ. Nova Scotia Dept. Agr. Mkting.; 41 pp.

13

Levac, B., M. Rousseau et P.-J. Bérnier. 1981. Hivernage des colonies d'abeilles. Publ. Québec. Agr. C.V.P.Q. (Agdex 616), 14 pp.

Levin, M. 1983. Value of Bee Pollination to U.S. Agriculture. Bull. Ent. Soc. Amer. (Winter, 1983), pp. 50-51.

McCutcheon, D. 1983. Overwintering Queens. Can Beek. 10 (10) : 221- 222.

Moeller, F.E. 1977. Overwintering of bee colonies. Publ. U.S. Dept. Agr. (Agr. Res. Serv.) 169 : 1-15.

Owens, C.D. 1971. The thermology of wintering honeybee colonies. Tech. Bull. U.S. Dept. Agr. (Agr. Res. Serv.) 1429 : 1-32.

Peer, D. 1978. A warm method of wintering honeybee colonies outdoors in cold regions. Can Beek. 7 (3) : 33,36.

Vickery, V. R. 1977. A successful method for wintering honeybees. Can. Beek. 6 (9): 116-117.

Vickery, V.R. 1985. The Current Status of Beekeeping in Canada. Macdonald J. (Ste-Anne-de-Bellevue, Que.) 46 (3): 36-37.

Vickery. V.R. and S.D. Willis. 1985. Wintering nucleus colonies. Can. Beek. Can. Beek. 12 (6) :136.

ECONOMICS
OF BEEKEEPING

If you are keeping bees for pleasure and take the honey only as a bonus, this discussion will not interest you very much. People will often go to great expense to indulge a hobby and may spend a great deal more than may be necessary to set up a few hives of honey bees.

If, however, you are a beekeeper that keeps bees, either on a commercial basis or to supplement other income, the economics of beekeeping requires careful consideration.

It is difficult to set out a standard plan for beekeeping that will satisfy everyone. Impossible is probably a more accurate term. There are so many factors to consider, not the least of which is the attitude and orientation of the beekeeper. Some hobby beekeepers may not even try to determine profit and loss. The fact and fascination of keeping bees far outweighs any monetary outlay. I must confess that I have a degree of agreement with this philosophy. On the other hand, I have kept many colonies of honey bees with profit as the purpose. I have to admit too that often I ended seasons with a profit even when profit was farthest from my mind.

The following sections are intended to provide prospective beekeepers with probable costs of equipment and other necessary items. Receipts may vary widely due to many factors. I will not attempt to provide accurate returns, but only possible returns that could be realized during good seasons with good management and with a steady market. During particularly favourable seasons, if everything happens as you hope it will, the returns could be even greater. On the other hand, the season could be a disaster, either in production or because of market conditions.

Expenditures

Outlays of capital for equipment can be variable, depending upon the size of the planned operation. In nearly all cases, the initial cost is by far the greatest expense. In a few cases the initial costs may be recovered during the first season but usually two or three or more seasons are required to recover the original investment. If the investment is made with borrowed capital, the break-even point will be later, how much later will depend upon the rate of interest at which the money was borrowed.

14

Size of Operation

A question that I am asked time and again is, "How many colonies should I start with ?". My answer always has been, "More than one." But, if the prospective beekeeper has no experience, I add, "but no more than four". A beekeeper who does not plan to ever keep more bees than enough to supply honey for his family and friends does not need more than two colonies in most seasons. Much depends upon the consumption per head of his family and friends. I assume they would consume more than the miniscule amount of about 700 grams (1.5 lbs.) that is about the national annual average. Consumption of honey in my home is about 18 kg (about 40 lbs.) and the children have long since grown up and gone.

If supplementary income is the aim, more colonies are necessary, varying from about a dozen to 100 or more. A beekeeper can keep 100 or more colonies as a sideline if a careful schedule is followed. More capital is required to pay for the number of hives and other apiary equipment and more expensive honey handling equipment of greater capacity. The same is true if beekeeping is intended to provide the main source of income.

How is the enterprise to be started? Will the hives be stocked with package bees or with nucleus colonies (fall or spring formed) or will full sized colonies be purchased? If producing colonies are available, they should provide a full honey crop the first year and will allow recovery of costs sooner than if the apiary is started with package bees or nucleus colonies.

Equipment costs

1. Hives, bees and apiary equipment.

A complete hive, that is all of the parts that make up one hive, will cost about $ 160.00 Canadian (U.S.$131.00). This will include the hive with a queen excluder, comb foundation and a feeder (tray type) but not the bees. Remember that honey is used by the bees to build the foundation into combs and the surplus honey crop will be reduced. If a large number of hive parts are purchased at the same time most dealers in bee supplies allow discounts of 5% to 15%, depending upon the quantity purchased.

Personal equipment, veil and hat, hive tool, smoker, perhaps gloves and possibly a bee suit, are items that may cost more than $100.00 but are one-time purchases that should last more than one season.

The cost of bees is variable. Package bees may cost $50.00 or more for enough bees for one hive. Nucleus colonies on four frames early in May may cost about $62.00 Canadian. There is also a cash outlay for sugar and for fumagillin to combat *Nosema* disease. Sometimes it is possible to purchase entire established apiaries. These colonies may be purchased for about $200.00 each, but this price does not usually include the additional supers the bees will need to store the honey crop.

There will be annual costs for sugar or prepared sugar syrup, antibiotics, transportation, honey containers and labour. In an established apiary there is the additional cost of annual replacement of about 20% of the brood combs.

2. Honey Room Equipment.

An outline of the equipment required for various sizes of operations is included in Chapter 9 (see Figure 9.13). Initial costs increase as the size of the initial operation is increased. Initial costs are one-time costs unless the size of the enterprise is increased, requiring greater capacity of honey handling equipment.

3. Labour costs.

A beekeeper may supply all of the labour in hobby beekeeping and in operations involving up to 100 colonies. This figure may be somewhat misleading as some beekeepers hire labour for a relatively small number of colonies while other beekeepers manage to take care of many more than 100 colonies. Labour costs tend to be seasonal, usually at the time of removing the honey supers and extracting the crop. Large operations may require labour from spring to late fall, but not during the winter. A beekeeper should keep account of his own time involved in labour with the bees. It is a legitimate expense and should be considered when tallying profit and loss and especially at tax time.

Labour costs are variable geographically and to some extent seasonally and probably will show slight increases with time.

4. Vehicles.

A beekeeper with only two colonies on the home premises can take off the honey supers and convey them to the extracting room in a wheelbarrow or even a child's cart. Larger apiaries, especially those that are located at some distance from the honey processing area, involve use of some sort of vehicle and the costs of transportation must be included. The vehicle may also be used in setting up apiaries, conveying additional equipment to the apiaries, etc., or for ventures other than the bees. The cost of use in beekeeping should be calculated separately from other use.

5. Power.

Electrical power, and perhaps steam as well, may be used in extracting, processing, packing, storage and sales of the honey crop. These costs should be recorded too, even if only a guesstimate is possible.

Receipts

The receipts include all cash or other value received for honey, beeswax or other product of the bees as well as any payments received for colonies rented for pollination of crops.

Factors affecting honey prices

Supply and demand operate as surely in the honey market as for any other commodity. In a poor season, when less honey is marketed, the price tends to be higher (except when there is honey carried over from the previous season - or large amounts of honey are imported). A bumper crop may tend to depress prices. The quantity of honey on the market at any time includes all local (Canadian or U.S., as the case may be) and all imported honey offered for sale at the same time. This does not include honey held back in storage, though large stocks of stored honey may tend to cause some price depression or maintain the price at a low level.

High quality honey, or packs of honey from known single plant sources (more or less) may bring premium prices, especially in specialty retail outlets.

Honey sold in bulk containers to honey packers (unstrained) will bring on average a much lower return, perhaps only half of the retail price at the time. There is an advantage in that payment is received for the entire amount and the costs for processing, packing and containers, storage, and labour are avoided.

The following prices were taken and adapted from "Annual Honey Report", Gleanings in Bee Culture, 117 (5) [May, 1989], page 261.

Bulk honey	Price, U.S.	Canadian equivalent
White, 60 lbs.	$0.63 / lb.	$1.67 / kg
Amber, 60 lbs.	$0.57 / lb.	$1.53 / kg
White, 55 gal.	$0.51 / lb.	$1.36 / kg
Amber, 55 gal.	$0.46 / lb.	$1.25 / kg
Packed honey		
Case, 24 lb.	$1.07 / lb.	$2.85 / kg

"Buy back" program in the United States

The U.S. government pays producers a flat price per unit weight for honey in storage. This honey must be bought back from the government before it can be marketed. The "buy back" price is lower than the price paid by the government. The advantage to producers is in receiving cash while the crop is unsold and the subsidy in the differential between "advance" and "buy back" prices. There is no equivalent program in Canada and this causes some depression of Canadian prices.

Competition from Imported honey

Honey is imported in bulk into Canada and the United States from Mexico, Argentina and China, with lesser amounts from other countries. Labour costs in these countries are less than the cost of labour in either Canada or the United States. Consequently, honey can be imported more cheaply than purchasing "local" honey, this causing a depression of prices for the local product in the importing countries. Often the price paid for local bulk honey is determined by the price paid for delivered imported honey. Occasionally honey from the western part of the continent is sent east in quantity and causes price depression.

All of this raises a question - is HONEY on the Canadian Agricultural Products List ? This is the list of products that another country, with little cash flow, is able to send to Canada in payment for Canadian goods sold to them. These products enter Canada at very low cost compared to Canadian production costs. If honey is on the Agricultural Products List, it is there to the detriment of Canadian beekeepers. Government authorities should be contacted to determine the actual status of honey with respect to foreign trade and, if necessary, lobbied strongly to produce a more equitable solution to the problem.

An Attempt at a Balance

a) Small operation

The cost of 4 hives, personal equipment, honey extracting equipment, power, vehicle and labour is approximately $1,400.00. Assuming a low yield per colony [70 lbs. = 32 kg] and packing for retail sales, the return at $2.85 (Canadian per kg) would be approximately $360.00. A higher yield per colony [110 lbs. = 50 kg] on the same basis would return about $570.00. I have many times, in very good locations, harvested an average surplus of 220 lbs. [100 kg]. At this rate the return would be about $1,140.00, or nearing the break-even point in the first season.

The 4 colonies producing a low average [32 kg] would begin to show a profit only after about 12 years. The higher yield [50 kg] would pay off the investment in 5 years, while the much higher yield [100 kg] could pay off the investment and show a profit of more than $600.00, or $150.00 per colony, in the second year.

Unexpected events may change the returns very greatly. Crop failures do occur once in a while, usually due to winter killing of a crop or to seasonal drought. American Foul Brood could wipe out the bees, with loss of combs and no crop at all. Never add up the profit until you see it in your bank balance.

b) Medium-sized Operation

The initial cost for bees, hives, honey handling equipment, plus labour,etc., for 50 colonies is about $16,500.00. At the low yield [70 lb. = 32 kg] and assuming retail sales at $2.85 per kg, no profit will be gained until the sixth year. If everything has been favourable, there could be a profit of about $60.00. If the original cash outlay was borrowed, interest costs will push the profit year to about the eighth year.

If the bees produced at a higher rate [110 lbs. = 50 kg] each year, the investment could be paid off during the fifth year and show a profit that year of $12,200.00, less the interest costs on borrowed money.

At the rate of 220 lbs [100 kg] per colony, the total investment could be recovered with a profit of nearly $9,000.00 in the second year.

The above returns could be only a "pipe dream" as many things can go wrong and the high average yields can seldom be reached. The figures certainly point out the necessity of high production per colony. The apiaries must be located at sites promising high production and attention to details is a must for the beekeeper.

I hope the foregoing has not dampened your interest in keeping honey bees. If you look upon beekeeping as a chore that has to be attended to, your success will be slower in coming and may never produce the results that could be attained from your efforts and the work of the bees.

I mentioned in an earlier chapter that many people keep bees (though not on a commercial scale) as personal therapy. The apiary becomes a place where the worries of the world are replaced by the fascination of observing and working with the little creatures that are at the supreme pinnacle of the insect world. How can I estimate profit and loss for these people ? As far as I am concerned, any monetary loss is far offset by by the calming influence of working a colony of honey bees on a fine afternoon.

I realize that commercial beekeepers will pay little attention to this, nor should they. Any beekeeper should realize that the bees *will* do their part; the profit and / or loss is the responsibility of the beekeeper. ❏

14

COMMERCIAL BEEKEEPING

There are four important points that mean success or failure in honey production by a commercial beekeeper: 1) apiary locations; 2) quality queens; 3) systematic manipulation of colonies; and 4) adequate feeding in times of need.

Location of apiaries

An apiary must have good wind protection and, in the economic flight range of the bees, enough floral succession from early spring to fall to ensure good colony buildup and a good yield of surplus honey. A plentiful supply of early pollen is necessary to ensure early beginning of population increase. The tree sources mentioned in Chapter 4, willow, poplar, red maple and alder, can provide the early pollen, and an apiary located near stands of these trees will have a distinct advantage over bees that must wait for bloom from later sources such as dandelion.

A commercial beekeeper often has to use rented land to set set up his his hives. The very best sites may not be available. He should be prepared to move an apiary to another site if he discovers that the production there does not match the production of his other apiaries. A location may look ideal, with good wind protection, adequate access for his vehicles, and perhaps even supplies plenty of early pollen but, if the bees are unable to store much surplus honey because of lack of succession or numbers of flowers, that apiary should be abandoned.

There should always be a written contract between the owner of the land and the owner of the bees. This should state clearly the area that the beekeeper is allowed to use and also any right of way that may be necessary to reach it. I know of a case where a land owner died and the property was sold very soon afterward. The beekeeper had nothing at all in order to prove his ownership of the bees and was forced to buy them from the new owner of the land.

How many colonies should be placed in a single location ? The number will vary. Some sites will be excellent for 50 or more colonies; others may not provide for the needs of more than half that number. It is advisable to maintain a strong pool of drone bees in any apiary location. Twenty colonies will provide such a pool. This is essential for mating queens that are replacements for failing queens that are superceded by the bees. The decision of the beekeeper on numbers of colonies should be based upon his own observations prior to establishing the apiary, or he may be assisted by information from other beekeepers in the general area. He (or she, and this is to be understood wherever I use 'he') may even be able to take over very good sites left open by other beekeepers that retire or move away.

Any commercial apiary should be located where it is not obvious to people or accessible to domesticated animals. It may be necessary to surround the apiary with an electric fence to keep away these and wild animals, especially bears.

15

Queens

The second important point is quality of queens. A commercial beekeeper must have a system for colony requeening if he is to have most of his colonies producing honey. Old queens or haphazard requeening can result in supersedure or even queen loss at a time when the colonies should be increasing in strength prior to the honey flow. All colonies should be requeened at least every two years.

Requeening either early in spring or in late summer or fall has been recommended by various authors. I prefer to requeen soon after the beginning of the major honey flow, about mid-June. Early spring requeening causes an interruption in brood rearing and bees do not readily accept queens early in spring unless they are being fed sugar syrup. This may be satisfactory if the operator can obtain quality queens at a reasonable price that early in the season.

I object to late summer or fall requeening too. Colonies of bees that are to be wintered need to have good queens producing many new bees in August and early September. These new bees are the ones that will carry the colony through winter and survive until spring. Older bees usually die before the end of the calendar year.

Requeening during the honey flow has several advantages: queens are cheaper than earlier in the season; the bees accept new queens readily during a honey flow; requeening causes an interruption in brood rearing and more bees become available as foragers to gather nectar. I recall a beekeeper that routinely checked through all of his colonies during the first week of the honey flow and killed all of the queens. The bees reared new queens and the cessation of brood rearing provided more field bees and the colonies were able to produce bumper honey crops. His apiary (50 colonies) was geographically isolated from other bees and his bees were of a superior line. This system can work well only with superior stock and in isolation and even then cannot continue indefinitely. Inbreeding will eventually bring about a situation in which many of the eggs laid by the queen produce diploid drones in worker cells. These drones are destroyed by the workers, but there will be only about half of the eggs that will produce worker bees.

The method of requeening will depend upon the availability of queens. Some beekeepers have access to supplies of capped queen cells for half the price of mated queens. They requeen by placing the queen cells between combs, after removing the old queens. Others purchase mated queens and introduce them in the mailing cages as outlined in Chapter 6.

In general, stronger colonies are less likely to accept new queens except when they have little brood. Weaker colonies usually accept new queens quite readily. However, strong colonies are much more likely to accept new queens when the bees are very busy, as they are during a honey flow.

Colony management

All colonies in an apiary are treated the same in all visits to the apiary except for a visit early in spring. At this time the colonies are checked carefully and are equalized in strength; that is, strong colonies are systematically weakened and weaker colonies are strengthened. Combs of brood or bees are taken from the strong colonies and are given to the weaker ones. At this time the brood combs of all colonies are inspected very carefully for disease. Combs from diseased colonies should not be moved to other colonies.

Brood is moved by first shaking the bees off in front of the colony from which they are removed and the combs without bees are placed in the hive of the weaker colony. The empty combs removed from the weak colony and placed in the other hive. Bees are moved by shaking them off the combs from the strong colony in front of the hive occupied by the weak colony. Young bees enter the new hive and the older bees fly back to their home hive. Naturally, a queen must not be on a comb from which the bees are shaken off. If she is, she will attempt to enter the new colony and will be killed. The strong colony will be weakened, perhaps too much, during the time while the colony rears a new queen, she becomes mated, and begins to lay eggs.

Some colonies may be so strong very early that they swarm before the honey flow begins. These can be treated as outlined above or, 2, 4 or even 6 combs of brood can be removed even to another yard to boost colonies there or to establish nucleus colonies. Brood must be kept warm during transit.

Thereafter, all visits to apiaries are planned so that supers, or whatever else may be required, are supplied to all hives equally. This applies throughout the season, including requeening, crop removal, fall feeding and winter preparations. If the owner of the bees is able to visit each apiary each time, he may well take note of certain conditions in certain hives, such as swarm preparations as indicated by large numbers of bees clustered on the front of a hive, and spend some time on the individual colony. In large operations, where teams of hired people attend to the routine apiary visits, it is usual that all of the colonies will be treated equally. This is necessary when many apiaries must be serviced. There is little if any time available for special attention to individual colonies.

Feeding the colonies in spring and fall is of prime importance. Too many times I have seen hives in spring in which all the bees were dead, but which had full combs of granulated honey. The sugar syrup fed in the fall is made into honey and is stored in the cells from which the last bees emerged. This places it in the area which will be enclosed by the winter cluster so that it is available to the bees. Antibiotics can be mixed into the syrup to combat bee diseases so that the colonies will not only survive, but will be strong in the spring.

Spring feeding gives the bees the incentive to rear brood on a large scale to make them ready for the honey flow to follow. The antibiotic fumagillin can be mixed into the syrup to combat *Nosema* to ensure that the population increase will not be affected by this parasite. Beekeepers who feed their bees terramycin (oxytetracycline) to "prevent" foul brood diseases should use the antibiotic mixed with powdered sugar along the ends of the top bars. The first treatment may be followed by another about ten days later. Great care must be exercised to ensure that no antibiotic is used at a time when it may contaminate the surplus honey that is to be removed from the hives.

Pollination rental

In small to medium operations, the owner of the apiaries may be able to supervise the handling and moving of at least some of the hives. If the number of rented colonies is large, particularly if they are to go to different rentors, the owner will probably not be directly involved in the transportation of the bees, but will leave that chore to the person or company that rents the bees.

In any case, the owner of the bees should make certain that signed written agreements clearly detail the responsibilities of both parties. Circumstances such as road accidents involving vehicles carrying the hives, poisoning of the bees, damage to the hives, etc., should be stated. The rentor of the bees should not be held responsible for queen loss during transit or loss of swarms from rented colonies. The period of time allowed until return of the bees should be stated within limits, but with allowance for weather conditions that inhibit bee flight.

The contract must, of course, state the rental cost of each colony for the rental period. This figure will be greater if the owner of the bees moves them to the pollination site(s) and

15

less if the rentor provides the transportation. The owner of the bees must agree to provide colonies that are strong enough to send out many foraging bees. Colonies started in the spring from package bees do not qualify and colonies started from spring-formed nucleus colonies hardly have enough bees for pollination of spring blooming crops. Wintered colonies (those wintered either in at least one, preferably two, brood supers) should be specified. Just as poor honey will not bring repeat sales, rental of weak colonies will probably mean no repeat rentals.

Migratory Beekeeping

In many parts of the world bees are moved to follow successions of blooming plants. Egyptians moved bees on boats and rafts on the river Nile to follow plant bloom. In Australia many colonies are moved southward in Queensland to follow nectar sources. In the United States many colonies are wintered in the southern states and are moved northward for the northern honey flows during the summer months. Very little north-south movement occurs in Canada, but apiaries may be moved from one location to another.

If any apiary has to be moved, the section on "Moving Bees" in Chapter 6 may be helpful.

Processing the crop

Consult the section in Chapter 9 on "Honey House Equipment and Processing the Honey - Medium to Large Operation (100 to 1,000 colonies)". Please note that some large operations, particularly in the west, may have 3,000 to 4,000 colonies.

Marketing

Established operations already have developed marketing strategy to dispose of their honey. This may be sale of the entire crop to a single large honey-packing company. The honey is extracted and strained and is delivered in bulk containers.

The price per unit weight is determined to some extent by the cost of imported honey landed at the packing company. In countries such as Mexico and Argentina, both of which sell honey to packers in Canada and the United States, and in some African countries, labour costs are much lower and consequently the price of imported honey often is low so that our producers, if they sell at the same price, find that their operations are close to the "break even" level. Canadian producers that export honey to the United States, or who are competing with imported honey from the United States, are disadvantaged by the "buy back" policy in that country.

There is a cost adavantage in selling the entire production to packing companies at a fixed price. The producer receives payment for the honey upon delivery and does not have costs for containers or storage or for labour costs in packing and sales.

Some enterprises pack their honey and, with ingenuity, market a very attractive product. Many sizes and styles of containers and packages, designed to appeal to consumers, are well received by retail outlets. Special displays in stores catch the attention of the buying public. The displays, the variety of products, and the attractive packaging, combined with the high quality of the products, have made the Labonte family enterprise a leader in Quebec. ❑

SOME ADDITIONAL NOTES

A seasonal schedule

Now that this book is nearly finished I feel that this would be a good place for a seasonal outline or schedule that a beginning beekeeper might find helpful. Although I have started at the end of the year, any individual can begin at any month that suits the particular beekeeping enterprise.

a) November and December.

If you have been keeping bees, go over the notes and records from the season just past. Look for mistakes in management, 'weak points' and places where management can be improved. Study the problems to prevent recurrence.

Make plans for the next season. List additional equipment (supers, frames, wax foundation, covers, or equipment for handling the the honey crop) that you will need. Order your supplies early. Often you can save money by ordering at lower prices before new catalogues are issued at the beginning of the new year.

b) January (or earlier)

Check all stored equipment and make repairs as necessary. Check for damage by the Greater Wax Moth. Order what you need for the coming season (if you have not already done so). If you plan to buy bees (packages, nucleus colonies or full-sized colonies), you should place your order early for delivery in April or May. If you intend to divide colonies in spring or to use the 2-Queen System, you will need to order extra queens.

c) February

Equipment repairs - don't put this off. Make new equipment ready for spring. If your bees are outside, you might have a look at them. There is little you can do at this time but you could check that the upper entrances are open. Lower entrances may be blocked with snow but this is not important. Dead bees on the snow or on the ground are the older bees that would not survive winter; without them the colony has a better chance to survive. If your bees are wintered inside you should check the wintering facility to be sure that temperature and ventilation are as they should be.

d) March

If you have put off the necessary repairs, get them done now. The time is fast approaching when you will need your equipment in good condition.

e) April

Unpack the bees and feed them. Conditions in your region will dictate the time to do this. The Atlantic provinces and coastal New England are kept cool at this time of year by the Atlantic drift ice and it is better to unpack later in the month (or remove the hives from the winter storage building). In Quebec, Ontario and most of New England, the colonies should be at-

16

tended to as early as the weather allows. As soon as they are unpacked, feed the bees with sugar syrup. As protection against *Nosema* add fumagillin to the syrup.

f) Mid-April to early May.

1) If you have ordered package bees they should be installed in hives and fed as early as possible (if they are installed on drawn combs). Check in 3 or 4 days for release of the queens and again 10 or 12 days later for presence of brood. 2) Nucleus colonies should be transferred to a super with 10 combs and fed. 3) If you are dividing (splitting) colonies, place the colony that will receive a new queen above the other one with a double screened board between them. There must be an entrance for the upper colony. 4) Establish 2-Queen colonies with those that are very strong. Check upper section with new queen as in (1). In cases of supercedure, requeen. It is a bit too early to allow the bees to rear a new queen.

g) Mid-May.

Remove all entrance reducers. Colonies from package bees may need another super if brood is emerging. Colonies started from nucs, especially wintered nucs, and unsplit wintered colonies need more space earlier. Add a honey super over a queen excluder. If some colonies are very weak they can be united with others. Check all colonies thoroughly for brood diseases.

h) Swarming period.

Generally 17 May to 14 July. Check the strong colonies every ten days by tipping up the top brood super, smoking lightly, and examining the bottoms of the combs for queen cells. If advanced swarm queen cells are found they must be removed. These colonies can be weakened by transferring some brood combs to weaker colonies. If the bees persist in making queen cells, use the Demaree system of swarm prevention.

i) June.

Colonies started from package bees or nucleus colonies could have the brood supers reversed, allowing more cells in which the queen can lay eggs. After the 'Honey Flow' has started, unite the sections of 2-queen colonies. Remove the old (lower) queen and unite using the supers containing brood by the newspaper method. Be sure that all colonies have plenty of room in which to ripen and store honey.

j) July.

Add supers as necessary. From July 1st (or as early as June 20th in early areas) to July 15th requeen the colonies that are to be wintered, except the 2-queen colonies. They have already been requeened. Check for queen acceptance and young brood.

k) Late July.

Remove and extract some summer honey if desirable. This may be delayed but, in any case, the colonies should have room to store more honey.

l) August.

Same as July. When most of honey has been removed, check for brood diseases.

m) September.

Remove remaining honey supers, extract and pack the crop. Colonies that are not to be wintered should be gassed. Weak colonies can be united to form stronger units.

n) Late September.

Feed sugar syrup to bring total weight of stored honey up to 18 kg (40 lbs) if in single brood supers; at least 32 kg (70 lbs) if in double brood chamber. (Actual colony weights will be about 30 - 35 kg (about 70 lbs) and 60 kg (130 lbs), respectively). Nucleus colonies formed in late summer or early fall will require at least 7 kg (14 - 15 lbs) of stores. Feeding can be continued into October if the weather is warm. Add fumagillin to the sugar syrup to counteract the ravages of *Nosema* during the winter months. Check the stored pollen. Each colony should have about three combs. If necessary, provide pollen or pollen substitute.

o) October - November.

The time for winter packing varies somewhat. The best time for packing for outside wintering or for moving hives to inside storage in southern Quebec, Ontario and the northern United States is about November 15th. In colder regions and in Atlantic coastal areas, packing should be done somewhat earlier. ❏

A GLOSSARY OF APICULTURAL TERMS

A beginning beekeeper will find that several words used in beekeeping do not mean the same as in conventional use. Other words will be new. The glossary presented here explains some of the terms that are part of a beekeeper's vocabulary.

AFB (American Foul Brood) - A serious bacterial disease of honey bee larvae. Usually means the colony must be destroyed to avoid spread to other colonies.

Apiary - Bee yard; Place where bee colonies are kept, or referring directly to the colonies.

Apiarist - A beekeeper.

Apiculture - The science and practice of beekeeping.

Bee escape - A one-way device that allows bees to pass from honey supers to the brood chamber, but not in the reverse direction.

Bee space - The space left by the bees between structures they build in the hive, about 8 mm (3/8 to 1/4 inch).

Brood chamber - Part of hive where brood is raised.

Capped brood - Following rapid larval growth, the bees seal the cells with wax. The pupal stage occurs in the capped cell.

Cell - A hexagonal or tubular depression in the comb; used for brood rearing and honey and pollen storage.

Chalkbrood - A fungus disease of brood. Larvae become mummified, chalk-like. May be found on floor of hive.

Chilled brood - Developing brood in cells are killed by cold. Found in outer cells or outer combs left unprotected when cluster is forced to contract, especially in spring.

Cluster - In winter the bees form hollow spheres and produce and conserve heat.

Colony - The bees, queen, workers and drones, working as a unit and living in an enclosed space, a hive or other places found by the bees.

16

Comb - A sheet of large groups of cells, back to back. In a hive the comb is surrounded by a wooden frame.

Demaree - A last resort method of swarm prevention. Queen and brood are separated. Devised by a man named Demaree.

Drawn comb - Cells are completely built on comb foundation.

Drifting - Young bees on orientation flights, or foraging bees returning loaded, enter hives other than their own.

Drone - A male bee. Larger than the others with squarish bodies.

EFB (European Foul Brood) - An infectious disease of larvae caused by a bacterium, *Mellitococcus pluton*.

Feeder - A structure of some sort (tray, can, etc.) for supplying sugar syrup to a colony of bees.

Fertilization - Uniting of male and female gametes: in plants this follows pollination; in bees eggs are fertilized as they are being deposited by the queen.

Fidelity - A honey bee works only one species of flowering plant at a time and will continue to work that source as long as it is available.

Forager Bee - A field bee; gathers nectar, pollen, propolis or water.

Foundation - A beeswax sheet with embossed cell bases.

Frame - The wooden part around a comb; 9 or 10 per super.

Fumagillin - An antibiotic fed to bees to control *Nosema* disease.

Greater Wax Moth - A pest that destroys combs, especially stored brood combs, by tunneling of the larvae of *Galleria melonella*.

Hive - A wooden (may be heavy plastic) structure, the house of the bees.

Honey Flow - Main periods when abundant nectar is available.

Honey Stomach - The first stomach of a worker honey bee, ahead of the true stomach; place where nectar is stored for transport and where conversion to honey occurs.

House Bee - Young worker bee, up to 3 weeks old, that works only inside the hive.

Hypopharyngeal glands - Glands in the heads of worker bees that produce Royal Jelly.

Nassonoff (Nasonov) Gland - A gland in the upper rear part of the abdomens of worker bees that produce an attractant pheromone.

SOME ADDITIONAL NOTES

Nosema - An internal parasite, *Nosema apis*, a protozoan, that infests and destroys the digestive tract of bees.

Nucleus - (often called 'nuc(s)'); a small colony of honey bees on 2 to 5 frames.

Nurse bee - A young bee, 3 to 12 days old, that feeds brood.

Package bees - Bees purchased by weight, formerly from the southern United States, now local or from New Zealand.

Parthenogenesis - Production of offspring without egg fertilization.

Pheromones - Externally secreted hormones that cause reactions in others.

Pollen - Male gametes, produced by anthers of flowers, required to be deposited on the pistils of the flowers in order to produce seed; pollen is collected by bees as their source of proteins and fats.

Pollen basket - The area on the hind legs of worker bees that is developed for carrying pollen; also called 'corbiculae'.

Pollination - Transfer of pollen from stamens to pistils of flowers.

Queen - The sexually active female bee; a colony normally has only one queen. She lays the eggs.

Queen excluder - Wire grid that confines the queen to the brood chamber but allows the worker bees to pass through.

Queen substance - A pheromone produced by glands in the head of a queen bee; this has a distinct effect on bees of the colony.

Robbing - A colony is attacked and destroyed by bees from other colonies; all honey is robbed out.

Royal Jelly - Rich protein food secreted by worker bees; fed to developing queen larvae.

Smoker - A fire pot with bellows, produces smoke to quieten the bees.

Swarm - Colony reproduction; the old queen and half or more of the population leave the hive to find a new home.

Super - The bottomless box that holds the frames; forms part of a hive.

Supercedure (supersedure) - Replacement of a failing queen; the bees raise new queens from very young brood. Only one new queen survives.

Tracheal Mite - A parasitic mite, *Acarapis woodi*, that enters the breathing pores of worker bees, breeds and multiplies there.

16

Venom - Toxic fluid from the poison glands of bees or wasps.

Virgin queen - a fully developed but unmated queen.

Varroa **mite** - A parasitic mite, *Varroa jacobsoni*, that attacks larvae and pupae in cells.

Wax glands - Paired glands on the underside of abdomens of worker bees that produce scales of beeswax.

Worker bee - A sexually undeveloped female bee; workers perform nearly all of the functions required by a colony of honeybees.

ADDITIONAL REFERENCES

Periodical publications

There are some periodical publications that are useful to beekeepers that want to keep up with events in the world of beekeeping. In fact there are many of them. I will not attempt to list them all but only those that I feel are the most useful to an average beekeeper of this region.

Gleanings in Bee Culture. Published by the A.I. Root Co., Medina, Ohio, 44256, U.S.A.

American Bee Journal. Published by Dadant and Co., Hamilton, Illinois, 62341, U.S.A.

Canadian Beekeeping. P.O. Box 128, Orono, Ontario, Canada, L0B 1M0, Canada.

l'abeille. F.A.A.Q., C.P. 656, St-Hyacinthe, Quebec, J2S 7P5.

Newsletters

A number of provinces and states issue periodic (sometimes monthly) newsletters. These keep beekeepers up to date on happenings in the industry, as well as the latest information on problems and how to solve them. Examples are: Bee sCene from British Columbia; Beelines from Saskatchewan; and Beekeeping Notes from Nova Scotia. There are many others.

Books

These references are listed in no particular order. They are books that I have read and enjoyed and some that have been very useful. The note on each book may help you to decide which ones you would like to read. I have not attempted to provide prices, as prices change with time (always upward). I have not given complete addresses of publishers but, as I have named them, the addresses can be obtained in most libraries. First check if the library has a copy of the book. Borrowing is cheaper and after reading it you can decide if you want a personal copy. There are many other books on bees and beekeeping, and many of them are excellent, but I cannot list them all. Authors not listed should not take offense.

The Hive and the Honey Bee. 1975. Dadant & Sons (Editors), 740 pages. Dadant & Sons, Hamilton, Illinois, U.S.A. This is an excellent source of information. Each topic is written by a specialist in that field.

The ABC and XYZ of Bee Culture. 1974 and other dates for other revisions. 712 +XIV pages. A.I. Root Co (Editors), Medina, Ohio, 44256, U.S.A. Topics are arranged alphabetically. This is the beekeeper's encyclopedia. There are many revisions.

The Complete Guide to Beekeeping. Revised Edition, R.A. Morse. 1974. 219 pages. Dutton & Co., New York. As the title suggests, this is a beekeeper's "guide". It is not as complete as I would like but this edition has a chapter on making honey wine. This makes it unique.

Garden Way's Practical Beekeeping. E.H. Tompkins and R. Griffith. 1977. 218 pages. Garden Way Publishing, Charlotte, Vermont, U.S.A. A down to earth publication on beekeeping.

The Joys of Beekeeping. R. Taylor. 1974. 166 pages. St. Martin's Press, New York. Easy and enjoyable reading.

Beekeeping the Gentle Craft. J.F. Adams. 1982. 182 pages. Doubleday & Co., New York. This book is also easy and enjoyable reading.

Honeybee Ecology, a Study of Adaptation in Social Life T.D. Seely. 1985. 201 pages. Princeton Univ. Press, Princeton, New Jersey, U.S.A. An in depth study of the ways in which honey bees are such successful animals.

The Biology of the Honey Bee. M. Winston. 1987. 281 pages. Harvard Univ. Press, Cambridge, Mass., U.S.A. and London, England. If you want to learn more about the biology of the bees, this is the book for you.

Bees and Mankind. J.B. Free. 1982. 155 pages. G.B. Allen & Unwin, London *et al*. An easy reading account of the ways in which humans and bees interact and the value of the bees to mankind.

Honey Bee Pests, Predators and Disease. R.A. Morse. 1978. Cornell University Press, Ithaca, New York.

America's Master of Bee Culture. The life of L.L. Langstroth. F. Naile. 1976. 215 pages. Cornell Univ. Press, London. Langstroth's life was not easy. He was plagued with mental problems but he was the first to discover the 'bee space' and to apply it to building a modern moveable frame hive.

Contemporary Queen Rearing. H.H. Laidlaw, Jr. 1979. 199 pages. Dadant & Sons, Hamilton, Illinois, U.S.A. 62341. This book is a detailed account of rearing queens and of artificial insemination written by the 'Master' of queen insemination..

Plants for beekeeping in Canada and the northern U.S.A. J. Ramsay. 1987. 198 pages. International Bee Research Assoc., Cardiff, U.K. This book has complete information on the plants available to honey bees for gathering nectar and pollen.

The Dancing Bees, an account of the life and senses of the honey bee. K. von Frisch. 1955. (Translated by D. Ilse). 183 pages + Plates I-XXIX. Readers Union, Methuen, London. [Also Paperback, Harcourt, Brace & World, viii + 182 pages].

I have copies of other books by von Frisch and I enjoy reading them again and again. The manner of communication of the bees is an intriguing topic to beekeepers and many others. This little book is a good one to start on.

16

The Life of the Bee. M. Maeterlinck, 1901. 356 pages. Musson Book Co., Toronto, and G. Allen & Sons, London. [Also Paperback, 168 pages. Mentor Books, New York]. A reader should not accept all of the 'scientific' accounts in this book but it is a joy to read and imparts the great respect that the author has for these little creatures.

Other publications on Beekeeping.

There are several publications issued by various authorities that are useful. Some of them are listed here but I have not tried to provide a complete list. These are guides to beekeeping that are generally lacking in detail, or that deal with a particular aspect of beekeeping.

BEEKEEPING in Eastern Canada. J.C.M. L'Arrivee. 1977. Agric. Canada publ 1600; 30 pages.

Beekeeping in Ontario. Reprinted 1976. G.F. Townsend and P.W. Burke. Ontario Ministry Agric. Food publ. 490; 38 pages.

Beekeeping in Nova Scotia - APIARY MANAGEMENT. Endel A. Karmo. 1975. Nova Scotia dept. Agric. Mkting, Hort. Biol. Services. (unnumbered); 41 pages.

BEEKEEPING IN THE UNITED STATES. S.E. McGregor *et al.* Rev. 1971. U.S.D.A., Agric. Research Service, Agric. Hndbk.No. 335; 147 pages. [More complete than others listed here].

Honey Bee Diseases and Pests. D. Dixon *et al.* 1987. Can. Assoc. Professional Apiculturists. 17 pages.

Bee diseases and pests of the apiary. P.W. Burke. Reprinted 1981. Ministry Agric. Food publ. 429; 25 pages.

Starting Right with Bees. [original by H.G. Rowe, 1957] Rev. by J.A. Root *et al.* 1976. 18th Edition; 96 pages.

Apiculture, Agdex 616, publications of C.P.V.Q., Québec Ministère de l'Agriculture et de l'alimentation, Ste-Foy, Québec.

There are many other publications. You should contact your provincial or state beekeeping organization for further information. Membership in your area organization is not expensive and is very worthwhile.

Finally, as I started with a quotation from Maeterlinck, 1901, I will finish with another by this author:

"To him who has known them and loved them,
a summer where there are no bees
becomes as sad and empty
as one without flowers and birds."

16

INDEX

Index

Index

Index

Index

Index

BEEKEEPING PROFIT AND LOSS STATEMENT

YEAR: _____

INCOME: Gross honey sales: _____

Beeswax sales: _____

Pollination fees: _____

Other income: _____

TOTAL   INCOME: _____

EXPENSES: Apiary equipment: _____

Honey House equipment: _____

Tools, etc.: _____

Supplies: _____

Hired labour: _____

Personal labour: _____

Vehicle(s), cost & deprec.: _____

Vehicle(s), operation: _____

Vehicle(s), insurance: _____

Insurance on building(s): _____

Telephone: _____

Interest on loans: _____

Miscellaneous: _____

TOTAL EXPENSES: _____

NET INCOME: _____

(This page may be photocopied)

HONEY PRODUCTION CHART

YEAR: _____

Colony No.	No. supers ___D ___S ___DS	Total Weight Honey	
		Gross	Net (Packed)
1. _____			
2. _____			
3. _____			
4. _____			
5. _____			
6. _____			
7. _____			
8. _____			
9. _____			
10. _____			
11. _____			
12. _____			
13. _____			
14. _____			
15. _____			
16. _____			
17. _____			
18. _____			
19. _____			
20. _____			
TOTAL HONEY			

D = brood size super, 9 1/2" = 61.3 cm
S = shallow super, 5 3/4" = 37.1 cm
DS = deep shallow, 6 5/8" = 42.7 cm

(This page may be photocopied)

COLONY CONDITION CHART

Date: _____

No.	Brood				Queen		Disease		Stores	
	P	F	G	E	+	−	+	−	+	−
1.										
2.										
3.										
4.										
5.										
6.										
7.										
8.										
9.										
10.										
11.										
12.										
13.										
14.										
15.										
16.										
17.										
18.										
19.										
20.										

P = Poor ; F = Fair ; G = Good ; E = Excellent

Queen: + = Good ; − = Poor

Disease: + = Present ; − = None

Stores: + = Adequate ; − = Low

INVENTORY, BEEKEEPING EQUIPMENT
Date: _____

Owner: _____   Page no. ___ of ___

Item/Description	No.	Condition	Est. Value
1.			
2.			
3.			
4.			
5.			
6.			
7.			
8.			
9.			
10.			
11.			
12.			
13.			
14.			
15.			
16.			
17.			
18.			
19.			
20.			

Prepared by: _____

(This page may be photocopied)

COMPARISON OF BROOD DISEASES

SYMPTOM	AFB	EFB	CHALKBROOD	SACBROOD
State of brood comb	Capped brood, sunken perforated cappings	Open brood, possibly some cells as in AFB	Capped and open brood cells	Capped brood cells punctured cappings
Age of brood	Older larvae or pupae lengthwise in cell	Usually young larvae coiled in cells	Older larvae, lengthwise in cell	Older larvae lengthwise in cell
Colour of dead brood	Dull, white thru brown to nearly black	Dull, white to yellow to dark brown, blotchy	Chalky white, may have black spots	Gray to brown, head darker
Consistency of dead brood	Soft, then sticky to ropy	Watery, granular	Chalky	Watery, granular fluid-filled sac
Odour of dead brood	Putrid	Sour	Yeasty	None
Type of scale	Flat on cell bottom, stuck to cell	Twisted, rubbery, not stuck in cell	Mummified, chalky brittle, not stuck in cell	Head black, curled to centre, brittle, not stuck in cell

(This page may be photocopied)

Bees emerging from centre of comb (top)

The bottom of this old comb has been torn down by the bees and rebuilt - all drone cells. (bottom)

Comb with capped brood (top)

Comb of honey, an outside comb from the brood chamber (bottom)

Honeybee on Aster. (left)

A 4-frame nucleus colony caged for pollination on a greenhouse bench. (right)

The hive of a 'double-queen' colony early in June. (left)

The hive of a 'double-queen' colony on the day of reuniting at the start of the honey flow. (right)

Queen rearing in Egypt. Look at those completed queen cells!! (top)

Endel Karmo demonstrating at the Maritime Beekeepers' summer meeting, Souris, Prince Edward Island, July, 1984. (bottom)

Mud hives in Egypt (top)

Bee-collected pollen in a C.C. pollen trap (bottom)

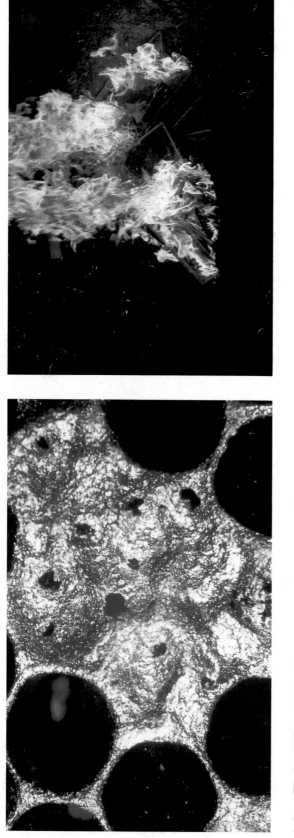

The "sure cure" for American Foul Brood. (top)

The same block of hives wrapped and with wind deflectors over the entrances. (bottom)

Sunken, perforated cell caps, a sign of disease. (top)

A block of hives ready for winter wrapping: 4 colonies in 2 brood supers below; 4 colonies in single brood supers in the middle; 8 nucleus colonies (4 frame) on top. The wires lead to